"My first knowledge of garden plants came through wild ones. Some one gave me that excellent book, the Rev C A Johns's *Flowers of the Field*. For many years I had no one to advise me (I was still quite small) how to use the book, or how to get to know (though it stared me in the face) how the plants were in large related families, and I had not the sense to do it for myself, nor trouble afterwards; but when I brought home my flowers I would take them one by one and just turn over the pages till I came to the picture that looked something like. But in this way I got a knowledge of individuals . . . I always think of that book as the most precious gift I have ever received. I distinctly trace to its teaching my first firm steps in the path of plant knowledge, and the feeling of assured comfort I had afterwards in recognising the kinds when I came to collect garden plants."

Gertrude Jekyll
1843-1932

BRANCH OF THE SPINDLE TREE.

A PASSION for NATURE

19th-century Naturalism in the Circle of Charles Alexander Johns

Author of *"Flowers of the Field," "A Week at the Lizard," "British Birds in their Haunts," "Botanical Rambles," "The Forest Trees of Britain," etc.*

By Deirdre Dare & Melissa Hardie

With an essay
"A Botanist Who Painted: Emily Stackhouse (1811-1870)"
by Clifford Evans

Patten Press & Jamieson Library
Newmill, Penzance, Cornwall
2008

This edition is published in 2008 by the Patten Press,
an imprint of Hypatia Publications:

Trevelyan House
16 Chapel Street
Penzance, Cornwall TR18 4AW

A CIP catalogue record for this book is available from the British Library.

ISBN 978-1-872229-58-4

Designed and typeset by Donna J. Anton

Printed and bound in the U.K. by
Cromwell Press
Trowbridge, Wiltshire

Dedicated to the memory of

MOLLY MATTHEWS
1908 - 2008

Granddaughter of Emily Johns Carrington
and great-niece of Charles Alexander Johns,
who did so much to restore interest in his life,
and who herself carried on faithfully the
writer-ly arts of the families of
Carrington and Johns

CONTENTS

PREFACE & ACKNOWLEDGEMENTS

In the 1990s, while researching the history of Helston Grammar School[1], I discovered the diary of Charles Alexander Johns for 1832-38, held by the Cornwall Record Office. It was written at the time when he was the assistant to the headmaster, Derwent Coleridge, second son of the poet Samuel Taylor Coleridge. With the diary was a letter, written in the 1970s, by his great-niece, Molly Matthews, and, to my delight and amazement, I was able to contact her and gain her invaluable interest. Both she and her daughter, Imogen Thomas, have continued to provide personal information and support since I undertook to research the life of their revered relation, the botanist, educator and popular 19th-century natural history author.

Over the past few years, many others have been unfailingly helpful as I explored the different phases of Charles Johns's life, the respect in which he was held by colleagues and friends, and his passionate love of and attention to the natural world. Dr David E Allen, a past president of the Botanical Society of the British Isles and of the Society for the History of Natural History, provided the botanical knowledge and natural history information that I lacked, while the research of Mary Nobbs and Val Cook added much to my knowledge of the schools that Johns established in Chipperfield (Callipers Hall) and Winchester (Winton House).

I was most fortunate to find as my publisher Melissa Hardie. For two decades she has been collecting volumes of historical importance in all fields of Cornish literature, and was immediately receptive to a publication about Charles Johns when I approached her with my manuscript. Her painstaking research has transformed my original biography into a far more substantial study, extending as it does to his extensive circle of friends and co-workers in the Victorian era.

We are both greatly indebted to Clifford Evans for the work he has been doing for many years related to the botanical prowess and

[1]Dare, D J (1996) *The Unknown Founder, The Story of Helston Grammar School from 1550-1972.* Truro: Kelynen Publications.

outstanding artistry of Emily Stackhouse, a friend and collaborator of Johns in Cornwall, and one amongst several who helped to make his work unique. The Evans collection of Johns's published works, posted over for our perusal from the United States, where he now lives, has been invaluable in allowing the dating of some queried editions and close scrutiny of the beautiful illustrative work produced for these by a largely unacknowledged band of artists. Also, Cliff's courtesy in permitting and providing some of Emily Stackhouse's illustrations, which he has owned until recently, is much appreciated. His own essay about Emily is included as an Appendix and his independent researches into the life of C A Johns have been a major source of confidence in what we have been able to find. The new owners of the Emily Stackhouse Collection of Botanical Watercolours is Mallett Fine Art of New Bond Street (www.mallettfineart.com), and James Harvey and his associates have been most generous and enthusiastic, not only in their part-sponsorship of this book, but also in allowing complete use and access to this superb collection of her work.

A full collection of Johns's published work, together with associated primary materials, is being gathered by the Hypatia Trust, and will remain in Cornwall for study by researchers in future. The Appendices have been prepared by Melissa Hardie for this purpose, and may be made available for on-line searches.

The archivists, librarians and staff of the following institutions have readily assisted with material and advice: the Record Offices of Cornwall, Berkshire, Hampshire, Hertfordshire and Suffolk; the British Museum of Natural History (Polly Tucker); the Courtney Library of the Royal Institution of Cornwall; Truro City Library; Plymouth Central Library; St Edward's Anglican Church, Shaugh Prior, Devon; Mitchell Library of the State Library of New South Wales, Sydney; Trinity College Library, Dublin; the Adyar Library & Research Centre, Adyar, India (Dr C V Agarwal & Mr C A Shinde, Librarian) and the Linnean Society of London. Many individuals have also contributed to this story: Mr R G Trethewey, Dr Paul Gainey, Bob Acton, Elizabeth Long, Dr Charlotte Mitchell, UCL; Canon Christine Redgrave, rector of Beenham parish church; Carol Hetherington, University of Queensland, Brisbane; Dr Rosemary White and her brothers, Derek and Gus White; Bishop Simon; Mark Barrington-Ward; Dr Ellen Jordan of Newcastle University, Australia; Dr Heiner Gillmeister of Bonn University, Germany; Leander Wolstenholme, Curator of Botany, University of Manchester; Mr W Michael Baron; and Ian Caldwell (Stackhouse descendant). We are grateful to them all for their rapid and generous response to our queries. Apart from all else, this kind of help shows how deeply engaged we all are with history and cultural inheritance.

Finally, our thanks go to Brenda Hull, Ann Round and Peter Waverly, who read and commented helpfully on the texts-in-process; and, not least, to Eric Dare, who supported, revised, improved early drafts and who has encouraged our efforts over the past few years of research and writing.

Deirdre Dare

CAKILE MARITIMA (*Purple Sea Rocket*).

Drawing by Emily Stackhouse

CRO Cornwall Record Office
FLS Fellow of the Linnean Society
FRAS Fellow of the Royal Astronomical Society
HRO Hampshire Record Office
HSS Hampshire Scientific Society
RCPS Royal Cornwall Polytechnic Society
RIC Royal Institution of Cornwall
SPCK Society for the Promotion of Christian Knowledge
SRO Suffolk Records Office

Note: Helston is the spelling employed in the text for all references to the town: Helleston, Hellestone, Hen-liston, Helstone, etc. for ease of identification.

Spellings: Throughout the 19th century (and earlier) there appeared to be no fixed form of spelling both names of people and places. Helston, as above, is a good example, but there were others in the course of this study, including sometime confusion of John with Johns, Boon with Boone, Bennet with Bennett, and numerous place-names used by Johns have formalised into different spellings today. Insofar as known, the modern-day spellings are employed for ease of reference. We are also grateful to Richard Fortey, former senior palaeontologist at London's Natural History Museum, who finally as late as this year, cleared up the confusion in these authors' minds between the spellings of the Linnean Society and the Linnaean taxonomies with which Johns was familiar. (See pp 171-3 in his delightful book, *Dry Store Room No.1, The Secret Life of the Natural History Museum.*)

C A Johns

INTRODUCTION

The readership for a biography of Charles Alexander Johns may be somewhat limited today, because, as a person, he was not a Wellington, a Brunel or a Dickens. To our knowledge he had no hidden life to confess as from under a stone, and he committed no staggeringly dangerous deeds. Though he looked at birth as if he was 'set for life amongst the gentry' into which he was born, in the strongly class-conscious society of the day, he was in fact destined to work against long odds to find and sustain a place there. He was an example, not unlike Thomas Hardy a generation or so later, about whom Francis Bacon wrote a full two centuries before:

> Reading maketh a full man, conference a ready man, and writing an exact man.

Johns followed the Baconian rule in every respect, reading widely, conferring with close and prominent family friends, pupils and scholars of the day, and then writing with both felicity and careful attention to detail. Because he did not publish sensational fiction or controversial theology, was neither radical nor bohemian in his ideas, his contributions to literature are now not widely remembered. He was, nevertheless, a famous man of his time, well-known and respected in the botanical world, and presents an enormous legacy to our own. His natural affinity with words and generosity of spirit, aside from his will and need to communicate, produced an accomplished author welcomed by young and old alike. Ultimately Johns became a passionate educationalist of great talent, sharing his knowledge both in the books he wrote and the institutions for learning that he founded and established. In Johns we discover a Victorian exemplar and natural historian – yes – but also a supreme innovator and an educational entrepreneur.

Charles Johns was a gentleman-naturalist, who through his personal interest in plants, alongside his teaching posts and ministry, wrote largely un-scientific books in fascinating variety, to inform and interest others – both children and adults – about trees, geological formations, birds, flowers and not least, social history, legends and customs amongst country people. He saw colour and detail in all around him, and his writings became his records of a life full of long-distance rambling and natural life acutely observed. He never quit learning or wanting to know, as his godson and nephew Charles Carrington tells us in his memoir. And he never stopped writing and revising his popular works for people of all ages, working up to the end of his life.

He did not pretend to be a scientist, rather an astute observer and conserver, eager to share what he found. Nonetheless, he was energetic, scholarly, reliable and conscientious. He keeps the innocent tourist as well as the learned pilgrim in his sights. And, always his examples are carefully chosen, carry a moral but not didactic message, and speak from the same circumstances as his proposed readers. Now that tourism plays such an important part in the Cornish economy, this small biography of a West Country teacher, may well delight the intelligent walker over some of those same territories and routes.

Today his books are collected, if at all, by horticulturists and botanic librarians for their descriptive content and their coverage of varieties and species indigenous to their time. They are also preserved and sought for Cornish collections for their broad historical content. The explosion of interest in the natural world, plants, gardening and the myriad changes that are predicted based on theories of global-warming may encourage the reader to look back on the life and times of Charles Johns as a simpler and less complicated paradise. Of course, it was not.

The Victorian age was a time of tumultuous change and turmoil. The introduction of the railways completely transformed people's ideas of place, time and distance from 1830 forward. The Reform Act of 1832 shook the political world to its core, and not least in Cornwall, where private fiefdoms and parliamentary seats were more numerous than anywhere else in Britain. The 1840s, a decade when Johns was establishing his career in the world of letters, was a time of economic depression as exemplified in the great potato famine in Ireland and subsequent migrations. It was also the period when cellular theory and biology were first voiced as the science of living beings and the essential structure of animal and plants. In the following decades the rapid accumulation of information and theories related to Darwin's travels and discoveries culminating in his *Origin of Species* (1859), alongside the controversies and social revolutions promoted by the Chartists in the national political sphere, the Oxford Movement in the religious sphere, and new ideas in art, literature, and social reform especially for women, all contributed to a time as complex and challenging to negotiate as our own.

Johns, though decidedly not oblivious to the political and religious movements around him, did not willingly engage with conflict and argument. Not energised in the same way by debate like his close friend Charles Kingsley, his appetites from childhood were engaged with the wonders of the natural world around him. His letterbook, however, reveals that he did correspond with senior politicians and strategists on subjects such as the spread of post offices, the need for education for the poor and, not least, involvement in the Boer War. Nonetheless, his high regard for social institutions such as learned societies, the monarchy and the churches was such that one would not find him in revolutionary circles of any sort.

His capacious mind lent itself to the broadest possible context, and later as a churchman he was described as neither 'high' nor 'low' but 'broad.' Certainly, botany for him was not a refuge. It was a passion taken up early in his life, one that required 'hard study and intense application,' and the acceptance of the fact that 'you set out fully prepared to encounter serious difficulties, and resolved to overcome them.'[2] He wished most of all to appeal to the intellect of his companions of any age to look to the natural world to find God, not in a priggish or puritanical fashion, but in an open and explanatory way.

> What though I trace each herb and flower
>   That sips the morning dew;
> Did I not own Jehovah's power,
>   How vain were all I knew!
>
> (CAJ, from *Botanical Rambles*, p 1)

From his own studies, poems and drawings and from those of his friends and family who joined him in his searches comes a framework

---

[2]*Botanical Rambles* (1846), pp 2-3, presents the study of the natural world by the individual as one of challenge-response in terms of approach, the outcome depending on one's attitudes and practice, well before the theory was crystallized by the historian Arnold Toynbee and applied to civilisations.

THE COUNTRY WALK.

COME, Charles and Sophia, and Emily, too,
Come down the green lane, papa's nothing to do ;
'Tis a calm, pleasant evening, and I think just the time
When, last year, we found the white violets in prime.
Like the snowdrops, they hang their heads meekly and low ;
But the snowdrops can't boast such a fragrance, you know.
Now, who will first find out the treasure again,
And who pry so closely, yet pry all in vain ?
Come, prattler, you must not yet scamper alone—
You may trip and fall down if you meet with a stone :

THE THRUSH.

So take papa's hand, and he'll lead you along,
And listen, pray do, to the thrush's sweet song.
All day, with his mate, he's been building a nest,
Where their innocent brood will be fondly carest ;
And now, though so tired, he hymns a sweet lay,
Nor ceases his note till the light fades away.
Who caused these fair flowers to rise from the ground,
And spread the green mantle of grass all around,
And taught the sweet thrush such beautiful strains,
Made the streams softly flow, and with trees deck'd the plains ?
'Tis God, my dear children, all powerful and good,
Who gave you your life, who provides you with food,
Whose blessings and mercies you daily receive,
And with whom, if you're good, you for ever will live.

H. I. JOHNS.

Poem by Henry Incledon Johns, father of Charles. Reprinted from *The Illustrated Spelling Book* by Maria Jacob (1854).

that quickens the heart of all those interested in the natural world. He inspires without preaching to the would-be botanist, artist and social investigator. And, rather than claim to be the 'omnipresent scientist,' his mission is to explain, to teach, and to put into the hands of the nature-lover – always his target audience – the references to historical and scientific facts that illuminate his subject. To describe a tree, he will tell you about Edward the Confessor's throne made of that wood. To describe a plant, he will tell you how Darwin found certain people eating it uncooked on his voyages. To describe a season of the year, he gathers poetry and quotations from his prodigious reading of poetry (see his 'readings diary' in Appendix iv). After careful perusal of his work, all of us might find topics to further investigate in our own time, not unlike Gertrude Jekyll and any number of others in theirs.

The writing style of Johns is warm, friendly, conversational and down to earth, un-stuffy, we can say with approval. It is not dry botanical treatise, and even to its author, as recognised in the Introduction to the third edition (1874) of *A Week at the Lizard*, first published some 30 years before, enticed the visitor.[3] He wrote:

> Published originally as a description of a little-known district, it opened a new scene of exploration to the tourist, and became a "guide-book," and has been quoted again and again as an authority. The introduction of railways and consequent facilities of locomotion, brought visitors, who required no "New Guide to the Lizard," because time works little change either on rocks or the vegetation of sea-cliffs, and the world are wont to prefer an original – the work, I mean, of an author who describes nothing but what he has seen – to a compilation.'

Johns then proceeds in the most straightforward way to tell his readers how to get to the Lizard the cheapest way, in the best kind of weather, the modes of transport, the accommodation you can expect to find at nearby Helston, the religious services on offer, the festivals, customs, industries and not least the times of the general post. Certainly his observations come from another and local world, less changing as a result of bureaucratic or political whim. In fact the book is a complete 'character' given by the author as referee, but not hagiography.

---

[3] *A Week at the Lizard* by the Rev C A Johns, BA, FLS London: SPCK, 1848.

Gently he chides the town's managers, about the state of the drainage and sewers, commenting on how much more attractive it could be to visitors! It comes to us as a social history of that part of Cornwall in the 19th century, or in modern academic terms as social anthropology, with appendices on the geological features of the area, a catalogue of birds observed in the Lizard district, and the plant life described and drawn. Unlike most guidebooks however, the *Week* stands as literature in its own right, and probably inspired followers such as Wilkie Collins in *Rambles Beyond Railways, or Notes from Cornwall Taken Afoot* (1851) and J T Blight with his *A Week at Land's End* (1861).

A Week at the Lizard was not, however, Johns's sole or even his first publication. And many more of his writings were devised as teaching materials and publications, printed for purposes largely outside the environs of Cornwall, but nevertheless continually showing reference to it throughout his life.

When G S Boulger had completed the revision and editing of the 29th edition of *Flowers of the Field* for SPCK in 1900, he received a letter of admiration and appreciation from the 'veteran chief of British botanists,' Sir Joseph Dalton Hooker (1817-1911), who had been acquainted with Johns all his life, but had survived him already by a quarter of a century. In the letter Hooker wrote to Boulger: 'When you shall have to prepare a still other Edition I venture to suggest that a few lines of Preface as to who Johns was; and an outline of the successive enlargements of his work would be very interesting.' Hooker, knowing full well who Johns was, though undoubtedly not in deepest detail, did not want others to forget. And Boulger was able to comply in 1911 when revising again the 33rd edition, by which time the long-promised *Flora of Cornwall* (1909) had been published, with sufficient biographical material to make the suggested memoir a possibility. Despite some flawed information that has been carried on through the following century, this is the picture with which we begin. The initial character given is correct: '…though the story to be told is but a simple tale of long-continued literary industry prompted by an enthusiastic love of Nature and a zeal for education' [Boulger, p ix]. That is the man and his circle of associates.

A bibliography is included in the Appendices for those whose appetites may be whetted by the telling of the events of his life and his circle of scholarly colleagues and companions. With some confidence, we believe it can be said that in the long catalogue of distinguished

Cornish naturalist literature, whether by visitor or native, Charles A Johns has a rightful and foremost place.[4] We take great pleasure in exploring and following the life of this almost-forgotten figure who walked with careful step along Cornwall's lanes and shores.

Melissa Hardie
Newmill, June 2008

East view of St Michael's Mount. Published by W. Penaluna, 1815.

---

[4]Certainly this was recognised by F H Davey in his magnificent effort to produce the *Flora of Cornwall* (1909), into which he placed first of six portraits of outstanding Cornish naturalists, that of Charles Alexander Johns. Unfortunately, there were also some bibliographic and biographic errors in Davey's account (probably as a result of reliance which he acknowledges, on the *Bibliographica Cornubiensis* of Boase & Courtney) of Johns's life which have subsequently 'infected' later records such as the *DNB* (Boulger), Freeman (1980) and to the present-day Simpson (2004 edition). Perfecting detail, of course, is always a work-in-progress, and it is to be hoped that the authors herein have contributed to a fuller and more accurate biography.

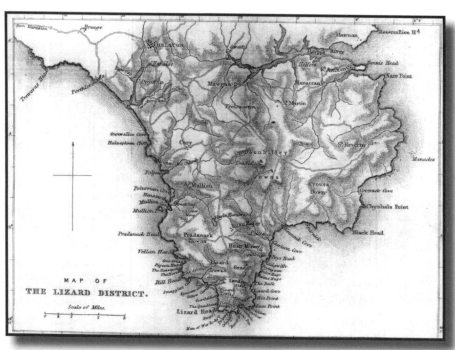

Map of the Lizard peninsula from *A Week at the Lizard*.

1

EARLY DAYS

In the far south-west of Cornwall sprawls a wild and beautiful peninsula, the Lizard, where for centuries farmers and fishermen have struggled to make a living. The rugged cliffs and powerful sea have brought shipwrecks and smuggling, while the isolation and tough conditions have created men and women of strong character, living close to nature. It was from such families that, in 1811, a gifted, ambitious young man was born, who was to make the Lizard well-known to his many contemporaries in the 19th century – and they responded in droves to the knowledge and enthusiasm for nature they found in his books.

Charles Alexander Johns was not born in Cornwall, although both of his parents came from long-established Cornish families. His father, Henry Incledon Johns, was born and brought up in the market town of Helston that is the gateway to the Lizard, and was baptised in the Church of England in the parish church, St Michael's. Latterly, however, Henry's father, Bennett John,[5] a surveyor or architect from nearby Wendron, had moved his wife, Anne, and their family to Plymouth Dock (that became 'Devonport' in 1823 by petition), where he worked in the drawing offices of the Royal Engineers.[6] Upon settling in Devon, 's' was added to their surname, which has laid a confusing

---

[5]Son of Alexander John of Wendron and his wife, Anne Jenkyn of St Keverne. His name Bennett is also found as Bennet interchangeably.

[6]The *DNB (From the earliest times to 1900)* erroneously names Charles Johns's grandfather as the Helston solicitor Tremenheere John. This may have been an uncle, but the exact connection is not known. This was probably taken by Boulger (entry author) from Boase and Courtney *Bibliotheca Cornubiensis*, which includes this same incorrect lineage. Bennett John's special duties involved the laying of plans for new fortifications and barracks to the town of Plymouth, in preparation for war with France.

Charles Johns's parents: Henry Incledon Johns, banker and artist,
aged 27, and his wife, Maria Boone, aged 17. Miniatures painted on
ivory at the time of their wedding in 1803.

blanket of questions for genealogists ever since.[7] John and Johns are
both familiar surnames in West Cornwall today, with traceable antecedents, the earliest possibly coming from Wales or Ireland to settle.

Charles's mother, Maria, was the daughter of George Boone (1745-
1837)[8] and Mary Incledon (1749-1833),[9] both of whom came from
St Keverne on the Lizard. There to stand in the village square and
or by the ancient church is to overlook the cliffs above the Manacle
rocks. Though not what is traditionally thought of as the seaside, the
rocks indeed being the cause of many shipwrecks, the lure of the sea is
strongly inbred in its local families. Maria's father had joined the navy.
Her mother, to be near her husband, moved further up the county to
Wilcove in Antony, just across the water from Plymouth Dock and
there Maria was born. Travel between the two locations was by ferry
at Torpoint, the newest of which had commenced operations in 1791,

---

[7]C M Matthews explains, '…it was after the move to Plymouth that the family began to write their surname in the English manner with a final "s." John is the
Cornish form.'

[8]Throughout the Johns diary, Boone is in fact spelled 'Boon' (the Cornish form)
as in most public records, however it has long been spelled in the family with the
addition of an 'e' (English form), no doubt a similar gentrification to John(s).
George Boone was a Warrant Officer R N (1748-1837).

[9]Both parents were related to Charles Benjamin Incledon of St Keverne, who
was a famous tenor, the 'Pavarotti' of his day. Incledon was at the height of his
career at this time (he retired in 1815), audiences flocking to hear him as Macheath
in 'The Beggar's Opera' by Gay and in works such as Haydn's 'Creation.' See Appendix ii for Incledon.

and provided quick transit to Truro from the Plymouth area. Robinson notes that 'It would appear that there was some kind of ferry in
operation from Torpoint to Devonport as early as 1730...'[10]

The marriage of Maria Boone with Henry Johns pleased both of the
distantly interrelated families, knowing that the couple could expect
a stable and prosperous future. Bennett Johns was no doubt satis-
fied that he had dissuaded his son from a youthful desire to become
an artist and poet, for which he had demonstrated early aptitude.
While acknowledging that Henry was a talented and keen artist, Bennett insisted that he take up a 'solid profession' befitting an educated
young man. Therefore, he had placed Henry in a junior position in
the principal bank of Plymouth Dock (established 1790), appropri-
ately called the Plymouth Dock Bank. Somewhat later Bennett would
also be instrumental in placing Henry's younger brother, Alexander,
in a similar position in a bank in Ireland, where another son, William,
would settle also, to become a solicitor. That placement of Alexander would prove in future years to be of immense importance to his
nephew and namesake, Charles Alexander.

This was an age when occupations and professions were often, if
not always, achieved through family connection, and within strongly
maintained lines of social class distinction. Henry, at the age of 25,
became a partner (though an uncomfortable one for reasons to emerge)
in the private bank that then was known as 'Shiells and Johns.' Thus,
with some pride, he could take his 17-year-old bride, Maria, back to
the comfortable and prestigious home of Bank House in Fore Street,
the wide street leading to the Dock gates. Robinson comments (p
140) in his extensive illustrated history of Plymouth, 'today most of
what was Fore Street lies behind the Dockyard wall and there is little
left to convey the dignity and importance of what was for two centuries Devonport's finest thoroughfare.'[11]

Home and family

Plymouth Dock (shortened to Dock in local parlance) of Charles's
youth was thriving, the wars with France having brought employment and wealth to the area. Of the 'Three Towns,'[12] Dock was pre-

---

[10]Robinson (1991) *Victorian Plymouth, As time draws on,* p 151.

[11]Very few of Fore Street's finest buildings survived the Blitz of World War II.

[12]Plymouth Dock, Plymouth, and East Stonehouse made up the 'Three Towns.'

Engraving: Devonport Town Hall, Column and Egyptian Building designed by
Foulston

Engraving: Fore Street, Devonport 1832 [Thomas Allom, engr.]

eminent and the most populous by 1821 – 35,000 in Dock compared with 21,000 in Plymouth. New roads had improved travel between the Plymouth district, Exeter and London, as well as westwards into Cornwall. When, in the mid-18th century, the St Aubyn family of Clowance and St Michael's Mount in Cornwall had inherited the Manor of Stoke Damerel, upon which Dock is built, they brought new life and a long period of expansion to the whole area.[13] A theatre was built in Cumberland Street and good hotels, such as Elliott's Royal Hotel in Fore Street. George Edgcumbe had joined with St Aubyn to build Stonehouse Bridge in 1773, linking the two towns of Plymouth Dock and Stonehouse, which in turn was linked on its opposite side with Plymouth. St Aubyn also granted leases of land in Stonehouse on which the imposing houses of Durnford Street and Emma Place were built for naval officers and other wealthy residents, and the new elite enjoyed a lively social life with balls, dinners, assemblies and visits to theatres and concerts.

The architect, John Foulston, completed the Town Hall for Dock in 1821 to offer assembly rooms and a magistrates' court, beneath which were the cells and police offices. Two years later, the Egyptian building to his design was also completed, with the intention of it to be the Classical and Mathematical School. By 1827 it had become the Proprietary Library. Foulston's other major commission in 1818-19 was for the design of the Athenaeum for the Plymouth Institution, where prestigious lectures were given by scholars and scientists. This was the prosperous area into which Charles was born, and where he spent his early childhood. Living in Fore Street as the Johns family did, they were fully in the middle of things, with construction and fulsome activity all around them. For Charles, with libraries, schools headed by friends of his parents and civic institutions on his doorstep, it was a rich, cultural environment in which to begin life.

His youthful parents were part of the business and social life of the Three Towns in general, much of which depended greatly upon the private local banks such as 'Shiells and Johns.' Henry will have approved or turned down loans to most of the leading figures and entrepreneurs of the area, and he and Maria were invited and attended the many celebratory dinners and various civic occasions. Though

---

In 1824, Plymouth Dock was re-named Devonport.
[13]Johns Autograph Collection, Appendix v: St Levan letter.

banking was just inside the divide between the professions and 'trade,' Henry was considered a gentleman and was also known as a literary figure.[14] Their friends and associates were amongst the clergy of the Church of England, the propertied classes and the literary and teaching circles of the day. Also the Incledon connection was a decided advantage, belonging to a well-established Devon family of note. They moved comfortably amongst the educated gentry of the city, and gave time and patronage to events that extended the importance and influence of Plymouth as a centre and a seaport.

Very soon after their marriage the Johns family began to grow. The first child, Henry (also styled Incledon), was born in 1804, and two years later their first daughter, Maria. Being attentive and loving parents, the death of their third child, Elizabeth, in 1808, brought them great sadness, but Sophia followed a year later. Then on the very last day of December 1811, their second son was born and christened Charles Alexander.

Alexander[15] was a well-established family name, but the name Charles had not appeared in the Johns family tree before. Though not known for certain, the name was possibly chosen because of their illustrious relation, the singer Charles Incledon.[16] Incledon had invited his cousins, Maria and Henry, before little Charles's birth, to travel up to London to hear him perform in Covent Garden and to join him for supper afterwards, mentioned frequently within the family as an unforgettable occasion.[17] Charles joined a warm-hearted, lively family, where two more sisters, Emily Heywood (named for her paternal

---

[14]Henry Incledon Johns Sr's first published work appeared in 1804, when he assisted Thomas Hewitt Williams with *Picturesque Excursions in Devonshire and Cornwall,* based on a series of tours in Devon and Cornwall, largely on foot. The composed guides illustrated by their own etchings and lithographs were to set a pattern which the whole family would later follow, especially Charles, with much success.

[15]Charles was given the second name of Alexander, after his uncle, Alexander Johns of Carrickfergus, Ireland, and grandfathers before that. See family tree, Appendix i and biographical notes in Appendix ii.

[16]Annotated historically as Charles Benjamin or Benjamin Charles Incledon, but popularly known as Charles Incledon. Appendix ii outlines Incledon's family connections with Cornwall.

[17]A letter from Charles Incledon to his cousin Henry I Johns on 1 December 1815, presaging a performance in Exeter and sending greetings to the Johns family is part of the Autograph Collection (Appendix v).

aunt) and Julia, and a brother, Bennett George,[18] were to join him in the nursery in quick succession. The children grew up with nurses, maids and governesses to care for them and to teach them, but the influence of their parents also was strong. Henry Johns encouraged their love of nature from their earliest days and of sketching the flowers, trees and scenes that they encountered on their frequent walks. Being a somewhat reluctant banker, this did not preclude his original love of poetry, music, art and nature. One of his early poems begins:

'Come Charles and Sophie and Emily too,
Come down the green lane, papa's naught else to do.'[19]

Within the dedicatory comments of this little book Henry remembered 'happy hours, when we have rambled together amid the inexhaustible beauties of Creation; and when, in the loveliness of Nature, I have taught them to recognize the beneficence of Nature's God. – It has been my constant aim to inspire them with a taste for rural pursuits and pleasures.'

On their many walks they learned the names of the wild plants, insects and birds that they saw and wrote them in their diaries and notebooks. Charles, particularly, always responded with enthusiasm to these forays into the natural world and especially enjoyed the family holiday visits to Shaugh Prior, also in Devon. A village on the edge of Dartmoor, between Plymouth and Tavistock, close to the beautiful valley where the rivers Plym and Meavey meet, it would remain an important focal place of special memory for Charles throughout his life.

Taking holiday lodgings there, sometimes several times in the year, the family with friends would sketch, walk and climb the craggy heights of the Dewerstone, a tor set high above Shaugh Prior. It was probably here at Shaugh Prior that the lifetime friendship between

---

[18]Baby Bennett (carrying his grandfather's name), the first sibling of that name, was born in 1919 and died in infancy. Bennett George was born the following year, and would follow in Charles's steps throughout his life. See Appendix ii for further detail of Bennett George.

[19]H I Johns (1832) *Poems Addressed by a Father to his Children* held by Plymouth Central Library, Devon. This little book, appearing after Charles Johns had gone to Cornwall to teach at Helston, was published by the author with a subscription list for its costs. One of the purchasers was Derwent Coleridge.

St. Edward's Church, Shaugh Prior, Devon

the Johns and Carrington families was cemented, a connection of importance to them all, as time would prove.

The whole Johns family and the Carrington family attended the village church of St Edward at Shaugh Prior when on holidays and developed a strong attachment to both the church and village. Back home in Dock they attended church regularly as a family, two and three times on a Sunday, at St Aubyn's Chapel[20] on Chapel Street near the port. Latterly this has become St Aubyn's Church.

Shaugh Prior was in the nature of a second home in the country, in retreat from busy Devonport life. In far distant years both parents, Henry and Maria, were to be buried in the churchyard there, following on from the earlier burials of two of their newborn infants, Elizabeth (1808) and Bennett (1819), and Sophia (1819) who had lived for only 10 years. Internal to St Edward's today is the memorial plaque inscribed to their friend, Nicholas Toms (N T) Carrington, though he is buried near Bath, Somerset, the acknowledged 'Poet of Dartmoor,' and an early mentor of Charles. It was probably in Carrington's private school that Charles's formal education was begun, though there are no formal documentary records.

---

[20]A proprietary chapel established first in 1770-71.

The economic crisis of 1825

When Charles reached the age of 13, a sudden shocking change of fortunes was to throw into chaos the comfortable way of life led by his family and many others. Since the end of the Napoleonic wars in 1815, unemployment and poverty had been increasing rapidly, leading to a major recession in the British economy. The effect on the Plymouth area, a naval and military centre, was perhaps even more dramatic. In 1825, financial crisis struck a heavy blow when up and down the country 79 banks shut their doors. Both Shiells and Johns[21] of Devonport and the Elfords' Plymouth Bank were amongst the failures.

It was a desperate time, and desperate indeed for Henry, Maria and their children. Their money, social position and even their fine home were lost, because the private banks depended wholly on the capital assets of the partners. As the major creditors were paid out, all was taken from those that 'owned' the bank. Some friends and many associates deserted them. The family was forced to leave Fore Street and to move to a much smaller house about a mile further inland at Park Street, which at the time was located on the outskirts of Plymouth. In turn, they had to dispense with the services of their domestic servants (equally, a dire circumstance for those helpers). At that stage in British social history there was, of course, no welfare state of any kind to support families, nor a national banking alliance to back up financial institutions. New sources of finance and support for the large and close-knit family had to be found as a matter of urgency.

Charles, with his parents and six brothers and sisters, moved into their new home, all having to adjust to cramped conditions and tight finances without servants for washing and cooking. Their father turned to the only other skill he possessed, his natural ability for drawing and painting. These were avocations, along with nature rambling, that he had never abandoned. This forthright adaptability on Henry's part to change course when obstacles arose, was not a lesson lost on his children, and would prove to serve them well.

Teaching was not only an acceptable gentleman's profession, though not an especially lucrative one, but also a means of ensuring further education for his children. Henry became professor of drawing to the Plymouth New Grammar School and advertised for pupils to whom he could give private tuition. He also exhibited and sold a

---

[21]See Appendix ii for more detail about Henry Johns and the bank failure.

number of his watercolours. Although living in a very different style from before, it seemed that Henry enjoyed this new way of life and exploited his creativity to the full for as long as he was able.

The older children followed suit by taking on new responsibilities. Son Henry, at age 21, had taken a teaching post in a small Plymouth school while continuing to live at home and contribute to the family purse. Undoubtedly it helped that Henry Sr's friend N T Carrington also ran his own private school, and could offer advice and support within educational circles. Charles's sister, Maria, 19, also remained at home to help her mother with the care of the younger children until her marriage. Even thereafter Maria, living nearby with her cler-gyman-schoolmaster husband, aided her parents with constancy, as did Emily and Julia who followed. Charles at 13, was closest to his younger sisters, Emily, 11, and Julia, nine. Bennett George and Jane, youngsters of five and three, were joined in the now bursting home by Anne, born in 1827, and John Jacob (named for his eldest sister's husband, Dr John Jacob, but always called 'Jack') two years later, who completed the family. It was a lively, often noisy, yet culturally active environment in which all were led by their parents and the older sib-lings to write, to paint and draw and to make music, talents they would be called on to exploit for a living in future.

As he grew, Charles developed a serious interest in botany that was recognised and encouraged within the family circle and by their friends. He was able to continue his education, despite their strait-ened circumstances, as both his father and his brother were teachers, and it was essential for the future of the family that the boys were edu-cated properly to take up recognised professions. Charles's objectives, tutored not least by his parents, but also by their circle of Church of England and pedagogic friends, were to apply himself to his studies so that he too could take Holy Orders, sustain a living, teach and publish his work. His exemplars were those men, all around him in the world of education and some known to his father, who today in the 21st century have come to be called the 'English Parson-Naturalists.'[22]

---

[22] *The English Parson-Naturalist* is the title of Patrick Armstrong's book (2000), subtitled *A Companionship Between Science and Religion.* The author labelling Johns as a 'popularizer' comments that some regarded his writings as 'lightweight' while acknowledging that he 'seemed to have the knack of producing the type of natural history books the public wanted.'

The parish vicar in the nineteenth century held a position much sought after by the young intelligentsia of the day. Akin to the popularity of a lawyer's, or solicitor's qualification in our times, it was only the country squire who held a more elevated and esteemed position in their communities. While the quality of livings varied considerably, both in their remunerations and desirability, this did not seem to deter many college-bound gentlemen.[23]

'An ornament to society' and an aspiring author

His attendance at Devonport Grammar School was an important and lasting influence upon Charles, because the Master there was the Reverend John Jacob LLD, who was also the Minister of St Aubyn Chapel. John Jacob married Charles's elder sister, Maria, and was himself a botanist of some repute. He certainly would have encouraged the boy's interest in plants.[24] Indeed, in Dr Jacob is found the amalgam of botanical fascination, academic authorship and religious devotion that were to become the guiding lights of Charles's future life.

Charles also became a pupil of Mr George Banks FLS,[25] a silversmith and engraver of Devonport, who had published *An Introduction to the Study of English Botany* in 1823,[26] with illustrative plates of his own. Amongst the subscribers to this work had been Charles's father Henry while still a banker. Banks gave a course of lectures on botany in the town in 1826 that young Charles, at age 14, attended and from which he probably took his inspiration to understand the classification schemes into which plant life was organised by various investigators.[27] From 1830-32 Banks produced *Plymouth and Devonport Flora* in eight monthly parts at 1/- each. Together, Mr Banks

---

[23]Evans, Clifford (2000) Reverend C A Johns's unpublished essay in private collection.

[24]In 1835 Jacob published 18 monthly instalments of *A West Devon and Cornwall Flora*. See Appendix ii for biographical sketch.

[25]Noted by F H Davey in *Flora of Cornwall*, Introductory pages xxxvix-xl, commenting that Banks contributed 13 first botanical records for Cornwall.

[26]Second edition in 1832, reviewed favourably in the *Gardener's Magazine* (J C Loudon, Editor) of that year.

[27]A quarter of a century later, in his famous *Flowers of the Field* (1851), Johns devotes Chapter 1 – An Introduction to British Botany, and the whole of Chapter 2 – Systematic Botany, to the terms and arrangement put forward by Carl von Linne, the Swedish botanist after whom the Linnean Society took its name. This grounding he owed to his school days, following in the footsteps of George Banks FLS.

and Charles wandered the countryside outside of the Three Towns,
collecting and sketching as they walked. Under the entry for *Asperula
arvenis,* Field Woodruff, Banks wrote, 'The author is indebted for the
habitat of this hitherto undiscovered British species of *Asperula,* to
his young friend and pupil Mr C Johns, whose unwearied ardour in
scientific pursuits cannot fail to make him an ornament to society.'
This is the first known mention in print of Charles as a botanist, but
not many years hence his long career in terms of published work was
set to begin.

The change in the family's fortunes and circumstances naturally
had a strong and lasting effect upon Charles. While loving the outdoor life and enjoying friendship and fun, he had a serious, idealistic
and ambitious side to his nature. He continued his education, not
only with John Jacob, now his brother-in-law, but also at the new
Plymouth Grammar School, where his father was employed. Here
he reached a good standard in the classics and pure mathematics, the
studies taught by grammar schools to prepare their pupils for university entrance, an objective that had long been in his sights. He also
made a much more intense study of botany, seeking new plants to
identify, name and discuss with others who shared his enthusiasm.
He was also adept at sketching, though never in this art as dedicated
or adept as his sisters. Nevertheless, in future publications there are
smatterings of his sketches, all of which are botanical specimens or
geologic formations.

Emily[28] and Julia, two of his younger sisters, tutored as Charles
was by their parents, proved to be exceptionally talented artists and
illustrated many wild flowers that he brought home. Charles laid early
plans to write a book '. . . to introduce the lover of Nature to an
acquaintance with the common British flowering plants, to teach the
unscientific how to find out the names of the flowers met with in the
course of country rambles.'[29] Fuelled by the similar activity of those
around him, his ambitions were not unrealistic. He had a keen desire
to go to university, to gain distinction in the world of botanical stud-

---

[28]Emily Heywood Carrington (EHC) would later collaborate with Charles
Johns on the SPCK publications, *Monthly Wild Flower* and *Monthly Gleanings,* by
providing six-stanza poems for each of the months of the year (1858-62). See Bibliography.

[29]Emily Johns Carrington's early records.

ies, and to enter the church. But now that this projected progress had stumbled on the rocks of family finance, an easy solution was not to be expected. He would have to work through the difficulties in a different way, and his ambitious and inquisitive nature would stand him in good stead.

By 1830, when Charles was 19, his father's health began in general to fail, following an initial stroke. Henry was suffering a growing paralysis, first of his legs and then of his hands, making it impossible for him to continue teaching. Sister Emily, at only 16, took over her father's private pupils, but the family was virtually destitute, and very frightened at this new turn of events.

The house was full with Bennett George (10 years), a scholar following in Charles's footsteps, Jane (eight) and Anne (three). Baby John was barely a year old, when this even more desperate state of affairs arose in all its force. Though 'Jack' was the last child, there were still the other mouths to feed. Of 12 pregnancies, Henry and Maria had eight living children, all at present remaining at home. The older ones knew that much was dependent on their efforts to keep the family together. Charles realised full well that he must put aside his purely academic ideas, at least for the moment, and find work to help support the family. At least by providing for himself, there would be one less to feed at home.

Their close friends, the Carrington family, were facing similar difficulties as N T's tuberculosis progressed. His school in Devonport had to be closed down in the face of his inability to carry on. Realising that he, too, was going to be shouldering the responsibility for his mother and brothers and sisters, Henry Carrington (N T's oldest son), at age 24, had borrowed sufficient funds to purchase the *Bath Chronicle* newspaper and printing works. In the early part of 1830 the whole family had removed to a rental property in Bath, where N T died in September of the same year.[30] Now the next generation of both families would become the mainstays. They were immensely fortunate in their friendship.

---

[30]Both Charles and Emily attended his funeral in Bath, and N T was buried in the churchyard at Combe Hay. The aforementioned memorial plaque in the church at Shaugh Prior attests to his deep love for Dartmoor.

Engraving: Devonport Docks. Published 1829.

Engraving: A south west view of Helston. Published by W. Penaluna, 1815.

2

THINKING AHEAD

Charles applied for the post of assistant master at the Grammar School in Helston, Cornwall, under its headmaster, Derwent Coleridge.[31] Henry Johns, in writing to recommend his son to his own 'old school' and to Coleridge, commented that Charles had given much time to botany 'which shows that he is studious.' Early in 1831, the appointment was secured for Charles and he began to make his plans for starting work in the early spring. He would be returning to his parents' native county and the home of many relations in the John, Incledon and Boone families. None of the ardour with which his mentor George Banks complimented him in print had cooled. Ahead of him was a new set of fields for his observations, and on these he set his professional sights. Never far from his thoughts was the need for further education and the advancement necessary to secure his family's future.

Young Johns was joining an exceptional headmaster who was to have a lasting influence on the educational development of the nation, and a lasting legacy of importance to Charles himself. The younger son of the poet and philosopher Samuel Taylor Coleridge, Derwent had grown up listening to the poetry and philosophical conversations that his brilliant father held with Southey (also his uncle and often surrogate father), Wordsworth and other Lakeland poets. All of these Charles was familiar with, as his avocation, following in his father's wake, was poetry. At St John's College, Cambridge, Derwent had spent much of his time involved with a group of intelligent and

---

[31]His story is told by the author of this book, 'Derwent Coleridge and his contemporaries,' Chapter 5, in *The Unknown Founder, The Story of Helston Grammar School*, from which some of background research is taken. His full biography is told in *The Unknown Coleridge, The Life and Times of Derwent Coleridge 1800-1883*, Hainton, R & G (1996).

influential young students, including Thomas Babington Macaulay, William Praed and Frederick Denison Maurice, discussing literature, philosophy, religion and politics, to the detriment of his personal studies. Leaving Cambridge in 1824 with an undistinguished degree, Coleridge had spent a short time teaching in Plymouth at the grammar school where, a year later, Charles's father became the professor of drawing.

While in Devon, Derwent Coleridge met and fell in love with Mary Pridham, daughter of the director of the Naval Bank in Whimple Street, the only Plymouth bank not to close in the 1825 crisis that had brought such disaster to the Johns family. Charles and his parents may well have met both Derwent and Mary in Plymouth at this time. Even if the Johns family did not know Coleridge personally before Charles went to Helston, it is certain that they did know the Pridham family socially, both having been banking families in the same district for some time.

Coleridge, at the youthful age of 27, had gone to take up his appointment as headmaster in Helston fully four years before Charles was even old enough to consider joining him, or to realise the necessity of a job rather than to continue his studies, as he had assumed. That same year (1827) Derwent had been ordained priest at Exeter, and licensed by the bishop there to take pastoral charge of the endowed school of Helston in the western reaches of Cornwall. A relation of his, another Coleridge (James Duke Coleridge, 1789-1857), was established in a living at Kenwyn, Truro, and had offered him work in his gift if all else failed. He thought the Helston post would stretch Derwent more, however, and recommended that he should accept the post there.

Derwent also had struggled, and would continue to struggle to overcome many setbacks, brought on by the rackety life of his father, his broken but loving family, and the straitened financial circumstances that always prevailed in the educational milieu. Coleridge became an additional model from whom Charles would learn much and find inspiration, and with whom he would remain in close touch throughout his life. The added aura of Coleridge for Charles was certainly the former's connections in the poetic and scientific circles of the day, names that he knew well through his avid reading and his own frequent writing of poems, especially about nature.

On a spring day in March 1831, Charles could have been seen

Derwent Coleridge (1850)

striding down Fore Street in Plymouth, passing by the large Georgian
house where he had been born, and hurrying on to enter the busy
harbour. He was to board the steamship *Sir Francis Drake* and cross
from Plymouth in Devon to Falmouth in Cornwall. He would have
been very conscious that, instead of going up to the university as he
had dreamed, he was travelling in the opposite direction to a remote
and relatively isolated place. It seemed at that stage his ambitions
would remain unattainable, but he was not giving up, as his diary
would show. It is inspirational now to remember that his work would
introduce many visitors to that remote area, who would otherwise
have been unaware of its charms until much later.

Naturally the Johns family were familiar with Helston and its
grammar school where both Charles's father and his uncle had been
pupils, and their cousins were involved in the civic life of the town and
nearby Wendron, where generations of his family had their home.[32]

---

[32]Indeed, if one views a list of the burials at St Keverne alone, during Charles's
lifetime there are some 14 Johns family memorials, recording concurrent lives,
many of whom exceed his own in longevity and most of whom carry the favoured

The next years spent in the Cornish homeland of his ancestors and relatives were to give Charles an ideal environment, not only for his researches in wild flowers and natural history, but also for the invaluable experience in educational methods under an unusual and energetic headmaster. He was also to meet and become friends with several others who would give him friendship, connections, support and encouragement for the rest of his life. There were many unknowns, but he seemed to see it all as a welcome challenge.

It is to be supposed that Charles, as a small child, may have accompanied his parents on visits to their relatives in the Helston area upon occasion, but he would not have travelled there by sea, rather by coach. His mother's parents, the Boones, who had been living in Antony near Plymouth while Boone was in the Royal Navy, latterly retired to Rosenithon, a hamlet close to St Keverne, on the Lizard, their own home country. From 1825, the steamship service had been running from Plymouth, carrying passengers to Falmouth on twice-weekly runs, and using two steamers – the *Brunswick* and the *Sir Francis Drake*. This speeded up the journey from Charles's home to his new term-time life in Helston that otherwise would have required lengthy travel by stagecoach.

Leaving Plymouth Sound by ship, Charles could watch the sea birds, the changing colours of the cliffs and coves, and the fleets of fishing boats. Unknown to him at that stage, but of momentous revelation to the world thereafter, from that same dock and within the same year, Charles Darwin was to set sail on *HMS Beagle*, after some weeks' residence in Devonport, for five years of wandering the world. For Charles Johns, the future was much less dramatic in its impact, but so was his voyage. After approximately six hours' travelling time, Charles Johns's steamship reached the large and thriving port of Falmouth, from where he journeyed on by coach and horses across the downs to Helston.

---

family names. In a fashion familiar to Cornwall even now, many families are quite closely interconnected through marriage. Charles was joining a community of his own cousins, their families (thereby his own) and their friends.

KYNANCE—from the Rill.

From *A Week at the Lizard*, 3rd ed, p 86.

Engraving: Helston Grammar School, 1835.

3

ARRIVING IN CORNWALL

O n the first occasion of his arrival, Derwent and his wife Mary (always referred to in his diary as Mr C and Mrs C) were waiting for the coach, to welcome and lead him to his new home. Charles would live together with the family in their large house on Wendron Street, assisting them in looking after the boys who boarded there, as well as teaching in the school at the bottom of the town. The Reverend Derwent Coleridge was also responsible for the spiritual life of his pupils, and assisted in the parochial care of the parish. This was the model of both teaching and pastoral care to which Charles also aspired, and of which the whole of his family approved and supported.

The previous Master had resigned during 1826, leaving parish and school in a run-down state. Appointed shortly after to take over, the following years had given Coleridge the opportunity to transform the affairs of both, and in these endeavours he would now have the assistance, and hopefully the friendship, of young and energetic Charles Johns.

Coleridge in writing earlier to Mary had described the new[33] schoolhouse to which Johns came, in graphic terms as 'a queer old everlastingly passagy, odds and endsy, roomy, stairsy, straggling, incomprehensible dwelling, with offices innumerable and an under-cellar capable of holding 500 dozen of wine....The garden is a delightful little spot, full of currant and gooseberry bushes with a strawberry bed and a little wall fruit, also one standard apple tree in the midst of a little grass plot.'[34] This was the schoolhouse from which Charles Johns

---

[33]Soon after Derwent's arrival in 1927, Lord Godolphin had bought a large house 'with gardens, tenements and blacksmith's shop attached' that he presented to the Grammar School as the Master's House where boarders could also be lodged.

[34]Hainton, Raymonde and Godfrey (1996) *The Unknown Coleridge*, p 93, London: Janus.

was to make his frequent forays into the countryside, to study and expand his knowledge of the world of natural things, and to which he would return in later years when he became its headmaster.

A description Johns would put into print some years later about Helston as a place is succinct and unremarkable, pointing to its location on the map of the district, situated on the side of the Cober Valley north of Loe Pool and Mount's Bay.

> This clean, and, on market days, busy little town, is situated at the root of the promontory which terminates in the Lizard, and on the west is distant from the sea a little more than two miles, being on the east three miles from an arm of the sea which terminates at a village called Gweek.
>
> (*A Week at the Lizard*, Chapter 1)

The Borough of Helston (Hen-lis-ton in ancient times, and a number of other spellings in between), with its Charter of 1201, was a town of some importance in the west of Cornwall as a 'coinage town,' to which tin was brought from the mines all around to be stamped and authenticated. Achieving that status during the reign of Edward I (1272-1307), more than a hundred tin and copper mines were worked in the district over many centuries. The local grandees and gentry tended to be mine owners, and the local miners attended the coinage halls around the Duchy to have their tin tested and weighed before being sold.

Coinagehall Street is the name of the main thoroughfare of Helston, noted for its charm and interest latterly by the poet and traveller, John Betjeman. In the period of Coleridge and Johns, it was represented, as a borough, by two Members of Parliament, handpicked appointments of the local patron, the Earl of Godolphin, who paid large sums of money for the power to nominate them. The Godolphin family had rebuilt the Church of St Michael's in 1761, paying 'all Church rates and other expenses incurred about the town, such as Lecturer's salary...'[35] Nonetheless, in ecclesiastical terms it did not attain its independence from its Mother Church of Wendron, the home of the John(s) clan, until 1848. Therefore Coleridge's appointment was to a curacy, rather than the higher level of rector.

The patron's financial support was critical for the grammar school

---

[35]Toy, H Spencer (1936) *History of Helston* pp 283-4 Oxford: OUP.

and its future. The mayor and corporation were responsible for the maintenance of the school, for appointing its masters, paying the annual endowment of twenty marks (£13 6s 8d), and providing two free places for poor boys of the borough. However, it is clear that Lord Godolphin also had a say in the appointments, especially as the head-master was frequently also the 'Lecturer' or curate of the parish.[36]

A typical 'pocket borough,' Helston was ruled by its mayor, Justice and Aldermen, who were able to keep the offices within a few fami-lies by constantly rotating the positions and re-electing themselves.[37] When Coleridge arrived, the mayor was Humphrey Millet Grylls Esq and the justice (ex-mayor) was Richard Gerveys Grylls Esq. The Coleridges had been welcomed by a leading group of gentry, includ-ing the Trevenens with whom they became especially friendly, Miss Emily Trevenen[38] being a particular favourite and associate of Mary and Derwent. They were not to be disappointed with the improve-ments and ideas that Coleridge would bring to his post. And from this general atmosphere of good will and generous patronage, Charles could expect to benefit as well. His eagerness to learn and to excel was not dampened in that environment, and the friends of the Coleridges became also his own circle of friends and acquaintances. At the same time, he associated himself at every turn with those of his old friends and family in Plymouth who continued their engagement with plant-hunting and botanical matters in general, and began correspondence with botanists when this was possible.

In Charles's journal, there is not a large account about his teach-ing or the school,[39] but from reports in other sources it seems that

---

[36]The term 'Lecturer' of Helston emanates from the patronage of Queen's Col-lege, Oxford, which institution had purchased it for its Michel Foundation, 'con-sequently, graduates of this college have usually occupied the rectory of Helston.' Toy, p 334.

[37]*Ibid* pp 284-5.

[38]Emily Trevenen's letters to Mary Coleridge and others, are part of the Rob-ert Wolff Collection of Victorian literature at the Henry Crowe Ransom Centre, University of Texas, Austin. See also Jenkyn, Ann Trevenen 'Appendix A: Emily Trevenen' in Dare, D (1996) *An Unknown Founder*. Emily was also the author of *Little Derwent's Breakfast, By a Lady* (1839), a collection of stories and poems for the amusement of Derwent and Mary's son.

[39]C A Johns Diary, held by Cornwall Record Office (Dec 1832-1838), CRO DDXII. p 111.

he settled easily into his new life, getting on well with Coleridge and Mary and making friends with pupils and parents. Like Coleridge, he enjoyed mixing with the more civic-minded and important members of Helston society, as he would have been recognised as part of the larger community because of his own family connections. In fact, of course, on a personal level he was financially very straitened and unqualified, with heavy responsibilities for his family at home. But, he engaged and enjoyed all the social and religious occasions that occurred with regularity throughout the school terms. The 'Annual School Meeting' was a major one of these, and one towards which the whole school worked.

For many years the school had held its Annual School Meeting in September, when the pupils joined past pupils for a service in St Michael's Church, followed by recitations and prize-giving in the school. The old boys would then enjoy a formal dinner at the Angel Inn, followed by a ball the next day. In 1831, only a few months after Charles Johns's arrival, the day before the School Meeting, the boys were examined on their work 'when their proficiency gave great satisfaction and was highly creditable to their teachers.'[40] Charles was included in the praise, though new to his post as second master. The next day proceeded with the service, the recitations in the school-room and in the evening prizes were presented to Vivian major, Rogers major and Moyle, sons of well-known local families.

The dinner at the Angel Hotel was described as 'sumptuous,' including venison, other game and the finest wines, and on the following evening 'the attendance at the ball was numerous and fashionable, and dancing was kept up throughout with unabated spirit.' Charles enjoyed both the dinner and the ball, as he continued to do over the following years, as oft remarked in his diary.

Interestingly enough, his journal begins with favourite passages from various books and newspapers, with cuttings clipped out and pasted in (some later extracted or torn out, leaving the book patchy in places). There is an excerpt from Knapp's *Journal of a Naturalist* regarding the predominance of yellow in English wildflowers. Further entries range from *Elements of Entomology* by Kirby and Spence, and thence to material from unknown sources on such diverse subjects as statistical information on casualties suffered in the French Revolution, the plight of

---

[40] *West Briton* newspaper 30 Sept 1831, p 2f.

Polish Jews, and Gardiner's *Discipline of Dublin University*. The dates these items were added are not always given, but the book appears to be divided in half, with published cuttings pasted into the first part, and diary entries starting in the second. This is the only diary located to this time, but leads one to suspect that there must have been a library of these, to record at least the references and cuttings that Charles would employ in his future works (See Appendix iv).

As Trenoweth so ably reviews Charles's prospects at that stage: 'He must have thought that he had found a plant paradise...The Lizard became Charles's living library, his outdoor workroom/laboratory, and the inspiration for his books. He would often walk more than 20 miles in a day in his search for wild flowers '"with no other companions than a volume of Wordsworth or Sutton[41] and a stout cudgel."'[42]

The entries in his diary reveal not only a conscientious teacher, serious in his ambitions and botanical studies, but a physically active young man, appreciative of food, wine and attractive young women, enjoying music and fun. To appreciate the mix of activity, ambition and emotion in a young man's life, at the best of times, is not an easy task, but his diaries and books speak for themselves. Interlaced as they are with the accounts of the walks he undertook, one is immensely impressed with his stamina. Without hesitation he flung himself into the pursuit of his life's passions.

[41]Reference to ? Rev Charles Sutton (1756-1846), botanist, Alfred Sutton (Partner in Seed Firm) or other.

[42]Roger Trenoweth quoting from Johns's letter to W J Hooker (November 1835). [Kew Archive].

Helston Grammar School door.

"The Flora Day tune is not to be forgotten by anybody who has ever heard it for the live-long day at Helleston. It never ceases for that day."

4

HELSTON LIFE, THE FIRST STEPS: 1831-32

For the first time, Charles Johns viewed the celebrated Flora Day dances, though probably not dancing on this initial occasion. The 8th of May was (and still is) Flora or 'Furry' Day in Helston, a very special day of springtime celebration that was probably pagan in its origins.

It began in the early morning with the 'Hal-an-Tow,' when a group of men and boys bearing branches of trees would parade the streets singing a song of welcome to summer. W F Collier,[43] writing some 60 years later, recalled how, when he was a pupil at the Grammar School, the boys went out to find leafy branches to decorate the school and that all the town was cleaned ready for the 'Furry' dance, which would wind in and out of shops and houses. The first to dance at 11 o'clock were the gentry: 'They were dressed in their best — the ladies in their brightest and newest Spring fashions; and the men — well, they wore colours more than they do now. Brown or green frock coats, or a bright riding tailcoat with metal buttons, nankeen trousers, and 'cheerful' waistcoats (as tailors called that gorgeous piece of apparel) were in vogue.'

Collier continued: 'After the gentry had danced their dance, the tradespeople did precisely the same, with the same band, the same tune, the same dance, through the same streets and the same houses.' Society in Helston was divided into three classes, and after the tradespeople, the working classes, such as the servants, masons or carpenters, followed with their dance. Charles attended these celebrations each year and included a description in *A Week at the Lizard* many years later, concluding that: 'In all probability it is a relic of very remote antiquity, and no slight confirmation of this opinion is

---

[43]Collier, W F (1889) *The Cornish Magazine* Vol 2, Jan-May pp 121-3.

afforded by the fact, that the air played while the dancing is going on is still traditional in Wales and Brittany . . .' (*Week*, pp 177-9)

24 August 1831

It was Charles's first summer as a teacher. Despite poor weather, he set out alone at 8am to look for rare plants in Kynance Cove. His equipment consisted of 'a walking–stick, a folio book for drying specimens in (which was slung over my back), a packet of sandwiches,[44] and a small flask of brandy.' Not realising where he was and ignorant of the tides, he collected various plants and then found himself cut off by the sea. He relates in great detail his unsuccessful attempts to climb the cliffs and his despair at the thought of having to spend 10 or 11 hours in the rain before the tide would allow him to escape. Finally, he made a determined effort to climb the cliff despite the danger, and reached the top with trembling limbs and tears of relief. The illustration to this 'perilous expedition' shows Charles teetering on the edge of a rocky ridge, carrying his book and pack – and wearing his top hat (*Week* p 101 'A Botanical Adventure'). He wrote down a thoroughly harrowing tale of his expedition the following day and confirmed that 'it was the opposite of an exaggerated account.' He followed those pages of description with heart-felt advice to climbers.

'It is much *more difficult* to descend than to ascend the face of a precipitous cliff, and therefore, *less dangerous*; and again, it is much *easier* to ascend a place of the same character than to descend, and, therefore, *more dangerous*. This will appear to be a paradox, and on that account it will, I hope, be remembered; but nevertheless, experience will prove that the maxim is a sound one. A climber, in descending, instinctively shrinks from climbing down any places where his body would be likely to be thrown off its balance, unless he can secure a firm footing and a good holdfast for his hands; and if he reaches a spot which is impracticable, he can make sure of being able to return by the way he came. On the other hand, in ascending, his body is thrown forward, he can see the nature of the rock which he is climbing, and has a far greater command over his hands and feet; in addition to which he is not likely to become giddy, for there is no necessity for him to look down.'

---

[44]D E Allen in *The Naturalist in Britain, A Social History*, points to this mention of a packet of sandwiches by Johns in *A Week at the Lizard*, as the first mention of them specifically by a naturalist in print.

From *A Week at the Lizard*, J W Whymper, 1874, 3rd ed, p 101.

On all his walks Charles was increasing his knowledge and understanding of the geological and botanical nature of the area. In his Appendix to *A Week in the Lizard* he traces the geological changes from Trewavas Head, west of Helston, to the southern tip of the Lizard, showing how the varied rocks affected the plant life (*Week* Appendix III pp 263-8). He collected and studied the flowers, ferns and mosses he found. Though not attempting to 'enter into a dissertation on the mineralogical or geological condition of the district,' he points the tourist interested in geology toward the 'rare opportunity of examining the magnesian rocks, hornblende, serpentine, diallage, and talc-slate' of the Lizard (*Week* p 263).

May 1832

Charles noted the title: '*Magazine of Zoology and Botany* – Letters by post should be addressed to Sir W Jardine, Jardine Hall by Lockerbie, Dumfrieshire. Books for view and parcels containing communications to the care of W H Lizars, Edinburgh or S Highley, Fleet Street, London' (Diary, p 1). He presumably sent for this magazine. Later he wrote notes from the *Journal of a Naturalist,* referring to the colour yellow in nature, and mentions, 'Rev Mr Kirby's identification of small caterpillar on brambles.' Many naturalists were also parsons, such as the Reverend Mr Kirby (1759-1850), who was vicar of Barham in Suffolk, a botanist and entomologist who had written, amongst other publications, a monograph on English bees. They regarded their study of nature as an activity that brought them closer to God and his creation and something to be shared with other enthusiasts.[45]

Armstrong makes the useful case for parson-naturalists as teachers or 'popularizers.' 'The nineteenth-century county or parochial flora was not generally illustrated, and the style was scientific and full of compressed detail. There has long been a demand for a different kind of volume, for natural history books that are a lighter read, and with illustrations that are easy on the eye. Clerical naturalists were often quite successful at filling this particular niche.'[46] Though this kind of analysis may read dismissively, this is not in fact Armstrong's intention. As part of of a continuum from 'compressed detail' only of interest perhaps to other dedicated scientists, through to the modern day, the parson-naturalists became an important bridge, and provided a network of correspondence open to everyone, and most readily to women.[47] Without these people, many of our modern societies, such as the Royal Society for the Protection of Birds and the National Trust, could not have evolved.

The increasing interest in plants and gardens throughout the country had led to the formation of Horticultural Societies, which held regular exhibitions. Charles attended and participated in these at every opportunity. W F Collier complained that Johns 'was not a good teacher, and did not make his lessons interesting, as Derwent Coleridge did. He heard lessons sharply enough, but was often all the time setting up specimens of botany, no doubt for publication, as I thought them beautifully done. I well remember now some very pret-

---

[45]Armstrong, Patrick (2000) *The English Parson-Naturalist,* pp 1-4 Leominster: Gracewing. Also D E Allen (1978), *The Naturalist in Britain,* pp 102-3 Harmondsworth: Pelican Books.

[46]*Ibid* p 61-2.

[47]The feminine discourse or 'dialogue' with nature in Victorian times is a fascinating study on its own, touched on in this book only in terms of the almost anonymous illustrators of Johns's work, but contemporary readers will find much to ponder in the work of Barbara T Gates and Ann B Shteir (see bibliography).

ty specimens of mosses in flower set up while I was hammering over Virgil.'[48] Collier accepted that Johns later proved to be an excellent educationalist and that there must have been some prejudice in his remarks, due to his displeasure at his own dull labours whilst Charles was indulging his passions.

" Holy Well," Trelill, near Helston, Cornwall.

Holy Well, Trelill, near Helston. From *A Winter Ramble in the Country*, 1847.

---

[48]Collier *Cornish Magazine, op cit*, p 118.

Engraving: Launceston. Published 1824 by Simpkin & Marshall, London.

5

WALKS & TALKS

January 1833

Charles also continued his botanical studies during the holidays. His expertise was sufficiently appreciated to lead to occasional invitations to give lectures, for which he was probably paid a small fee. In this new year of 1833, Charles would also publish a piece of his own work for the first time, and presumably at his own expense. He wrote *Chronological Rhymes on English History* to amuse and aid his pupils on what might seem a dry subject.

At the beginning of the year he was invited to the Launceston Institute of Botany. Crossing from Plymouth to Saltash, he was met by a man with a gig and taken to the then county town of Cornwall, where Mr Darke, the Secretary, greeted him and they dined together. 'About 30 Ladies and Gentlemen attended the lecture' he wrote, and Mr Darke returned to the Inn with him afterwards, where they 'supped together.' The next day Charles explored the town and admired the ruined castle, and the church, 'the body of which is very beautiful having nearly every stone richly carved and ornamented' (Diary p 117). He returned by way of Tavistock, where he dined with Mr Edgecombe, returning home to Plymouth by the Tavistock stage coach.

Charles generally enjoyed his journeys between Helston and Plymouth, unless the weather conditions were too unpleasant. He records a journey from Falmouth to Plymouth at the end of term as 'a delightful passage,' taking from 10.30 am to 4.30 pm. On the return trip to Falmouth, in January of 1833, he notes his expenses for the boat, dinner and the post-chaise to Helston as 'Porter 6d., Boat 9d., fare 12/6, dinner 4/- including brandy & waiter, Boat 1/-, chaise 7/6, Porter 6d., in all £1-6-9' (Diary p 118). He seems to have travelled in pleasant style, despite his need to save money.

February

On 8 February, Charles made the comparatively short walk to the
fishing harbour of Porthleven (two and a half miles) 'to see wreck
of the *John and Mary* from Cork for Plymouth laden with pork and
butter stranded on the beach about 100 yards east of the pier – her
bottom knocked out – part of ye cargo lost – no lives lost'(Diary p
119). He continues: 'She mistook the light at Penzance pier-head for
the Lizard and seeing a light at Porthleven (which was a man carrying
a lantern) mistook Porthleven for Falmouth and ran in as the weather
was very bad. She was sold this afternoon.'

On a fine afternoon, he walked to Gunwalloe cove on the Lizard
with Davis (a pupil). Very thirsty, he went into the public house and
asked for some bottled porter, '"had none." "Some of their best beer?"-
"Very sorry had none, their beer had not done working," obliged to
drink some cider.' On other outings, he went to a mill to beg for a
piece of bread and butter, and to a Redruth inn for bread, cheese and
porter.

> *13 February:* 'Walked to Merthen after dinner although ye weath-
> er was very unpromising the wind being hard and the sky much
> obscured by clouds – took tea and on my setting off on my return
> found it a decidedly bad evening, pitch black, raining fast and blow-
> ing hard – coming across the fields I was forced to hold my stick out
> before me to avoid running against the gates.'
>
> (Diary p 118)

Romance was obviously not a subject that Charles avoided thought
of at the age of 22, and his entry for Valentine's Day of that year shows
oblique reference:

> I know not whether it be ominous of discord to newly married peo-
> ple to have bad weather on Valentine's day the year they are married;
> if so those who enter the connubial state this year will have a fair
> prospect of foul weather not only during the *lune de l'absinthe* but
> also *du miel,* for about twelve this morning we had a tremendous
> storm which lasted two hours . . . .

Charles regularly walked the 10 miles from Helston across the wild
Goonhilly Downs to St Keverne to visit his grandparents, George
and Mary Boone. On 16 February, he left Helston at 12.30pm on

'a lovely sunny day' arriving at Rosenithon, just beyond St Keverne, at 3.15. He found his grandfather (always referred to as Mr Boone) 'as usual hale and strong, he had walked to Helford 6 miles and back again one day without feeling any ill-effects' (Diary p 120). Not so, his grandmother Mary, who he found just recovering from a third paralytic seizure which nearly killed her. Mr Boone was about 88 years old at this time and Charles was obviously proud of him. The following day was wet, but after visits to church and to friends Charles records that he walked back to Helston in two and three-quarter hours.

Three days later, the weather was very stormy. Charles writes: 'Rigged myself in foul-weather clothes and walked to Porthleven.' On Loe Bar, a sand barrier between the large freshwater lake in the Penrose estate and the sea, a mile east of the harbour, the waves were 'mountainous high,' and Charles describes their towering shapes and how he tried to protect his ears from the sand particles blown fiercely against him. 'I could compare it with nothing but a drizzling shower with the exception that the stones were rather harder than ye drops of water, but they were quite as numerous; I could not bear to hold the back of my hand to the shower for more than a half minute.' Returning home at noon he found Coleridge preparing to take the same walk. Charles writes that he turned back with him to walk the two and a half miles there 'as I was not tired . . . We found ourselves up to the knees in water several times being surprised by the waves. At four o'clock I was quite ready for my dinner' (Diary p 122).

24 Feb. 1833. 'Went with Mr C to Crowan, 5 miles, where he was to take the duty for Mr Grylls who was ill. We left at a quarter to nine and reached Crowan at ten or rather before. Dined on roast fowl at the vicarage. After dinner I went to Clowance and amused myself with teasing a surly old swan. He had once chased Sir John St Aubyn from the pond to the house a quarter of a mile and was very near being put to death, but was saved at the intercession of Mr Grylls. He had, however, one wing broken which prevented him from doing much mischief. He swam round the edge of the pond by my side, and when I held my stick at him bit it in a very resolute manner, till getting vexed he sprang out of the water and very nearly caught my leg. He looked very awkward when out of the water and when he attempted to run after me (not being able to use his wings) he looked so very ridiculous that I could not contain my laughter, with his outstretched neck, his ponderous carcase and seven-leagued steps he appeared to be falling on his nose every minute. Mr Coleridge preached again in the evening and we arrived home at 9.0 pm.'

(Diary pp 123-4)

LOE POOL.—from Degibna Wood.

A month later, he visited the Porthleven area again, to see the Bar cut. 'From the wetness of the season the Loe Pool had risen so high that the Bar had been cut through once and broken itself twice and was again cut through today' (Diary p 125). When the water could not escape from the lake, the lower part of Helston would be flooded and, according to ancient tradition, the mayor would place three halfpence in a stout leather purse and send it to the Lord of the Manor of Penrose, asking permission to cut the Bar.[49] Charles continued:

I went down at 12 o'clock, it had been cut three hours and the water was then running out with very great violence – the channel was I should think more than 50 yards wide. The manner in which the stream met the waves of the sea was very beautiful. They appeared to struggle against one another till one drove the other back. The current had washed the sand in such a way that a high wall was formed on both sides, when I amused myself by sitting on the top and the formation being very unsubstantial a great piece of the embankment … gave way and we slid very gently together to the bottom.

This description reveals not only a young man of high spirits but also a writer of exactness and imagination, which was to appeal to his many readers in later years.

Charles's walks took him west along the cliffs to Breage and

---

[49]Cowls, Bert (1982) *Looking Back to Yesterday* Helston: p 102.

beyond, and east to Gweek and Falmouth; he walked to visit the Duke of Leeds' estate at Clowance and the mansion of the Vyvyans at Trelowarren. Sometimes he walked alone, but more often he was accompanied by friends or pupils, those who shared his interest in the flowers and ferns of the unspoiled countryside, especially on the Lizard. All this walking made him hungry and thirsty, and he would record his experiences of enjoyable or less palatable fare. Later in the year, he records a walk towards Wendron for 'a good tea on cold roast pork and eggs at Lenderyou's' (Diary p 132).

March
Helston Grammar School had flourished under Derwent Coleridge. By March of 1833 Charles could write, 'the number of boarders having increased from 14 to 21 since I have been here I this day wrote to Mr Coleridge requesting an increase of salary. He agreed to give me all the French £20 and £32 a year for this half, which latter sum he would increase at Midsummer to £40 and Midsummer twelvemonth to £50' (Diary p 124). Charles was proving a valuable assistant, but his diary notes continually remind him that more study is needed if he is to progress beyond that position.

His family was always closely in touch with Charles, and at the end of March his mother wrote saying that she would visit him at Helston on her way through to her parents at St Keverne, as Mrs Boone was very ill and had sent for her. The following day he hired a gig to collect his mother and bring her back for tea with Mary Coleridge,

Engraving: Trelowarren, c 1830, *Lyson's Cornwall.*

before seeing her to the Henwoods where she slept the night, before
Mr Henwood took her on by gig to St Keverne the next day. Maria
Johns remained in Cornwall until 20 April, when Charles, after a walk
around the town with her, saw her off by the Mail in the evening.

April

Charles enjoyed his contacts with the gentry and visits to their homes
and gardens, and he even donated his labour from time to time. Over
the Easter holidays he was invited to spend several days with Mr Benjamin Sampson and his family at their home, Tullimaar, Perranwharf,
not far from Truro.[50] Their son was a pupil at Helston Grammar
School, and Charles writes: 'We left Helston at half past twelve in
his phaeton which had been sent for us and arrived in rather more
than an hour and a half. The house is situated very beautifully near
a branch of the river on which Truro stands, opposite to Carcleugh'
(Carclew) (Diary pp 128-9).

After dinner, Mr Sampson, with son Vivian ('an old pupil now at
Harrow') and Charles, rode in to Truro to take tea with Mr Wilson,
the attorney, though Charles says no more about the reason for the
visit. He visited Truro again the next day with Mrs Sampson to bring
home her niece from boarding school there and to go shopping in this
fashionable Cornish town, with its own Coinage Hall for assaying tin,
its fine Georgian houses and Assembly Rooms.

On the following day, Good Friday, Charles writes that he was first
invited to admire Mr Sampson's garden, with its terraces and shrubs,
'when Mr Henwood[51] the Geologician came up with a very important face holding a stone in each hand' (Diary p 130). Henwood was
indignant that someone had removed a quantity of a rare mineral,
chalcedony, found by men working on a road. He reckoned that he
could have sold this mineral for a hundred pounds, while the men
were given only a few gallons of beer.

The family then attended Perran church, where the preacher was
a Mr Webber, but Charles wrote: 'The church is very small and badly

---

[50]In the late 20th century, the home of the Nobel Laureate Sir William Golding
and his family.

[51]William Jory Henwood, born in 1805 in a nearby house in Perranarworthal,
was to become a distinguished scientist and mining geologist, and the family were
friends of the John and Boone families in Cornwall. A brother was a medical doctor.

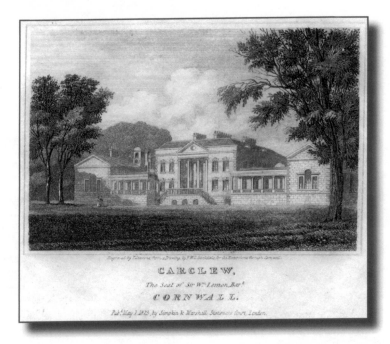

CARCLEW,
The Seat of Sir W.ᵐ Lemon, Bar.ᵗ
CORNWALL.

attended with no singing' (Diary p 130). After dinner they visited
Carcleugh (Carclew), the beautiful mansion of Sir Charles Lemon,
and admired the house, grounds and greenhouse before joining for
tea with the family. Charles was particularly impressed by some very
tall fungi, which he thought must be about 14 feet high. He described
the architecture of the house in some detail.

Their next visit was further afield, to Thehiddy (Tehidy), the grand
home of the Basset family near the north coast and not far from
the mining towns of Camborne and Redruth. Francis Basset, who
became Lord de Dunstanville, had made his fortune from the prof-
its of Dolcoath and Cook's Kitchen, two of the richest mines in the
county.[52] Again, the house with its fine pictures, the grounds and the
greenhouse were inspected and admired. The party returned via Carn
Brea, a craggy hill above Redruth, on which stood a castle once held
by the Basset family.

Charles surmised that the granite stones and rock basins scattered
on the top of the Carn suggested that they had been used by Druids
for their rituals in pre-historic times, a common attribution at the
time for all such stones. He noted that there was a woman living in

---

[52]Gill, Crispen (1995) *Great Cornish Families* p 7. Tiverton: Cornwall Books.

Engraving: Cambre [Carn Brea] Castle, from Redruth. Published 1824 by
Simpkin & Marshall, London.

an old chapel or watchtower on the hill, so that she can 'entertain
the numerous parties, which visit Carn Brea in the summer' (Diary
p 131).

On Easter Day, Charles first accompanied Mr Sampson to his
Powder Mills 'in a valley 2 miles away.' This was Kennall Vale, where
gunpowder was produced for use in mining. Founded in 1812, Benjamin Sampson was its first manager and was proud to show the
young man the various processes, powered by many waterwheels,
producing high quality powder.[53] Charles was interested to learn
all he could about the life of the area and his stay at Tullimaar,
aside from its social interest, taught him much about an industrial
process with which he was completely ignorant. After attending
church with the family, Charles rode to Helford Passage, accompanied by his host, who saw him onto the ferry that crossed to the
Lizard peninsula. From there Charles walked on to his grandparents
at Rosenithon. Sampson had shown great hospitality to his son's
young teacher and Charles was grateful.

---

[53]Acton, Bob (1991) *A Second View from Carn Marth* p 89. Truro: Landfall
Publications.

Benjamin Sampson, like Derwent Coleridge, was a founding officer and committee member of the new Cornwall Polytechnic Society.[54] The Annual Exhibitions awarded cash prizes to the entrants in various categories to include Natural History, and the advent of such a programme in Cornwall

Engraving: "Carn bré Castle" with a distant view of Redruth.

was something to delight the heart of Charles. He became a subscribing member in 1835, and by the following year was acting as a judge for the Natural History section. Through the Polytechnic and its annual exhibitions came the possibility and opportunity for a large acquaintance amongst the more educated gentry of the county. One of the prominent vice-presidents of the Polytechnic was Edward Pendarves, MP for Truro, a notable member of the Stackhouse extended family, of nearby Trehane. This acquaintance was to prove important to Charles.

May

8 May: According to Collier (Note 29), 'The boys of Derwent Coleridge's school were, of course, gentry,' and they joined the eleven o'clock dance during Flora Day, along with their masters and their partners. Charles does not write down the name of the girls he danced with, but on 8 May 1833 he notes, 'Flora Day. As usual, except Yeomanry cavalry danced with their ladies instead of each other – great improvement' (Diary p 139). He dined that day with the Misses Cunningham and spent the rest of the day in music and singing. '…½ past 10 walked with them to Trelil.' The Cunningham girls,

---

[54]Established that year (1833), by the gentry of the county, at Falmouth, at the suggestion of Anna Maria Fox and her sister Caroline, who came up with the name 'polytechnic' for the learned society, the purpose was to promote learning and exhibition of arts and industry within the county, and to encourage fine workmanship and competition. Under the initial patronage of Lord De Dunstanville, his untimely death the following year meant that in short order the society gained the accolade of Royal patronage (1835) with its patron being HM William IV, and its vice-patron the illustrious Davies Gilbert, DCL, FRS.

Miss Mary and Eliza, and their mother lived at Trelil, a house just outside Helston on the road to Falmouth.[55]

Early entries in his diary show that Charles was exploring the possibility all along the way of studying for a degree at Trinity College, Dublin, as an external student. It is not clear why Trinity College was his objective, except that both of his uncles, William and Alexander Johns, were prominent people in Ireland, making the destination one of interest and more potential comfort than an impoverished student could find elsewhere. Also it was known that at least some of the work toward a degree could be done on a non-residential basis. He noted down the annual charges as '15 guineas including three items of College Tutors' and Professors' fees. The charge for entrance including a half-year's fee in advance is 15/- for Pensioners and 30/- for Fellow Commoners' (Diary, pp 15-6). Then follows a list of the Greek and Latin books, which 'every young gentleman who proposes to become a Student of the University is supposed to have read with care and is examined (upon) at his entrance.' These entrance exams took place generally in July, October and November and a certain number of passes must be achieved each year.

Soon after these entries in the diary, Charles pasted in two cuttings from an Irish newspaper, one referring to William Guinness of No 26 Upper Ormond Quay, advertising the latest fashions in men's coats, waistcoats, etc. Charles was visualising himself as a student in Dublin (Diary p 28). After the increase in his salary, in March he had written, 'made up mind to read for Dublin.'[56] Now the problem was how.

Due to the consuming interest he had developed even before his arrival to teach in Cornwall, Charles stayed in touch with some

---

[55]Cornish meaning: 'Trelulla,' or Lulla's Farm or settlement place. There is another Trelill, a village near Bodmin. Trelil Farm is spelled with one 'l,' but the Holy Well remains nearby carries two, and is located at Wendron on the Lizard, near the ancestral homes of the John family.

[56]By the 1830s Trinity College, Dublin, already had a long and distinguished history. During the 18th century, the city had become renowned for its culture and fine architecture, and distinguished scholars such as Oliver Goldsmith, Jonathan Swift, and Edmund Burke were educated at Trinity. Just opposite the college stood the Bank of Ireland where his uncle, Alexander Johns, had contacts. As Charles could not afford to attend Oxford or Cambridge, he grasped the opportunity to become a non- residential student at Trinity, which was fast rivalling the English universities in the quality of its teaching and research.

botanical acquaintances who were spreading their scientific discoveries by correspondence with each other. Not unlike collectors of today they exchanged ideas and specimens and prepared papers for publication. This avid attention to nature's design and detail stirred him ever harder. On one of these early walks Charles made a discovery of his own. The plant was '*Bromus mollis, B.Lloydianus*,' Soft Downy Brome-grass, which he found was abundant between Gew Graze and the Lizard. Examining the specimens he had picked, he discovered the genus of the plant, but could not find the species. He wrote a description and sent it with a dried specimen to 'one of our first British botanists, whose address I happened to know.' This was probably W J Hooker LLD, then Professor of Botany at Glasgow University. 'In a few days I heard, to my great satisfaction, that my plant was a new variety, never having been observed previously to my finding it at the Soap Rock. Though it was then new to botanists, I have since remarked it in great abundance both here and on other parts of the coast' (*Week* p 242).

June

Holidays meant that Charles returned to Plymouth and his friends and family there. This year it also brought a great sadness. Charles was deeply shocked by the death of a close family friend, Miss Elizabeth Sparrow of Cattedown, Plymouth. From home he had walked to her house with a note from the family to Elizabeth, 'expecting to laugh and joke with her.' Instead he found the house and windows closed and discovered from a neighbour that she had died.

> 'I had never before known what Death was . . . One or two of my schoolfellows had died and I was sorry to hear it, said it was distressing and soon forgot. A brother and sister had died before I well knew what Death meant. My grandfather [Bennett Johns] had died, but he was an old man . . . this stroke was so unexpected, the victim so young and high-spirited, and I had looked forward with such pleasure to meeting her, and instead of finding her ready to join in the jokes which had several times passed about seeing her immediately on my arrival to hear that she was dead – dead! It was not credible.'
>
> (Diary pp 141-2)

Charles followed her funeral procession from Cattedown to the Baptist Chapel, describing the 'sable coaches and their melancholy contrast with the white hatbands of the bearers.' Commenting on the service, he wrote: 'I very much missed the consolatory burial service of our church, the place of which was supplied by an extempore address (of great feeling certainly) from Mr Nicholson.' Charles picked a walnut leaf as a memento and seemed half in love with Elizabeth. However, she had been engaged elsewhere and had been visiting her fiancé to see their future home near Kingsbridge when she caught influenza, dying 11 days later. 'It is very remarkable that a few days after the funeral I went to Cattedown to enquire after the family and found the windows again closed and on enquiring as before at the next house, found that Mr Sparrow's father was dead.'

Naturally, holidays also gave Charles the chance to enjoy outings with friends of his own age and indulge occasionally in parties with music, picnics and drink, even the occasional cigar. He often walked with his sisters, one visit to Sheviock with Julia, a walk with Emily the following day to Devonport for the purpose of going to St Germans (in Cornwall). One fine day he walked some 15 miles from Plymouth to visit friends at Tavistock, where he enjoyed 'some first rate claret.' The next day at Lydford, he and his friend, Reeves, went to 'a hovel called an Inn' and had a glass of cold rum and water with their bread and butter. They made up for it later at Tavistock, dining on 'Salmon-peel and duck.' The following morning, while Reeves hired a pony, Charles walked to Morwell rocks and on to Morwellham, where they dined on 'bacon and eggs and finest strawberries' (Diary pp 146-7). This gave Charles the energy to walk back to Plymouth via Denham Bridge and the valley of the River Tavey. Like most young men, his thoughts dwelled on his stomach, and promises made to it.

July-August

On 2 July, after an early breakfast with Reeves, they boarded the *Sir Francis Drake* on a trip to Torquay, when the band of the *Caledonia* played on board, which Charles much enjoyed. He dined with a party of 19 at Machette's at 3.30 p.m. and, after visiting an abbey nearby, returned to the boat. On the journey back, 'there being a very tolerable bass singer on board we amused ourselves by singing Glees.' It was a glorious night with a full moon and Charles did not arrive home till one in the morning. The next day he walked five miles to Sheviock 'to get rid of the lassitude occasioned by yesterday's raking!' (Diary p 148). A few days later there was a family outing to St Germans, when

Charles sent up their names to his Lordship the Earl before they began to explore the grounds. They took a picnic of sandwiches, veal pasties and wine, and Charles smoked a cigar. Away from the constraints of the school, he reveals himself as a normal, sociable 22-year-old.

Charles had already experienced by now the illness and death of a number of people close to him and more was to follow. In March 1833, his grandmother, Mrs Boone, had sent for his mother to come to St Keverne as she was very ill. She recovered, and Maria returned to Plymouth in April, but by June, when Charles visited his grandparents, Mrs Boone had lost the use of all her limbs and was failing. She died on 29 July, 'aged 74, after a long and painful illness.' She had suffered a stroke 30 years earlier and in the last six months had been in agony from dropsy.

Two days later Charles set out on foot from Helston at 5am to attend the funeral at St Keverne church. He arrived at 8am and his grandmother was buried at 11, 'borne to the grave by six old and young women, about 100 people being present' (Diary p 166). He returned that evening 'on foot, not in the least tired.' Nine days later he walked again to see his grandfather, who was 'as well as one could expect, (having) lost a companion of 52 years.' They walked together to Trenance and on to Porthoustock 'to call on Mr and Mrs Joyce, just married.' The next day Mr Boone, aged 88, accompanied his grandson for three miles on his return to Helston.[57]

A little later in the month, Charles organised a visit to Kynance Cove, on the rugged coast of the Lizard, eager to show the Cunninghams and their friends the rocks, caves and sea features that he loved so well. This was a very special outing when Charles wanted to impress the ladies with his knowledge of the rocks and plants to be found there, but the day did not start well.

'Rose very ill-prepared for this day, the pain in the soles of my feet and chest having increased by pains in the limbs and a slight headache. I had arranged a party to Kynance with Mrs and the Misses

---

[57]Mr Boone remained hale and hearty for several more years. In April 1835 Charles wrote that he met his grandfather on the day after his 90th birthday, 'half a mile from his house carrying a rake, hoe, shovel, fork, basket all on his shoulders at once!!' (Diary p 212). Despite a fall the following October, Mr Boone lived on until March 1837, when Charles mentioned in a draft letter that his grandfather had recently died (Diary p 239).

KYNANCE COVE—from the "TAR-BOX."

Frontispiece to first edition of *A Week at the Lizard*, 1848.

Cunningham, Mr and Mrs Faning and Miss Jenkyn. We were unable
to get a van as we wished but managed to hire a covered cart rather
ancient and shabby, but no matter we were in search of pleasure and
did not mind trifles. We started from Turnpike gate[58] at half past 9
and the shaking of the machine did my head no good. At Bochym[59]
we walked some distance and I felt very ill and though all the party
were earnest in their entreaties that we should return I held out not
wishing to spoil the pleasure of so many.' (Diary 168-9)

They arrived and Charles had a sleep. 'I awoke much better so far
relieved that I climbed round the Asparagus Island[60] before the tide
went out putting the ladies to great fright and then to the top of the
island where I was again sick.' Returning to the party he writes, 'We
explored the caves and sang glees, not with much spirit certainly on

---

[58]The Turnpike stood at the crossing of the road from Falmouth to Helston and
the road from Redruth to the Lizard.

[59]Bochym, a manor house about halfway along the road to Kynance.

[60]Asparagus Island, a large central rock, named after the plant (asparagus offi-
cionalis) growing on the top, and surrounded by the sea at high tide.

my part and entered our machine again giving up all idea of visiting the Lizard' (Diary p 195).

On their return to Helston Charles insisted on walking back to Trelill with the Cunninghams, but could not manage to eat a pasty! He did not get back to Wendron Street till 11 in the evening and took two pills before sleeping and 'expected to rise quite well,' but in the following weeks he became worse and worse.

20 Aug: 'I heard there was a neck to be cut that evening in the neighbourhood and went to the ceremony. The Neck is a handful of wheat the last cut on an estate which is preserved until the next year. About 30 or 40 stalks were left standing near the middle of the field which was cut down by the whole body of reapers, myself and the ladies included. This done, a man raised it with both hands above his head exclaiming "I 'ave un! I 'ave un!" The first reaper – "A Neck! A Neck! A Neck!" when the whole party set up a huzza. This was repeated three times and the ceremony was concluded.'

September
From the last week in August, when he 'felt myself mighty queer,' Charles was ill and only notes reached the diary.

26 to 30 Aug: 'Ill in bed.'

31 Aug: 'Came down stairs about the middle of the day just in time to receive a parcel from Mr Book (who had just returned from Plymouth) containing inter alia apples and plums. Stayed down but a few minutes being too ill to sit up.'

2 Sept: 'Wrote home saying I was just recovered from an attack of jaundice.' Mr Henwood, the surgeon, having tried medicine, bled him and applied 'a strengthening plaster' to his chest. However, Charles records:

10 Sept: 'Spasms more violent particularly towards evening relieved by a powerful dose of opium which threw me into a stupor lasting many hours, but not at all refreshing me' (Diary p 172).

By 15 September he was slowly improving, but Mr Henwood advised that he should go home to Plymouth to convalesce. 'I called on my friend in the afternoon, and he took me to Trelill where I sat an hour, ate an egg in milk and rode inside the Mail to Falmouth. The cholera just broken out there.'

23 Sept: 'At home I found all pretty well except my father who in my absence had lost the use of his right arm but had learnt to write totally with his left. My mother had just recovered from an attack of the same disorder as myself.'

Charles did not return to Helston until 20 October, two months after the outing to Kynance, and when he returned to Cornwall he brought Emily, Julia, Bennett, Reeves and Stevens[61] with him. In that week, he also notes that he 'commenced Hebrew.'

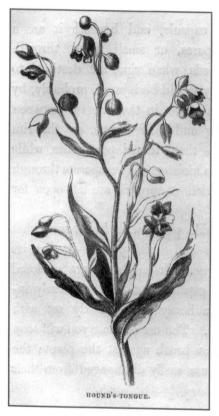

HOUND'S-TONGUE.

Hound's-Tongue. Drawing by Emily Stackhouse for *A Ramble in Autumn*, 1852, p 42.

---

[61] It has not proved possible to trace Charles's youthful friends Reeves and Stevens, as their full names are not given in his diary, and no more is known about them except their residency in the Plymouth area.

6

THE KINGSLEYS & *PHILANTHUS*,
LOVER OF FLOWERS

The Kingsley family is first mentioned in Charles Johns's diary in October 1833, when, because Coleridge had to go into Penryn for an appointment, Johns was given the task of 'guide to Kingsley and sons.' This was the beginning of a life-long acquaintance and friendship with the family as a whole, and Charles Kingsley in particular.

30 Oct: Mr C went to Penryn and left me to act as guide to Mr Kingsley, a clergyman from Clovelly who had brought two sons to school. A lovely day, Mr Kingsley and his sons very fond of Natural History with every branch of which they had some acquaintance without being adepts in either one. Returned to dine with Mrs Coleridge . . . .

There were only eight years separating the young schoolmaster and Kingsley Major, his pupil, and their friendship was based immediately upon their love of nature. Charles Kingsley wrote later of 'going long rambles with him [Johns] on the neighbouring moors and on the sea coast, in search of wild flowers, and helping him in the study which each loved so well' (Kingsley Letters p 26). Collier described how Johns would take some of the older boys out with him to study botany on holidays and half-holidays, saying that, 'we looked on the tin cases for holding specimens, which they hung round their shoulders, as a priggish sort of affair, not to be compared for a moment with the manly fishing-basket.'[62]

[62]Collier, W F *Cornish Magazine* op cit, p 119

Nov 6: Walked to Gunwalloe to get some reeds (*Arundo Phraquintis*) for writing Hebrew; found them to answer even better than the Persian reed, being not so pithy and more easily made.

November-December

Johns records in his diary: 'cholera first appears at St John's.' Coleridge decided the school term should end early on 12 December instead of the 19th, 'but most boys sent for earlier.' On 2 December, Kingsley Major was 'attacked with violent English cholera which alarmed us a little; he continued ill during the week and I sat up with him half of three nights' (Diary, p 177). Charles Kingsley's illness caused Mary and Derwent great anxiety, and Johns's attentive care was much appreciated by the Kingsley family. Undoubtedly, these experiences put a seal upon their beginning friendship.

More trouble was to follow for the Kingsley family and also for the school in the new year of 1834. Herbert Kingsley, the younger brother of Charles, did not settle at all well in Helston and Johns tells his sad story in his diary, writing in Latin rather than English. This may merely have been because he wanted to practise his Latin, as all the entries from mid-January to mid-May 1834 are in Latin. However, these weeks cover all the references to Herbert, and Johns may have thought that the classic language offered some protection from prying eyes.

It seems that Kingsley minor was unhappy and wanted to run away. In February, he stole a silver spoon from the school, sold it and disappeared. While searching for him Johns was thrown from his horse, but not badly hurt. Dr Henwood, helping in the search, returned from Falmouth saying that Herbert had been seen in the town enquiring about sailing ships. Soon afterwards the boy was caught by the local bailiff, aptly named Hawk, who handcuffed him and brought him back to the school in disgrace. Mrs Kingsley was sent for and came at once. She pleaded that expulsion would not only ruin the boy for life, but also kill his father, the Vicar of Clovelly. Somewhat reluctantly, Coleridge agreed to keep Herbert at school and punish him in other ways.[63] We can only imagine the discussions and tears that must have taken place.

Soon after this episode, Herbert's father invited Charles Johns to

---

[63]Hainton, *op cit*, p 125.

Drawing by Ann Catherine Johns for *Home Walks and Holiday Rambles* (1863).

stay with the family at Clovelly during the summer holidays, and Charles looked forward to it with expectation. Before the holidays, though, young Herbert fell ill in Helston, with rheumatic fever. He seemed to be recovering, but on 19 May unexpectedly died. Derwent went to Clovelly the following day to inform the parents and to bring them back with him. Herbert was buried in Helston a day or two later on the north side of St Michael's churchyard. The tombstone was inscribed simply with the letters and date: 'H K 1834.' Later this inscription was added: 'Herbert Kingsley, brother of Charles Kingsley. Died at Helston Grammar School, May 1834. Aged 14 years.' These sad events clearly brought Charles Johns closer to the Kingsley family as his diary and their own memories testify. It is a story too, that has been glossed over in most of the many biographical memoirs of Charles Kingsley.

When term ended in June, Johns left Helston together with the Coleridges, Misses Elizabeth and Lucy Cosserat and Richard Powles,[64] in a barouche to travel to Falmouth. The next day they boarded the *Sir Francis Drake* in misty rain and Johns writes that Mary Coleridge (not a good sailor) and Lucy were sick on the journey to Plymouth.

---

[64]Richard Cowley Powles, was a particular friend of Charles Kingsley. He was the pupil deputed to present an inscribed Bible to Johns upon his leave-taking. See Appendix ii.

View of Clovelly

Two weeks later, Johns went on board Plymouth's second steamer, the
Brunswick, to meet Charles Kingsley's younger brother, Gerald, coming from the naval college at Dartmouth.[65]

They travelled together to Bideford, where Mr Kingsley met them
and took them on to Clovelly. Charles Johns much enjoyed his stay,
going out in a boat with Gerald, walking on the cliffs, helping in
the Sunday School at the Rector's church and assisting in the hay-
field. Charles's younger sister Julia joined them at one point and
Johns writes of an expedition to Hartland when he, with Mr and
Mrs Kingsley, Miss Cadel and Julia travelled in a 'car,' while Gerald
and his brother Charles Kingsley rode on ponies. There they visited

[65]Few sources agree as to the number and order of the Kingsley children, but see
Appendix ii under Kingsley to detail all of those known to date.

Roman remains and Johns was horrified to find that the old Abbey building had been destroyed and rebuilt in a 'modern' style. However, exploring in Hartland Bay he discovered some rare barnacles on the sea-shore to add to his collections. The weather was good, for on the following day, after going fishing with Mr Kingsley, Charles enjoyed a swim in the sea.

In Helston, Charles had enjoyed mild flirtations with young women he met. At home in Plymouth, however, he fell in love more seriously with Miss Rebecca Yolland. The Yolland family lived near Ivybridge, on the road heading east from Plymouth to Exeter. Charles first mentions them in 1834, when, on 22 July – Regatta Day in Plymouth – he rode on horseback with Mr and Miss Yolland, to Merafield, their home, and writes, 'the pleasantest day I had spent for the holiday.' The next day he went sailing in the *Shampacket* and, while on board, wrote some lines to Miss R Yolland, 'who had the day before during a ride to Ivy-Bridge rallied the Author on his predilection for Botany.' This long poem refutes the accusation that he is like the herbalist who picks the flower he seeks, but is unaware of the beauty around him:

My thoughts are feasting by the woodland shade
The rugged pathlet and the bright cascade
Where the tall foxglove peeps into the brook
And royal ferns adorn each watery nook...

...Then Lady deem not that an idle hour
Which holds me in communion with a flower
In her that Nature's still small voice would hear
When Nature weeps with her must shed a tear
Smile when she smiles, be gay when she is gay
And watch her varying moods from day to day.'

(Diary pp 37-8)

From Helston, Charles attended the Royal Cornwall Horticultural Society's exhibitions whenever he could, sometimes entering his own specimens. In the summer of 1834, Mr Moyle took him to the RCHS's exhibition at Truro's Assembly Rooms, in which Charles had entered a group of indigenous plants. A full report appeared two days later in *The West Briton* (29 August 1834, p 2c):

'At twelve o'clock, when the adjudication was finished, the doors were opened for the admission of Members and their friends, and in a short time the room was filled with company, consisting of the leading Gentlemen of the County, and a large assembly of the gayest of Cornish youth and beauty. A band of music, as usual, occupied the gallery and played at intervals during the meeting.' This was a social occasion in Truro and was usually followed by a formal Dinner and Dance in the evening.

The president, Lord Boscawen Rose, spoke at length about the entries in various sections, referring to the Cottagers' section, which had been introduced a year or two earlier, 'to better the condition and improve the moral feelings of the labourer.' The winners in most other sections were well-known members of the gentry, including Sir Charles Lemon of Carclew, Lord De Dunstanville of Tehiddy, W Pendarves of Pendarves, B Sampson Esq of Tullimaar and Mrs T Grylls of Cardinham. It was the entry of the last-named which caused Charles Johns to write to *The West Briton* under the pseudonym *Philanthus*, lover of flowers.

Mrs Grylls had won the Indigenous Plants section with an entry of 30 named specimens. The names of other winners did not include Charles, whose entry was probably included as one of those that 'fell short of the number specified in the lists transmitted to the Secretary and forwarded to the Judges.' Then, as now, these judgements led to hurt feelings, and Charles wrote a rather pompous and scathing letter.

It was headed *Nomina si nescis, sperit cognitio rerum* (if the name is not known, one expects this to be judged). After praising most of the exhibition, he referred to a 'glaring error' in the naming of three of the specimens in Mrs Grylls's winning entry: 'Leontodon palustre' should have been 'Leontodon Taraxacum'; 'Stachys annua' for 'Galeopsis Ladanum'; and 'Torilis nodosa' for 'Coronopus Ruellii.' He suggested that it was like naming a bunch of carrots 'a Brace of Summer Cabbages,' and continued:

> Sir, I think that the Society, if one of its objects be to promote the science of Botany, should appoint as Judges, men competent, or desirous (I know not which epithet to use), to correct such glaring errors, whereas, by awarding First Prize to this identical group of misnomers, they have confirmed the unfortunate Botanist in his mistake.[66]

---

[66] *West Briton*, 13 September 1834 p 4c.

Hypnum proliferum.

Drawings by Charles Johns of
specimens found on Cornish
rambles. From *A Ramble in Spring.*
Clockwise, from top left: *Luzula
campestris, Hypnum proliferum* and
Hypnum triquetrum.

Hypnum triquetrum.

The judges, whose names Charles said he avoided discovering, were the Rev R Lampen and Mr W B Booth (Sir Charles Lemon's head-gardener), who probably felt less than kindly towards their anonymous young critic.[67] 'Dined at Mr Grylls with Coleridges, Mr & Mrs H. Grylls, Mr & Mrs Gerveys Grylls, Mr & Mrs Glyn Grylls. Discussion on Botany and letter about Mrs Tom Grylls discussed 20 minutes – not found out' (Diary p 200). Only Mary Coleridge knew Charles's secret and obviously kept it, discreet woman that she was.

The following month, the Horticultural Society's exhibition was held at the Falmouth Polytechnic Society's building and Mary Coleridge, with little Derwent and others, travelled there from Helston. Charles was taken by gig with Mr & Mrs Punnet, a happy occasion for the latter, whose prize was announced in *The West Briton*, 24 October 1834: 'Indigenous Plants – most rare plant (Adiantum capillus, Veneris, rare and new habitat) 10s Rev J Punnet, St Erth.' After dining at Pearce's and having tea at Selby's, they called at Alfred Fox's house, Rosehill, at 7.30 for Mrs Coleridge, who had no doubt been admiring the garden there. The Fox families were creating beautiful gardens in the area that are still enjoyed today.[68]

Because George Banks FLS had sent some plant specimens from Plymouth that he and Charles had found in their search of the south west of England to W J Hooker at Glasgow, the latter had become aware of Charles as a potential collector for him.[69] This thrilled and inspired Charles, as he readily admitted to Hooker. By including extracts from the first of Charles's letters back to Hooker, we understand how the youthful botanist has worked up to this time.

Helston, September 1834 to Professor W J Hooker, Glasgow
The receipt of your very kind letter afforded me very great pleasure,

---

[67]William Beattie Booth (c1804-74) was a Scot, like most head-gardeners in England at that period. He became an Associate of the Linnean Society in 1823, and a member of the Botanical Society of London in the mid-1840s.

[68]Penjerrick, Glendurgan, Rosehill and Trebah gardens

[69]W J Hooker (1785-1865) had established his world-famous herbarium of preserved plant specimens on the basis of early travels, keen passions for plants and independent means. In 1820 he became regius professor of botany at the University of Glasgow and with Thomas Hopkirk established the Royal Botanic Institution of Glasgow, developed the Glasgow Botanic Gardens, and continued his massive contributions to British botany as editor, author, and scientist.

William Jackson Hooker

inasmuch as it put within my reach under favourable auspices a correspondence which I have long desired; and has given me a new stimulus in the pursuit of my favourite study. I have not been in the habit of drying plants on an extensive scale, contenting myself with enough to supply myself and three or four friends, the sum of my Botanical acquaintances, but an excellent opportunity for a commencement offers itself now, as most of the rare Cornish are in perfection during the Autumnal weather, and I have therefore procured a stock of Herniaria Glabra, Scilla Autumnalis which I shall have great pleasure in transferring to your Herbarium. Physospermum grows only in the neighbourhood of Bodmin, and I am sorry to say it is too late in the season to obtain it.

Only a few days before I received your letter I had sent for a stock....Asperula arvensis I most certainly did discover, and gathered it supposing it, till I examined it to be A. Cynanchica. Not finding it in the *English Flora* I went to Banks's for the purpose of referring to *Loudon's Encyclopedia*, and not till after I had found it to be A Arvensis did he examine it. The specimens he sent to you we gathered together after I had taken him to the place.

I have condensed all the information respecting the plants of the

South West of England that I can at present recollect into the following desultory remarks, some of which I hope may be useful.

Fedia Dentata is an extremely common plant in cornfields in all the west of Cornwall and not rare in the neighbourhood of Plymouth. I have found it also in the North of Devon.

Sanguisorba Officinalis is not confined to the North of England; I have found it in the N. of Devon on the banks of the Tamar and on Goonhilley Down, Cornwall, at the latter place 5 or 6 feet high.

The little Myosotes which I have enclosed grows on sand bans and dry hedges in the neighbourhood of the Lizard: is it your Collina?

Perhaps you will be kind enough to tell me whether the Erythraea is pulchella. I found it with these on a sandhill at Whitsand Bay, Cornwall.

I have a quantity of Illecebrum in drying for you for which I have discovered three new habitats in swampy ground South of Helston.

It is said that Tamarix was introduced into the district of the Lizard from St Michael's Mount by a cartman who picked a stick to beat his horses with, and on arriving at his journey's end stuck it into a hedge at the Lizard, and from thence it spread till it became a common hedge shrub.

Erica vegans is commonly but erroneously supposed to be confined to the Serpentine formation of which the whole of Goonhilley Down is composed. I have however found it in several places four or five miles from Goonhilley: in one, in great abundance and perfection. Near the Trellawarren [sic] Lodge on Goonhilley where it grows among tall furze it rises to the height of 5 or 6 feet.

I have repeatedly found Polygonum Aviculare (var B) and have remarked in addition to what you say, that is minutely frosted with transparent glands, which at the edges of the leaves are so large as to give them the appearance of being stipulated or rather ----lated (?).

Sedum Album I found last July covering a wall near Coddon Hill, Barnstaple.

Cerastium Tetrandrum was in great abundance on the sandy parts of the coast between the Lizard and Penzance. I am sorry to differ in opinion from you: But I am vainly inclined to suppose that the Cornish C Tetrandrium is different than semidec. I have examined a great many and I never found the number of calyx-leaves or stamens vary and I once found semidec growing amongst ——— nearly twice the size and nearly erect.

Of Linaria Spuria [? indeciph] I shall be pleased to send you specimens which I gathered near Mullion, and L. Elatine is very common.

Coronopus Didyma grows abundantly in the neighbourhood

——*[omitted words]* town which I have visited in Devon and Cornwall.

About 3 years since I found Lepdium latifolium growingon a heap of rubbish from the Limestone quarries at Cattedown near Plymouth. I shall be able to send a specimen, and I am not aware that it was ever found in the west before.

Erodium Moschatum was at Penzance & Helleston *[sic]*; and near the Lizard I have found it undoubtedly, growing on the cliff, as has my brother-in-law, the Rev Dr Jacob at Whitsand Bay, Cornwall.

Maritimum grows abundantly along the coast, with occasional patches between the Lizard and Penzance. I also found it growing in the North of Devon spreading on a sand bank and covering ——*[omitted words]* around a foot in diameter.

I discovered this year, a new habitat for Lathyrus Aphaca on the embankment between Laira Bridge and Saltram during excavations for the new victually office at Devil's Point, Plymouth.

I found a large heap of Earth entirely covered with Papauer Rhoeaes and Anthemis Tinctoria most certainly exposed to the air.

I have sent a young plant of Ulex, which species I cannot say. I invariably find them with divided leaves till some time after the Colylidones —— have disappeared.

Reseda suffruticulosa was grown for three years on a pile of rubbish on Helston Downs, undoubtedly wild.

The variety of Asplenium —— I enclose grows abundantly on an old wall or heather hedge close to Helston and last year a solitary specimen of Briza Minor in a cornfield near —— in the South of Cornwall.

When Hooker later (1835 *Flora*) was to include Charles's habitats for two species, the youthful botanist was so gratified that he waxed eloquent: 'If any description of vanity be pardonable it must be that which a young man feels when he finds himself admitted into a fellowship no matter however remote with the scientific men of his day, and such beauty I must plead guilty to feeling on my having been classed among the Botanists of England by her first Botanist.'[70]

---

[70]Letter to Hooker from Johns, 5 June 1835 (Kew archives).

Flowers in remembrance of Rebecca Yolland. 'January'
painted by Julia Johns. From *Monthly Gleanings from the
Field and Garden* by C.A. Johns (1859).

7

MOMENTOUS TIMES

The year of 1835 proved a very important one for both Charles Johns and for Derwent Coleridge, but for several different reasons. By the beginning of the new year it was clear that the Yollands and the Johns families were very friendly with each other. They holidayed together at Shaugh Prior and soon after Charles spent a day at Merafield and wrote a love poem in Rebecca Yolland's 'snap book' while staying overnight. A few days later he was there to escort Rebecca and his sisters, Emily and Jane, to St Mary's Church at Plympton.

Ten days later, he walked to Stoke Damerel where his sister Maria and Dr Jacob lived, to fetch Rebecca, as she had been staying with them, getting to know the family. A week later, 'Walked to Merafield with Mamma – dined there – lovely day. Emily and Jacob came out in the afternoon' (Diary, p 208). They must have stayed overnight, for the next day comes the entry, 'Walked to Devonport with (the) Misses Yolland, met Emily at Stoke and walked to Saltram Bridge with Miss Y.' Apparently, there was no chaperone on this walk. In early February Charles visited Merafield again and walked with Rebecca's sister, Mary, 'who was just recovering from an illness.' Three days later he was there again 'to wish goodbye,' before returning to Helston in the *Drake*.

Two months passed when, in late April, Charles 'was surprised to have call from mother on her way to St K' [Keverne]. Maria had travelled to give her son very bad news; Rebecca was mortally ill and had spoken to Emily, asking her to tell Charles that he could see the album in which he had written of his love, because she had left a message for him there. Rebecca asked Charles to sow some flower seeds in the garden at Merafield, where she hoped that he would gather the flowers when she was in her grave.

Charles did not record her death in his diary, but in June he wrote an emotional entry describing his visit to Rebecca's grave in the churchyard of Plympton St Mary, where he chose a flower in remembrance. He walked on to the Yolland's garden, filled with sad memories and thinking of Rebecca's last words to her mother: 'Never speak to a dying friend, you may awake them' (Diary, p 216). Picking a rosebud, he wept, and then called on Rebecca's mother and brother, 'both dreadfully cut up.' They talked of Rebecca's acceptance of death 'as a delightful excursion.' Written separately at the beginning of the diary, Charles recalled the happiness of the days spent with her in January in these sad lines:

> Yes, the tales that Memory tells are sweet
> As the balmy breath of an April morn,
> The happiest hours we have spent were fleet,
> They passed while we knew not the joys they had home,
> Till we eagerly snatch'd them from Time's rolling stream
> As we grasp at the shades of a fading dream.'
>
> (Diary, p 59)

Underneath he wrote: 'The delightful hours which I have spent at Merafield are flown swiftly into the dreamy land of the past. She is dead, the light of the once bright home extinguished and she sleeps with her sister in the silent grave.'

A few weeks later Henry Carrington, now from Bath, joined Emily and Maria, her mother, John Jacob, Julia, Charles and (friend) Reeves for a visit to Mount Edgcumbe; on another outing to Sheepstor, which started at six in the morning in an open carriage, they breakfasted at Meavey and Emily stayed there to sketch Meavey Oak. Charles, Reeves and Carrington walked up river to a splendid viewpoint and then down through the wood to a waterfall. Carrington remarked that it was indeed more beautiful than any scene he had observed in Switzerland.

Charles must have felt keenly of the death of Rebecca Yolland, watching the happiness of Henry Carrington and his sister in their developing love. He walked to Plympton St Mary, to Rebecca's grave and picked roses, and later wrote that he dined at Merafield and 'felt wretched' (Diary, p 226). The next day, after seeing Carrington off on the Bath Mail coach, he wrote in his diary, 'Interna Emily literas a C. accipit' ('Emily accepts private letters from Carrington'). Though at the time he did not know it, this successful courtship between Emily and Henry was to make it possible for Charles to attain his ambition of an university education.

8 May 1835

Coleridge took the opportunity to combine the opening of the new schoolhouse, built beside his home in Wendron Street, with the celebrations of Flora Day. With the assistance of Charles, he assembled his pupils at the old schoolroom at the bottom of Coinagehall Street and they processed up to Wendron Street with the Mayor and Aldermen of the Borough, 'to take formal possession of the new building, the approaches to which were tastefully decorated with rustic arches of evergreens and May flowers.' In the new schoolroom Coleridge gave 'a most impressive address,' which was followed by 'the recitation of two suitable poems by their authors, Powles and Kingsley.' The Reverend R G Grylls responded 'in terms which must have been most grateful' to the headmaster and 'with great feeling subsequently admonished the assembled pupils.' After enjoying 'a cold collation,' the company inspected the 'spacious School Room and Library, Dining Room, porch and vestibule, and above these 3 large dormitories and the same number of smaller rooms.' The porch front was elaborately designed in 'Tudor style,' incorporating the Borough Arms, and at the back the two bay windows looked out upon the playground. This impressive building had been designed by George Wightwick of Plymouth, whose work was growing in popularity in Cornwall, and whose design had been chosen a year earlier for the imposing memorial to Humphry Millett Grylls, which still stands at the bottom of Coinagehall Street.[71]

In Latin the memorial tablet reads:

> The Town Council, in whose hands lies the patronage and preservation of the school, in conjunction with a large number of old pupils and supporters of the school, who contributed to the expenses, ordered to be erected, in the year of our Lord 1834, this building intended for the purpose of educating boys in Greek and Latin literature, and in all other subjects that pertain to a pious, cultured and happy life, when the old building, situated for a long time in the lower part of the town, seemed too small for the number of pupils.[72]

---

[71]Pearson, Alan 'George Wightwick 1802-1872' *Old Cornwall Magazine*, Vol 9, no 78.

[72]The tablet remains in the present Godolphin Club building. The Tudor porch and entrance to the school can be seen set back beside the building.

This was an important step in Coleridge's ambition to make his school the equal of public schools such as Eton or Rugby, so that parents would feel confident in keeping their sons at Helston until they were ready for Oxford or Cambridge. Collier gives a good picture of how the school was arranged within the building:

> There were no classrooms in those days. We had a large schoolroom, with good desks of oak well arranged, which held us all; but he [Coleridge] had a small library attached to the schoolroom - not his own well-furnished library – where he took his classes; [not only] the head-boys, of course, but all the classes in turn. We used to call him "Maister" behind his back, and his wife... "Misses". They lived in a house in the street, apart from the schoolhouse, access to which lay through a small court.[73]

A prospectus[74] following the move to the new school shows that higher fees were being charged for boarding, ranging from £34 per term for younger boys up to £42 for boys over 16. Extra charges were made for visiting masters of writing and arithmetic, dancing or fencing, drawing, music, mathematics (taught by the headmaster) and botany (taught by the assistant master). The fee for 'Parlour Boarders,' including board and tuition, was £100, a considerable sum. These pupils lived with the Coleridges as part of the family, as did Charles.

June

Henry Carrington called on the Johns family in Plymouth. On finding that Charles had gone to visit Mr Hore,[75] curate of St Luke's Church, to admire his plants, Henry walked on to join them and found them 'discussing a bottle of Port and smoking cigars' (CJ Diary, p 219). Henry spent most of the next few weeks with the Johns's family, going with them to Shaugh Prior, on outings to Dartmoor, climbing the Dewerstone and making clear his desire to marry Emily, the sister closest to Charles in age and affection.

The Johnses' family holiday in June led to Charles taking his longest and most strenuous walk on record. The group had gone to Shaugh Prior to spend time sketching and exploring the countryside. Charles,

---

[73]Collier, *op cit*, p 117.

[74]The Helston Museum holds a copy of the prospectus.

[75]See Appendix ii: William Hore.

with his sisters Emily and Julia and other friends including Henry, hired a fly and two horses to make a trip across Dartmoor to 'Prince's Town.' He describes the 'utter barrenness and desolation' of the moor, where there were plants but no human cultivation. The church seemed 'a part of the moor,' and the trees in Wistman's Wood 'to have been there since Creation' (Diary, pp 221-2). These woods would appear again in future in one of his published papers. At Prince's Town he enjoyed a meal of ham and freshly caught trout.

Two weeks later, having stayed with his friends in Tavistock, Charles walked to Lydford, where he met 'a disciple of Culpepper' and they discussed the use of plants as medical cures. After visiting Lydford Castle, he set off to walk over the moors, crossing rivers and leats, and exploring 'Briton hut remains' as he travelled from tor to tor. When at last he found a road he felt too weary to continue to Prince's Town and followed the railway back to Tump,[76] where he had a glass of hot gin and water. On reaching Plymouth at 10.30 in the evening he reckoned that he had walked nearly 40 miles — and 'was blamed for walking so far!'(Diary p 229).

July
Visits to the Horticultural Society's exhibitions took place through 1835 and Charles continued his searches for rare wild plants, mosses, shells and geological specimens, both in Cornwall and Devon. During the summer, the Kingsleys were staying with the Calmady family, who lived in their manor, Langdon, at Wembury, near Plymouth. They introduced Charles to the family and he was invited to dine with them, afterwards walking in their spacious park and inspecting Mr Calmady's herbarium. While the Kingsleys were staying in the area, the two young 'Cs' went for long walks together hunting for plants. Johns was now an acknowledged member of the band of keen botanists who exchanged information and specimens and were building up a systematic record of the indigenous plants of England. And Charles Kingsley's appetites were growing all the time.

August
On 1 August, Charles returned from Plymouth to Helston with

---

[76]The meaning of 'tump' is a mound of earth. Here it probably denotes the name of an inn.

Derwent and his young son. A month earlier Mary had given birth
to a daughter, named Emily after their friend, Emily Trevenen.
At the christening on 5 August, Charles stood in as godfather
for Henry Nelson Coleridge, Derwent's cousin, along with John
Heyrick Macaulay,[77] and Emily Trevenen, who was one of the
two godmothers. The September school meeting brought praise
for Coleridge and the new buildings, and Charles Johns's health
was proposed by Mr Treweeke, rector of Illogan, who spoke of his
'scholastic exertions and kind manner towards the boys.'[78] Charles
was grateful for this vote of confidence, but all this time, as wit-
nessed in his diary, he was anxiously seeking ways in which he
could find the money to begin degree-work and get forward into
his life's career.

   Charles discovered that he had been mentioned in the report of
the July meeting of the Horticultural Society in Falmouth (1835).
The vice-chairman, C. W. Popham Esq. of Trevarno, Helston, had
said that the collection of indigenous plants 'were, perhaps, the
most interesting to British botanists of any which have previously
been exhibited.' After praise for the specimens from Miss Rodd and
Miss Warren[79] (frequent prize-winners), he referred to Mr Sleeman and Mr Johns, who had entered 'a similarly interesting group
from the neighbourhood of Helston.'[80] Charles replied in print,
saying that the entry was *not* from him, 'being at the time absent
from the County, and not knowing what Mr Sleeman was about
to send, nor what he had sent till I saw his name and mine in *The
West Briton*.' Referring to a plant entered by Miss Rodd, who had
claimed that 'it was hitherto unknown in England,' Charles continued: 'The *Orobanche Rubra* is not as your correspondent states,
new to the County. I found it myself six years since, at Kennack,
and more variety at the Lizard. Professor Hooker, to whom I sent

---

[77]A friend of Derwent's from Cambridge, and a cousin of Thomas Babington
Macaulay, who as master of the new Proprietary Classical and Mathematical School
in Plymouth, had offered Derwent his first teaching post of third assistant master.
From 1832 he was headmaster of Repton School, Derbyshire.

[78]*West Briton Newspaper*, 2 October 1835, p 3a.

[79]Miss Elizabeth Warren, a particular friend of Emily Stackhouse (Appendix),
a frequent winner of horticultural prizes, whose botanical career is outlined in F H
Davey, *The Flora of Cornwall*. She was also a friend of Charles Johns.

[80]*West Briton* 31 July 1835 p 3a.

specimens, informs me that about the same time with mine (last May), he received others from Yorkshire, precisely similar.'[81]

September

At the annual school meeting, after recitations were given to 'a numerous assemblage of Ladies and Gentlemen,' Powles and Kingsley came forward and presented to Mr Coleridge, in the name of the whole school, 'a very handsome silver salver, richly chased,' and inscribed in Latin. Powles spoke briefly, referring to 'this trifling token of our affection and respect'; Coleridge was 'much affected' and replied with 'a long and eloquent speech.'[82]

Soon after, 16-year-old Caroline Fox[83] wrote in her diary: 'Papa and I spent the evening at the Derwent Coleridges' at Helston.' Charles was also present. 'It left a beautiful impression on us, and we visited the lovely little sleepers, Derwent and Lily, saw the library and the silver salver presented by the boys, and best of all, listened to his reading of passages from 'Christabel' and other of his father's poems, with his own rare felicity.'[84] It was through occasions such as this that Charles nurtured and enhanced his own life-long interest in poetry, and to which he could hearken in later years when verbally illustrating his books.

Caroline Fox. Etching by Herbert von Herkomer after S Laurence.

Coleridge had greater plans for his school. His dream was to make Helston's Grammar School 'a place of classical education of the highest class, for the extreme West of

[81] *West Briton* 14 August 1835, p 2f

[82] *Royal Cornwall Gazette*, 23 October 1835, p 2f

[83] Caroline Fox (1819-1871), the daughter of Robert Were Fox, FRS of the distinguished Quaker family of Falmouth, sister of Barclay Fox and of Anna Maria with whom she inspired the creation of the Royal Cornwall Polytechnic Society. Caroline is now considered to be one of the foremost diarists of the 19th century. Her letters and diaries, as edited by various authors, remain in print today and are an excellent record of the intellectual and literary life of the nation, as well as a cultural calendar of Cornwall.

[84] Fox, Caroline (1882) *Memories of Old Friends* edited by H N Pym. London: Smith, Elder & Co.

England.' He began to raise money so that 'the unsightly buildings' (old cottages), which hid his new school buildings, could be
replaced by 'a group of collegiate edifices,' but he was later to realise
that, although the school might be described as 'the Eton of Cornwall,' there were not enough local families of sufficient wealth and
class to support his ambitions.

In November of 1835 Charles received a letter from Henry Carrington offering financial help to further his studies. Henry realised
that if Charles could qualify and become ordained he would then
be able to earn sufficiently well to support his ailing father and the
family. This would release Emily from her cares to become Henry's
wife. Charles's formal letter to Coleridge followed a few days later,
showing that he did not want to be reliant on Carrington if he could
possibly earn enough himself. However, the financial problems of
the Coleridges and the school meant that Charles was persuaded
to accept Carrington's help, while continuing to offer teaching support at Helston in term times. On 3 December 1835 he recorded in
his diary that he had written to his chosen tutor at Trinity College
Dublin, Dr Gannon, to confirm his entry as a student at Trinity
(Diary p 234).

His continuing correspondence and exchange of plants with W J
Hooker at Glasgow gave him such great pleasure and growing confidence, that he wrote to him in November 1835 to ask if Hooker
would help him to become a Fellow of the Linnean Society of London.[85] Hooker, who was known for his encouragement of young botanists, happily agreed. Both of these steps, university and society, were
the necessary ones for his future. There was no flagging in his resolve
to prepare himself. Now for the entrance exams in Dublin, after the
years of preparation and reading.

On 21 December, the end of the school term, he walked from
Helston to Penryn, slept there and the next day travelled to Plymouth on the Mail coach, writing, 'hard frost, desperately cold'
(Diary p 234). Henry Carrington and Emily were waiting for him
at Elliott's Hotel in Fore Street, Devonport, and together they rode
in the coach to Plymouth, where Charles and Emily said farewell
to Henry as he journeyed on to Bath while they returned home to
their parents.

---

[85]Letter from C A Johns to W J Hooker, 21 November 1835 (Kew archives).

On Christmas Day, Charles attended St Andrew's church and wrote: '.... stopped to the Sacrament – never so cold in my life before' (Diary, p 235). The next day, after visiting Mrs Yolland with Emily, Charles suffered pain in his chest in the night and was given a mustard blister. Mr Jupe the doctor was called, who bled him and sent him to bed for most of the following week.

WYCH ELM AT ENYS, CORNWALL.

From *Forest Trees of Britain* (1849), Vol II, p 123.

Plymouth Jany. 11. 1836

My dear Sir,

A serious illness occasioned by travelling on the outside of the Mail during frosty weather has prevented my making my most cordial acknowledgements for the flattering testimonial you were kind enough to draw up, as well as for the highly valuable signatures you were good enough to obtain.

I hope ere this you have received my little parcel. it was forwarded to Miss Warren according to your wish.

Nor I have not yet received your parcel nor indeed do I expect to do so till I return to Hillerton. I am in a few days about to proceed to Bath for change of air and thence to keep my term at Dublin. I have therefore directed that it should not be forwarded till I am again settled. lest it should be mislaid or injured.

I am looking forward to a rich harvest next year a fair proportion of which I hope will find a storehouse in Glasgow.

This testimonial was enclosed in a very kind letter from Dr Graham which I am only now enabled to acknowledge

I am
My dear Sir
Yours most truly
C. Johns

Belated thank-you letter from Charles Johns for the
Linnean Society testimonial of W J Hooker (1836).

8

BEGINNING FORMAL STUDIES

January-February 1836

When Charles finally did venture out in early January, he developed a severe headache and Mr Jupe ordered 'a dozen leeches to the temples.' None of this was a promising preliminary to an important journey. Unfortunately, he missed meeting an important visitor to the Coleridges in the period he was away from the school due to illness and his entrance examinations.

The distinguished poet Robert Southey came to visit his nephew, Derwent, and Mary, as he had long promised them he would do. Southey had married a sister of Derwent's mother, Sarah Fricker, and in many ways Southey had stood in as Derwent's father when Samuel T had found himself incapable of attending to family life. That would have been an occasion that Charles would have highly savoured.

Later in the month Charles travelled to Exeter, slept overnight at Mr Jeffrey's and then continued on to Bath the next day, reaching York House, Carrington's home, between 7 and 8pm. Henry was waiting for him and after they had dined together he took Charles to the theatre. He returned to York House 'pretty well tired.' The following day Henry accompanied Charles to Bristol, expecting to see him off on his journey by packet steamer to Dublin that evening. But, more difficulty lay ahead. 'Hurricane in night – put off journey till 26th – returned to Bath.' On the 26th he records: 'Left Bath at 8, sailed soon after noon in the *Star Packet*. Tolerably fair weather till toward evening, eat a good dinner and was followed 3 or 4 hours by a sea quite expecting from my looks that my dinner was to be transferred to him. Miserably sea-sick – was promised fair weather when we came under the Irish coast (which) we had for a short time when a fearful storm came and carried away a sail etc. – finally we reached Dublin at 8 o'clock' (Diary p 236). To add to his miseries, he then found that the lodgings he had booked for the earlier date were now engaged, so he slept at an inn.

The following morning he called for his cousins, Alexander Johns's sons, the elder of whom was already a student of law at Trinity College, and the other who soon would be so. Charles's first examination was taken before Dr Gannon and Dr Sadleir (to become Provost in December 1837) – '15 lines of Homer etc,' which Charles passed. In the evening he dined with Mrs French, a relative of Alexander Johns's wife, Emma, as he did on at least two other recorded occasions. She seemed pleased to offer hospitality to the young man, and Charles made sure to call on her again before leaving Dublin.[86]

Another contact was Miss Byrne, to whom Charles took a letter from his sister Emily, walking in rain and snow to find her. On his second day, he called on Dr William Allman, professor of botany, who later took him to the Botanic Gardens at Glasnevin, a special pleasure for Charles. William Johns, his cousin, accompanied him to the college chapel and took him to visit Dublin's two cathedrals, Christchurch and St Patrick's. On another day, he took Charles to the Zoological Museum in Phoenix Park, the second oldest public zoo in Europe.

Glasnevin Chain Tent, 2007   *(Photo: Philip Budden)*

These visits for learning and pleasure came between further examinations in classics before Mr Peter, mathematics with Mr Hart, and 'Catecheticals' on St Luke before Mr Todd. All of these he passed satisfactorily and was recorded as entering 'Trinity College on 18 January 1836 at the age of 24 as a pensioner' (that

---

[86]See notes for the French family connections in the entry of Alexander Johns in Appendix 2.

is, he paid a fixed sum annually). After realising this long-held dream of admission to Dublin, on 5 February Charles wrote: 'Packed up – at Quay found Steamer not going off.' He left his luggage and, after calling again on Mrs French, walked in the Park. At 6pm he set off by carriage to Kingston, where he took the Mail Packet at 7pm, arriving at Holyhead at 2.30am and went to bed. Four and a half hours later he climbed onto an outside place on the stagecoach, arriving at Shrewsbury at 9.30. At 11am he continued in the Mail coach, reaching Bristol on Sunday morning. From there he took the first coach to Bath and the next day, 'Outside the Tam o' Shanter to Exeter,' followed by 'Outside the Regulator to Plymouth.' On 11 February he writes, 'Helleston by Mail.' It must have taken Charles some time to recover from this nightmare journey, but his school-mastering, even for the time being, was not at an end.

Although Charles had written of his decision to enter studies at Dublin, first in 1833 and started to study Hebrew in that year, the records of Trinity College show that he did not officially enter until 1836, eight months after the opening of the new Helston school buildings.[87] The problem, of course, was financial, and these worries were not over.

In a letter to Coleridge he wrote that he had borrowed £20 from a friend to be repaid 'when I get my first living of £500 per annum,' but he was reluctant to take on further debts. He acknowledged that, while not extravagant, he might be considered 'unthrifty.' He could not be a burden to his family in Plymouth, 'entirely supported by the extraordinary, the wonderful exertions of the best of [sisters, crossed out] daughters,' a reference to Emily and Julia, but also to Maria living nearby. He then continued to suggest ways in which D C might provide him with a larger income by making French compulsory or mathematics 'an essential branch of their [the boys'] education which I might undertake in the evenings.' He finished with expressions of regret if he should have to leave the school and Coleridge and his family.

There follows a page in the diary that is empty except for a list of expenses that add up to £33 19s 6d, and after comes a reference to 'his endeavours to obtain employment in the holidays.' His letter must have been unsuccessful for a second is written, saying that despite the loan of £20 from a friend he has had to borrow another £10 and even so is unable to pay his Christmas bills, 'a predicament, which is

---

[87]Letter to the author from Trinity College library, 24 April 2001.

as unpleasant to me as novel' (Diary, p 111). After leaving the examination hall on the last occasion, he had only his money worries to fill his mind: 'The college fees are £15 per annum and each visit to Ireland cannot be reckoned at less than £15 more making £45. I find it impossible to pay for clothes, travelling etc with less than £50, in all about £95. It is impossible that I out of £70 [his teaching stipend] a year can pay £90 and therefore if I wish to prosecute my undertaking any further I must either find some means of increasing my income or of diminishing the expenses to be incurred.'

Charles, by then, had successfully passed the entrance examinations at Trinity College and was ready to begin his studies as a non-residential student if only the money involved was found. In this letter he suggests that one alternative was to look for a similar teaching position near Dublin, which would enable him to continue his course. In further entries in the diary Charles refers to the care he has received under Derwent and Mary's roof, and on 13 February 1836 he writes a short letter expressing sadness at leaving Coleridge and the family, but, 'My object however must be effected and I've no other road to it than the one which I have marked out for myself' (Diary p 112).

Derwent Coleridge himself was never without money worries. The new school buildings had brought more pupils, but the old house was in constant need of repair. A month after Charles's last letter, Coleridge was exploring the possibility of moving his family elsewhere and becoming a housemaster at Harrow School, but nothing came of that.[88] Nothing came of Charles's decision to leave Helston either, and that was due to further and continued support as proffered by Henry Carrington late in the previous year. The money promised to allow for his Irish visits meant that Charles could remain in Helston, and continue his reading and studies in the knowledge that he could continue to enter for the Dublin examinations, as he became prepared through his supervised studies (supervised by Dr John Jacob, of Plymouth).

Charles's abilities were recognised by the wider community on 15 March 1836, when, aged only 25, Charles could add FLS after his name. The certificate of recommendation stated:

C.A. Johns Esq. of Helston, Cornwall, a Gentleman well versed in Botanical Sciences, being desirous of becoming a fellow of the Lin-

---

[88]Hainton, *op cit* p 139.

nean Society, we the undersigned do recommend him as eminently deserving of that honour & one likely to become an useful & valuable member.

He was proposed by W J Hooker LLD, Regius Professor of Botany at Glasgow University, soon to be knighted and to become the first director and creator of the Royal Botanic Gardens at Kew. The certificate was posted in one of the Society's rooms, with the name of the proposer and  seconders,[89] and left for several weeks for any existing Fellows to add their names. Eventually there was a ballot to confirm the election.

This was the official recognition he needed to support the dogged determination he had shown over and over again to become a specialist in botanical subjects and a respected teacher and scholar. Though Charles probably would never converse with all those distinguished men in the world of natural science that signed his nomination papers and confirmed his place in the Linnean Society as a member, his name was now in the realm of known botanists.

September

Charles was in the newspapers again. After mention of the prizewinners at the horticultural shows of 1836, came the paragraph: 'The rare plant, Elatine hexandra, together with several very nicely prepared dried specimens, among which is one of a new species or variety (not determined) of Orobanche, having come to hand after the day named by public advertisement for receiving the indigenous plants, could not be taken into competition or full consideration suitably to their merits, but the judges had thought proper to award an extra prize of 10s to the whole, to mark their sense of Mr C A Johns's ability and diligence in obtaining interesting botanical acquisitions.'[90]

At the annual school meeting the following September, Charles

---

[89]Seconders were listed as Robert Graham, R K Greville, George Loddiges, Dr Patrick Neill, and Thomas Thomson, all botanists of international standing with Scottish connections to Hooker, quotes from whom Charles would later employ in his books. (See Writer's Notebook, Appendix iii.)

[90]*West Briton* 30 September 1836, p 2e.

was presented by the pupils with a handsomely bound Bible inscribed, 'To Charles Alexander Johns Esq. FLS, as a small testimony of affection and respect,' and this was also reported in the newspapers.[91]

Later in 1837 an eminent geologist, Henry Thomas De la Beche,[92] invited Charles to leave his teaching and take part in a geological survey of the area as part of a national survey. The government at the end of the 18th century had established a body under the Board of Ordnance with the task of providing a map of the whole of Great Britain on the scale of 1 inch to 1 mile. When the sheet for Cornwall and Devon was being prepared for publication in 1832, De la Beche, then secretary of the Geological Society of London, was commissioned by the government to put on to this the known conformation of the geology of Cornwall's mining districts. Seizing his chance, De la Beche suggested that a team of geologists should be recruited to repeat this exercise in other parts of the country. Out of what was originally intended as a short-term project, a permanent Geological Survey of Great Britain was surreptitiously contrived, with De la Beche as its salaried director from 1835. He was inviting Charles to join this team and work in an area where mining was of first importance, but at this point the future of the project was uncertain.[93]

Charles was tempted. In a draft letter to the geologist, who was staying in Falmouth, he wrote that he had only received De la Beche's letter the previous night as he had spent two or three days at St Keverne on the death of Mr Boone, 'the old gentleman whom you may remember to have called on with me on the day of my geological birth' (Diary pp 239-40). It seems that Charles's interest in geology had been set alight when De la Beche had previously visited the Lizard peninsula, and been introduced to him as a likely and willing candidate in his work.

---

[91] *West Briton* 6 October 1837 p 3a.

[92] De la Beche (1796-1855) had begun the geological survey for a map of England at his own expense, and then it was officially taken up. By 1836, he and his daughter, Elizabeth 'Bessie,' had become friends with the Fox family of Falmouth. In 1848 he received a Knighthood for his work. (See *Barclay Fox's Journal*, as referenced in n 63.) D E Allen (*op cit*, p 77) describes De la Beche as 'the master operator' of the 19th-century natural history scene, and the worthy heir to line of grand interventionists descending from Sir Hans Sloane and Sir Joseph Banks. See Appendices ii and iv.

[93] Allen, D E *op cit*, Note 19 pp 87-8.

Charles thanked him for his offer of the post, writing that his 'present mode of life, though it has many and great advantages, does not chime in exactly with my tastes – it is somewhat too sedentary and has too much sameness for one of an active temperament of body if I may use the expression and who wishes to push ahead. Indeed if I were to dwell much upon the abstract idea of a schoolmaster's life and compare it with the life of a man of Science I should be much inclined to jump to conclusions and accept your offer unconditionally.'

He does not know what is involved in the survey, what the emolument would be, and what would happen to him when it finished. He would have to be absent to sit his exams in Dublin and he needed to earn sufficient for his College expenses. Finally, he referred to the kindness of Coleridge and his family, whom he would be leaving. Coming to the notice of De la Beche was important indeed, but this was a critical decision for Charles and it emphasises how difficult it was for scientists and naturalists of the day to advance far without independent means. However, he returns to his need to gain a degree and his desire to enter the church. Then he would be able to 'settle myself comfortably for life.' There was no further mention of the survey, and Charles returned to his struggle to become a graduate and a clergyman.

THE CORNISH CHOUGH.

The Cornish chough. From *A Week at the Lizard*, p 125.

The Old Library. Trinity College, Dublin.

The Old Library Long Room. Trinity College, Dublin.

9

TO IRELAND – A NEW COMPANY
OF NATURALISTS & THINKERS

The extra work involved in his Trinity College studies, carried out alongside his continuing teaching responsibilities at Helston, left little time for his diary. It continues only with his draft letters to De la Beche, turning down his offers, and to 'Reverend Sir' at Dublin. The latter, presumably, was a professor of the Divinity School, and Charles wrote to him after successfully passing his examinations in April of 1838. At that stage he became a Junior Sophister, entering the third year of his degree. He wrote that he had tried to seek advice from him previously, at that time, 'on a subject peculiarly important to me as affecting my future prospects of life.' But, the Reverend was too busy to see him.

Charles was writing his drafts and letter to the Reverend Sir while staying in Ireland with relatives north of Belfast. He describes his desire to enter the church from an early age, the approval of his parents, and their financial difficulties after 1825. He writes that he is glad that life has not been too easy for him, enabling him to be a schoolmaster for the past seven years at Helston Grammar School. Having been told that he could gain a degree 'without residence,' he was now shocked to find that he must spend two years in full residence in order to obtain the 'testimonium' necessary for ordination.

This prospect seemed above and beyond his means and he asked whether any Bishop would supply such a testimonium or ordain him without it in his special case? Perhaps he could gain a divinity testimonium by attending one term at Cambridge or Oxford? What would the 'Reverend Sir' recommend? In a postscript Charles adds that he would be spending the next four weeks with his uncle, A Johns Esq. at Carrickfergus, and then return to Helston, Cornwall, 'at either of which places I shall be exceedingly obliged for a reply' (Diary pp 242-4).

The Rubrics. Trinity College, Dublin.

All Charles's pleas were to no avail, but somehow the money was found to fund his final two years at Trinity College, Dublin. Most probably Henry Carrington, who married his beloved Emily during 1838, continued to support his brother-in-law, and his uncles in Ireland may also have helped. However it was managed, and we do not know for certain as the diary comes to its natural end, Charles must have enjoyed these years greatly. The separation from Helston, the school and the Coleridges was tinged with sadness, but after almost eight years, this also was an expected separation, and only the beginning for Charles toward his chosen professions. Mary and Derwent wished him well, considered him part of their family circle, and knew he deserved the opportunity of studying. Derwent by this stage was already casting around in earnest for his own next move, though it was still a year or two before that transition was effected.

Charles was a natural student, keen to study and clear in his objectives. Not only did he have a natural affinity for languages, but music, drawing and composing poetry were part of his everyday life. He succeeded in winning four vice-chancellor's prizes in Latin and Greek verse, and his reading amongst the poets, divines and naturalists was prodigious.[94] He had his own lodgings in the Rubrics, the splendid Georgian buildings of the College, where he already knew the Public Theatre well, because it was used as the examination hall. Now he could enjoy concerts, plays and important meetings in this hall and

[94]See Appendix iv: A Naturalist's Reading List.

attend the chapel, where a choir sang for the Sunday service. Charles, with his love of music and his sincere religious devotion, regularly attended. He was free from his duties as a schoolmaster most of the time, while returning to Cornwall with some regularity when breaks were possible, and could enjoy the life of the lively city of Dublin and the countryside around. Since the age of 19, he had not been without the need to earn his living, so this was indeed welcome respite.

Charles's involvement with Cornwall and its institutions was not, however, at an end. Throughout 1838 and 1839, he remained on the Committee of the RCPS for the Helston area alongside Coleridge, Glynn Grylls, M P Moyle, James Plomer and the Rev Canon Rogers. His friend, the Rev W S Hore, came from Plymouth to join Charles for a walking tour of the Lizard, a time when each of the young botanists made noted discoveries that later came to print.[95] In the 1838 Annual Exhibition in September, he was awarded a fourth prize for his model of a conservatory (for plants) in the Natural History section. In the following year's exhibition he was awarded a second prize for 'Twenty Cards of Botany,' not unlike the kinds of small publications that would be elaborated from his work in future years by publishers.

While following the rigorous course of the Junior and Senior Sophister, Charles attended lectures in botany given by Dr William Allman and became a frequent visitor of the National Botanic Gardens at Glasnevin, an easy walk for him of four to five miles from the college. Professor Allman is recorded as a member of the Botanical Society of London. Charles was also a member, as were John Moore and James Mackay, both curators of the Dublin Botanic gardens in the 1840s. William Andrew, an army agent, was the local secretary in Dublin for the London Botanical Society, and Charles was in ready contact with them.[96] Encouraged by such as Professor Allman, Charles

[95]Hore, W S (1845) recalling the 1838 ramble in another joint account in 1845, in *The Phytologist*, pp 235-9.

[96]Allen, D E (1986) *The Botanists* Appendix 2, pp 5-6, 203-215 Winchester: St Paul's Bibliographies. The London Botanical Society, founded in 1836, provided for the growing popularity of botany, in part due to 'the lively teaching of the subject by the professors of botany at the universities: W J Hooker at Glasgow (later to become Director of Kew), Robert Graham at Edinburgh (who had been Hooker's predecessor at Glasgow), and J S Henslow, Charles Darwin's teacher and friend at Cambridge.'

Glendalough, 2007

Glasnevin Palm House, 2007   *(Photos: Philip Budden)*

made outings to the countryside, especially to the Wicklow Mountains, where he searched for rare mosses[97] and wild plants and visited the monastic ruins at Glendalough. This sixth-century Celtic settlement founded by St Kevin; its beautiful lakes and mountains would have appealed to Charles's love of romantic scenery and remind him of his Celtic heritage. Throughout his rambling literature there are brief but telling references to time spent in Ireland, and to flora and fauna found there.

Soon after he completed his degree work and qualified for ordina-

---

[97]The source of at least some of the mosses in his published work, *Flora Sacra* (1840).

tion, Charles produced a small book, *Flora Sacra*, with the sub-title 'the knowledge of the works of nature conducive to the knowledge of the God of Nature,' by the Rev C A Johns, BA, FLS.[98] This collation of poetry, Biblical text, combined with the natural content of his searches, was to set the pattern for Charles's future literary style, and may have been influenced by the style of Dr Allman.[99] Always he drew in others to his work in an informed inclusiveness, whether that be famed poets or the lesser known, and with some frequency his family and friends. The book was printed by his brother-in-law, 'H E Carrington, Printer, Bath,' and published in London by J Parker, Strand.[100]

For the title page Charles chose a quotation from Bishop Thomas Newton (1704-1782) which resonates clearly throughout Johns's earliest writings, giving a kind of motto to his life as a naturalist.

> True philosophy is the handmaid of true religion; and the knowledge of the works of nature will lead us to the knowledge of the God of nature, the invisible things of him being clearly seen by the things which are made, even his eternal power and godhead.

The contents of *Flora Sacra* are a series of 23 pressed mosses, each fixed (tipped-in fragments of actual plants) to a page with the botanical name above and a Biblical quotation beneath. On the opposite page is a quotation or poem by Keble, Milton, Cowper, Wordsworth and others. Opposite *Spaghnum obtusifolium* is a poem by Carrington

---

[98]A rare copy of this book was presented to the author by his descendant Molly Matthews. The Clifford Evans collection also holds a copy. This small book, published and dated in 1840, introduces some confusion as to the accurate dating of Charles's ordination to the Diaconate. According to *Crockford's Clerical Directory*, he was not ordained until 1841, but in 1840 his authorship as The Rev C A Johns B A, F L S is already in print. However, this may safely be explained in that the *testimonium* was guaranteed at the conclusion of his degree work at Dublin, and may already have been scheduled by the Bishop of Exeter at the time of going to print. Both his degree and ordination are documented as granted in 1841.

[99]William Allman (1776-1846) is said to have made little contribution to botanical knowledge despite his professorship in botany at Dublin from 1809-44, and was satirised by Erinensis (Dr Peter Hennis Green) as reported in the *DNB* from the 1925 *Lancet* as 'far gone in swaddling . . . sedulously occupied in strewing the philosophy hall of the University with "green rushes," and constructing a new "railway" to heaven, out of flowers and scraps of scripture.'

[100]See Appendix ii for a brief summary of this very important publisher in Johns's life.

(Henry's father, N T Carrington), and opposite *Trichostomum lanugnosum* is a rather wistful poem signed C A Johns, in which he compares the untainted praise of 'nature's music' with that of a 'sinful mortal' such as himself. He wonders why he cannot respond so joyously to God as Nature does, and why his prayers die on his lips?

Sabbath Morning in the Country

Gladly shines o'er heath and mountain,
With quickening ray the summer's sun;
Sparkles bright the bubbling fountain,
Its waters carol as they run.

High in air the lark is soaring
To God enthroned in heaven above,
From pipe unwearied ever pouring
Songs of gratitude and love.

Flowers of loveliest hue are flinging
Incense on the passing breeze;
Mute tho' their voice, to God are singing
Lowly herbs and loftiest trees.

Where the budding woodbine twineth
Shadowy branches of the oak,
The weary ox at length reclineth,
Loosened from the galling yoke.

Now no more through field or fallow
Sounds the thoughtless ploughman's song
Nor shepherd, 'neath the drooping sallow,
Drives the bleating flock along.

Sabbath stillness reigns around me,
Earth and all her myriads rest,
Heavenly calm and peace surround me,
Wafting quiet through my breast.

Why, then, with nature's music blending,
Soars not from me the holy song?
When nature's praises are ascending,
Why dies the prayer upon my tongue?

Why, when my heart with joy is beating,
Starts from mine eye the sudden tear? –
The praise that nature is repeating,
Alas! I cannot offer here.

Sinful mortal breathes to heaven
Prayers that savour of the earth,
When nature's meed of praise is given,
In heaven they claim their heavenly birth.

Away, then, where the anthem pealeth
Loudly through the cloistered roof,
Where priest to guilty man revealeth
Deeds of mercy, words of truth.

With fellow sinners there addressing
Praise to the Omnipotent above,
With them I'll sing, with them confessing,
Grace despised and slighted love.

CAJ 1840

Across from the entry for *Hookeria lucens*, under which Charles writes parenthetically ('The leaf is a beautiful object for the microscope.'), is a long quotation from the greatly respected botanist and founder of the Linnean Society, Sir James Edward Smith (1759-1828), who published *English Botany* between the years 1790-1814, in 36 volumes. With the choice of this text for his book, Charles would seem to be setting the framework within which he conducted his life thereafter.

A short extract suffices:

. . . Some studies seem to contract the mind; but such is not the character of natural science, which enlarges the understanding by a perpetual display of the power and wisdom of God, and encourages our best hopes by sure testimonies of His goodness . . . Let those who hope to inherit these promises [of God], and those who love science for its own sake, cherish the same benevolent dispositions. Envy and rivalship in one case are no less censurable than bigotry and unchari-tableness in the other. The former are as incompatible with the love of Nature, as the latter with the love of God; and they altogether unfit us for the enjoyment of happiness here or hereafter. –

The book ends with *Hypnum Commutatem*, a quotation from Hosea (xiv 5-7) and the triumphant lines written by Derwent Coleridge's father:

> Glory to thee, Father of earth and heaven!
> All conscious presence of the universe!
> Nature's vast ever-acting energy!
> In will, in deed, impulse of All to All!
> Glory to thee, Father of earth and heaven!
>
> S T Coleridge

Crom Yew, County Fermanagh, Ireland. From *Forest Trees of Britain*, Vol II, p 311.

10

ORDINATION & PUBLICATION

Charles completed his studies at Dublin in 1839-40,[101] though the award of a Bachelor of Arts was not made until the spring of 1841, together with his ordination as a deacon by the Bishop of Exeter. In 1842 his priesthood was confirmed (*Crockford's* dates). This was a time of great pride for the wider family, in response to Charles's determined and inspired work for both his degree and entry to the clergy of the Church of England. At home in Plymouth and still living at Park Street, were his mother and father, now known as an artist, his unmarried brother Henry, age 37, his sister Maria Jacob nearby, age 35, and sisters Julia and Jane. His youngest brother, Jack, was also living at home and working as a junior clerk at a local bank.

Ordination ceremonies for Charles were conducted by Bishop of Exeter Henry Philpotts (known as 'Henry of Exeter'),[102] in whose diocese he would serve his curacy. It is not known why the particular parish of Yarnscombe, near Great Torrington and Barnstaple, was chosen for Charles, or anything about the basis of his acceptance of it. Bishop Philpotts was a high churchman, and much given to debate and controversy, though this probably had little or no influence upon the day-to-day activity of a newly appointed curate. According to parish records (Devon) the tithes of the Yarnscombe parish had been

---

[101]Barclay Fox, p 179 and n, in his February 1840 entries reports having 'the felicity of meeting Johns, our new little curate' [meaning newly-qualified curate rather than working locally] 'whom Derwent Coleridge describes as a "harmless man," which I should say was just.' The meaning of these remarks is unclear, due to the lack of context for such a judgement. By the following year Coleridge had appointed Charles to his staff yet again, hence it is to be supposed that the term applied to 'causing no harm,' i.e. not a trouble-maker.

[102]Bishop of Exeter from 1830 to his death in 1869, at the age of 91. Appendix v lists two letters and a photograph from Henry Philpotts in the Johns's letter book.

commuted (to fixed payment of clergy) in 1840, and at just that period Charles Johns began to serve as an assistant at approximately the rate of £136 annual stipend. The rectorial payment was not too much more, at the rate of £152. This was not yet a salary from which Charles could begin to repay Henry Carrington, but he could help his family a little.

Yarnscombe was not far from the port of Bideford, well-known to his friends, the Kingsleys, but not a place that inspired much joy in the Reverend Johns. His assignment was to the parish church of St Andrew, and it is not known whether or not he worked with another, or lived alone in the small stone parsonage nearby. The reasons for his unrest he outlined in a letter to Hooker, who had recently become the director of the Botanic Gardens at Kew: 'I am now located in a very dreary miserable parish in Devonshire where my duties have been to perform the work of a missionary with very little escape to my amusements to study the mosses and *Hepaticae* and to prepare for publication the little volume which I enclose for your acceptance [*Flora Sacra*]. I shall shortly hope to remove to London where I shall have the satisfaction of paying my personal respects to you instated in your new office.'[103]

By the following year, he was indeed in London. In fact, Charles's new employment, a chaplaincy related to St Mark's College, was to effect a welcome reunion with his former colleagues and friends, and a permanent escape from the full-time parish work of a country cleric. His work was within the geographical parish of St Luke's, Chelsea, where the Reverend Charles Kingsley (Senior) since 1836 had accepted the living, moving his whole family up from Devon. The Kingsley's family home was in the old rectory, Church Street, and there Charles Johns was always welcome and treated as family. To equal that pleasure, Charles was once more to become an assistant to Derwent Coleridge, who would continue to encourage his ambitions in the educational world, to which Charles believed he was more suited.

Coleridge, from the peak of success at Helston in 1835-37, had found that the number of pupils attending his fine new Helston Grammar School had decreased. Improved roads and the spread of the railways had made it easier for wealthier parents to send their sons

---

[103]Letter from C Johns, dated 7 May 1841, held by the Royal Botanic Gardens, Kew.

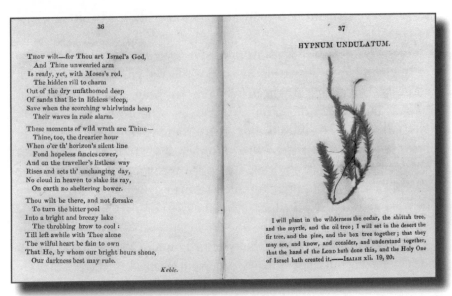

Flora Sacra, pp 36-7. Poem by John Keble.

away to the established public schools. But also the recession in the mining industry was in full swing through this period, and private schooling was not the first priority in local families. In 1840, Derwent had written: 'My boys are all doing well at university – their testimonials are loud and constant in my favour – nothing is neglected which can contribute to the health or comfort of the boys – I have first rate assistance – I am lauded to the skies – yet the school rapidly dwindles.'[104] An unhappy coincidence of that same year, probably adding to the Coleridges' general frustration, was the birth of a still-born son in Helston in early February.[105] Therefore, simultaneously with Charles Johns's return from Dublin to the West Country to take up his first curacy in Devon, the Coleridges were casting around for pastures new. Charles was well aware that they were looking to move because he came to Cornwall to visit when he could, and he knew that Coleridge was asking his friends and colleagues to recommend him for a curacy in the Home Counties. Feeling to be at a crisis point in Cornwall, and after trying a number of options which for one reason or another failed, Derwent was offered an excellent opportunity

---

[104]Hainton *op cit* p 157.
[105]*West Briton*, 7 February 1840, referring to the birth on the 2nd.

to influence the future of education through the preparation of its teachers.

From early in the 19th century the National Society of the Church of England had been setting up schools for the poor throughout the country. These gave Anglican religious teaching, as did the school in Helston, though the latter was a private school requiring fees. By 1840 the Society had decided to open a training college in London to provide teachers for the growing number of Church Schools. When a principal was advertised for, Coleridge was appointed, after a first choice of another clergyman failed to materialise. In January 1841 he became the first principal of St Mark's Training College in Chelsea.[106]

Chelsea in 1841 was on the edge of London. Where the built-up area ended lay nursery gardens and beyond them a large house, Stanley Grove, standing in eleven acres of ground between the King's Road and Fulham Road. This became the new training college, and Coleridge was responsible not only for staffing the college and recruiting the students, but also for the Society's Boarding House for Men at Cannon Row, Westminster, and the Women's Boarding House at Smith Square, Westminster. These two institutions had been established earlier to enable adult teachers to follow a short course of study and training at the National Society's Central School in Westminster.

Coleridge lost no time in appointing as his assistant William Crank, who had been latterly on his staff at Helston. He then asked Charles Johns to be in charge, as a chaplain, of the older masters in training at Cannon Row, perhaps as a favour to give him an initial foothold in London. A year later, Charles's younger brother, Bennett Johns, became the master in charge of the new Practising School built in the grounds of Stanley Grove. Bennett remained there for five years, prior to his own entrance into the Anglican ministry, and long after Charles had moved on in his teaching career. Bennett too had received his degree of MA from Dublin, and was following his brother step by step.

Derwent's ambitions for St Mark's and the young students trained there went well beyond the expectations of the National Society, that

---

[106]St Mark's College became the College of St Mark and St John in 1926, and moved from Chelsea to Plymouth in 1973. Called 'MarJohn' in brief, it is affiliated to Exeter University, more than fulfilling Derwent Coleridge's ambitions.

the college should produce teachers of the three 'R's, the doctrine of the Church of England and no more. His aim was to provide his students with a liberal education to the highest level of which they were capable. While other Victorian training colleges kept a rigid distinction between the training of elementary schoolteachers and education at secondary level, Coleridge sought to bridge that gap, and many of his students entered the church and taught in grammar schools. He also encouraged the use of music in the daily services held in St Mark's Chapel, engaging a singing instructor to teach all the students to sing unaccompanied. His liberal outlook and methods were spread by the teachers leaving the college and not least by Charles and Bennett Johns in their future careers in education.

In 1841, the National Society purchased Whitelands, a house adjoining Chelsea Hospital, as a training college for prospective schoolmistresses.[107] The Head of this institution was to be 'a lady in mind and manner,' to be helped by a clergyman and masters 'under the general direction of Mr Coleridge.'[108] The lady superintendent appointed was 'a rather splendid Scottish* widow named Mrs Julia Field, who was assisted by her unmarried daughter.'[109]

Caroline Fox's diary entry for May 1842 explained the transition from Cornwall to Chelsea retrospectively:

> The Derwent Coleridges have given up the school at Helston and settled near London, at St Mark's College. To-day he showed us over the place with great delight, himself so completely in keeping with it... Their object is to train up a class of teachers intermediate between the present aristocratic constitution of the Church, and the extremely ignorant set who have now to fulfil its inferior offices.

John Seed's study outlines the religious framework for students:

---

[107]Whitelands was later to move out of Chelsea to the southwest London area of Roehampton, and through various metamorphoses become Roehampton Institute (of Education) and latterly University of Surrey, Roehampton, maintaining always its emphasis on education and teaching.

[108]Hainton *op cit* p 176.

[109]Cole, Malcolm (1982) *Whitelands College, The History* p 3. *Though referred to in this text as a 'Scottish' widow, it has been found that Julia Field, widow of James Field of Bath, Somerset (d 1822), was born and raised in Co Galway, Ireland (see entry in Appendix ii for further explanation of the 'Scottish connection').

Church influence saturated the day to day life of the college.... local churchmen provided much of the teaching in the early years, including Derwent Coleridge, Principal of the nearby male Anglican training college St Mark's, and Charles Kingsley (Sr),[110] the Rector of Chelsea, father of the writer . . . . Kingsley, the rector, not only came to Whitelands to teach the students in the 1840s, he was also a member of the new College Council from 1849.[111]

So the several friends from the West Country were together again.

Whitelands College 1841-70. *Courtesy of John Seed.*

In Charles's position as chaplain, he may not have had formal teaching responsibilities, and he was there mainly amongst young men of his own age preparing to be teachers both at home and in the mission field. These were not the youths of gentlemen's families to whom he was accustomed. His letters to Hooker, by this time appointed to the position of director of the Royal Botanic Gardens at Kew, supply us with the best information about this short period in his life, and

---

[110]Charles Kingsley (Sr) was appointed Rector of Chelsea in 1836, and St Mark's College happily was situated within his parish.

[111]Seed, John (2005) *Training Female Schoolteachers in Victorian London: A Study of Three Colleges*, Chap 1: 'A superior class of parochial schoolmistress' Whitelands College 1841-70. www.billygriff.sathosting.net

it is clear that his botanical interests were as strong as ever. His post brought him into contact with teachers in training around Britain and also further afield. On the occasion of a friend bringing home for him from South Africa a box of seeds, he planted them in the grounds of St Mark's, Chelsea. When he sent a list to Hooker, he offered to supply him with any of the seeds or plants that he might want.[112] Another letter refers to his 'black friend in Bermuda' from whom he had received a package of specimens which he shared with Hooker. This friend was one of his pupil teachers at Cannon Row.

In the summer of 1842, Charles and another friend[113] made a botanizing tour in Scotland, during which three days were given over to the mountains. His opportunity to describe it in some detail would come some years later (1846) in his first book of excursions, entitled *Botanical Rambles*, when he employed the Scottish highlands as his case study for the finding of mountainous plant life. Herein are almost 30 pages of travelogue about a high-spirited pair of naturalists out to enjoy themselves.

I started from Glasgow, in one of the small steamers which ply on the Clyde, and sailed down the river to Dunbarton, distant about seventeen miles. I was told that, if I completed my short tour without more than one exposure to soaking rain, I might consider myself very fortunate. In addition, therefore, to my usual botanical apparatus, which consisted of a large tin box slung across my back for collecting specimens of plants, a stout knife to answer the double purpose of cutting and digging, a stock of blotting-paper and boards for drying, at the close of each day, whatever plants I might find, I furnished myself with that most unromantic appendage, an umbrella…I was accompanied, too, by a friend, who, though he was familiar with every spot that we intended to visit, was as anxious to renew his acquaintance with them as I was to commence mine, and was prepared to go wherever he thought I should be most gratified, and to do anything that would give me pleasure.

(*BR*, p 115)

---

[112]Letter to Hooker from Johns, 30 August 1841 (Kew archives).

[113]Though remaining unnamed in the text, this walking companion was probably William Mawdesley Best (?1809-1869), a lawyer friend and writer on legal subjects (*DNB*) from the Inns of Court in London, whose original home had been Haddington, East Lothian. Best was in the following year to be one of the witnesses at Charles's wedding ceremony.

Of Charles's courtship of Ellen Field and the general tenor of their long marriage, nothing is known, and this is to be regretted. Whereas Chitty in her biography of Charles Kingsley was able to reveal in her own words 'a whole new side to Kingsley's character, the side that he used to refer to as "the forbidden depths,"' there is no such excitement or titillation of the senses as revealed in the life of Johns. The lack of any documents, personal letters, or much reference in the correspondence of others, with a few minor exceptions such as references in the letters between Charles's sister Emily and her husband Henry Carrington, leave us with a characterless feeling about the marriage which was the only one for each of them. This is not necessarily a bad thing, as we are all entitled to our 'hidden depths,' but as Chitty argues in the case of Kingsley, 'It is as well that the love letters *have* become available, for other sources of original material are few.' What was true for Charles Kingsley prior to these revelations, is certainly also true for Charles Johns. The closest we come to the man is a deep familiarity with his writings. And, in the latter stages of the research for this monograph, an autograph album of writings, signatures, envelopes and letters, contributed by various members of the family and close friends, has also come to light. Some of these letters, when addressed to Johns personally, are employed within the text.[114]

On 22 June 1843 Charles Alexander Johns, Bachelor and 'clericus,' married Ellen Julia Field, spinster, at the parish church of St Luke's, Chelsea. They were married 'according to the rites and ceremonies of the Established Church,' by Licence, by the rector, the Rev Charles Kingsley (senior), in the presence of William M Best and Bennett G Johns (witnesses for Charles) and Ellen Richards and Maria Johns Jacob (for Ellen). Charles was at that time living in Smith Street, close to Ellen's residence at Whitelands, and the father of each, though Ellen's father was already deceased, is described as 'Gent' on the marriage certificate. Charles was 31 years old at the time of his marriage, Ellen 10 years younger.

---

[114]The entire list of autographs appears in Appendix v, indicating a wide circle of friends and acquaintances.

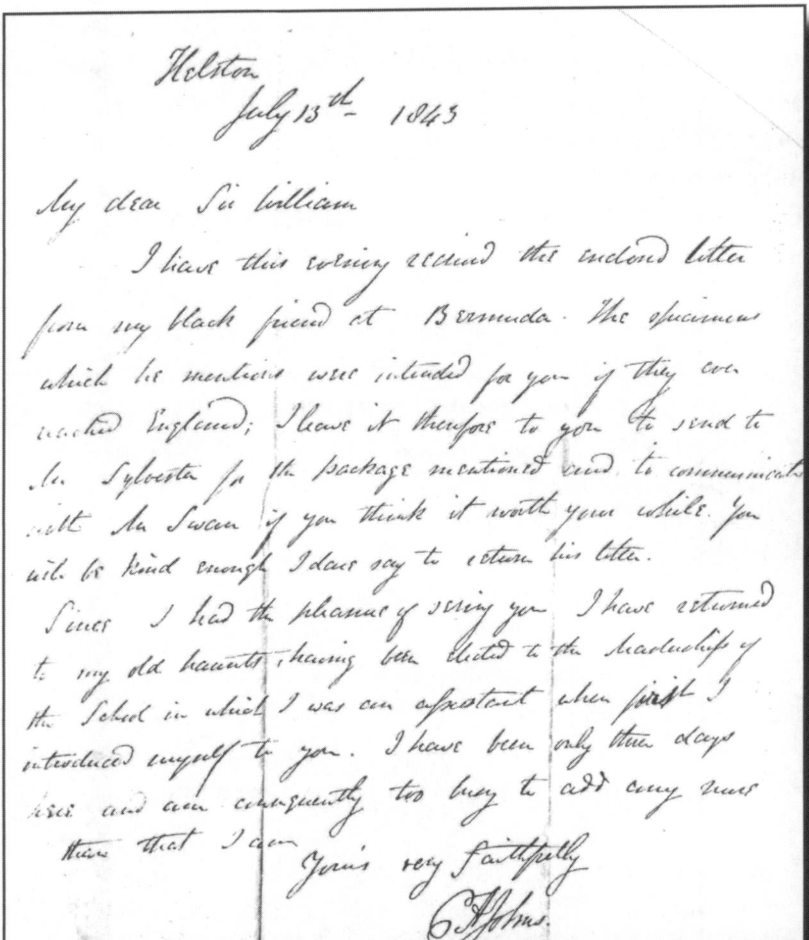

Helston
July 13th - 1843

My dear Sir William

I have this evening received the enclosed letter from my black friend at Bermuda. The specimens which he mentions were intended for you if they ever reached England; I leave it therefore to you to send to Mr Sylvester for the package mentioned and to communicate with Mr Swan if you think it worth your while. You will be kind enough I dare say to return his letter.

Since I had the pleasure of seeing you I have returned to my old haunts, having been elected to the Mastership of the School in which I was an assistant when first I introduced myself to you. I have been only three days here and am consequently too busy to add any more than that I am

Yours very faithfully

C A Johns.

Letter from Charles Johns to William Hooker (1842).

THE

PHYTOLOGIST:

A

POPULAR

BOTANICAL MISCELLANY.

CONDUCTED BY

EDWARD NEWMAN.

VOLUME THE SECOND.
(CONCLUDED).

pt. 3.

LONDON:
JOHN VAN VOORST, PATERNOSTER ROW.
M.DCCC.XLVII.

Johns and friend William Hore contributed findings from
the first publication of *The Phytologist.*

11

HELSTON, CORNWALL –
IN HIS OWN RIGHT: 1843-47

A letter written by Henry Carrington some years later mentioned that Charles had experienced problems with the Committee (of the National Society or of St Mark's is not clear), 'on account of the manner in which he conducted affairs at Manchester Buildings.'[115] It is not known if his failings in their eyes referred to time spent away from his responsibilities at the Men's Boarding House at Cannon Row, but by early 1842, after only a few months in post and before his marriage to Ellen, Charles had been seeking work elsewhere.

In March of that year came Johns's first foray into the field of published scientific journalism, when he contributed a note on mosses found at Leith Hill, Surrey, to *The Phytologist*, in the first volume of that new botanical miscellany.[116] This was a popular journal to which Charles and his circle of botanical friends would contribute over many years. One letter to Charles, sent by the noted bookseller and zoologist, William Yarrell, early in that year, makes a formal arrangement for him to be interviewed by a panel at the Royal Entomological Society in London. Perhaps this was a thrust at finding a curatorial or administrative post at a related

---

[115]Emily Carrington's album, now in possession of her granddaughter, Molly Matthews.

[116]A magazine (1842-1863) under the editorship of George Luxford and management of Edward Newman. In its statement of intent, the opening comment is '*The Phytologist* owes its existence to the desire of recording and preserving fact, observations and opinions related to Botany in general, but more especially to British Botany. Prior to its commencement *these* had no appropriate receptacle.' It had become by 1844, when its second volume of issues opened 'the medium through which all our British botanists communicate with the public' (Preface, *Phytologist*, 1845).

learned society. Another publication by Charles within the year, however, appears to demonstrate that a primary desire was to continue in some kind of teaching capacity. Late in autumn, appeared his *Short Sermons for Children*, published again by J W Parker of the Strand who had produced the *Flora Sacra* for him.[117]

The hoped-for move, wherever it was to be, would necessarily have to carry with it the reference of Derwent Coleridge. And indeed, on 6 April 1843, the minutes of the Borough of Helston record that the Council approved the appointment of the Reverend Charles Alexander Johns, former assistant to Coleridge, as Master of Helston Grammar School.[118] A month after their marriage Charles and Ellen began their new life together back in Helston, when the school reopened on 25 July.[119]

It had been four to five years since Charles left Helston and its grammar school, as a full-time teacher, and without doubt he was pleased to renew old friendships with those such as Emily Trevenen, the close friend of the Coleridges, the Fox family, the Grylls family and numerous others. He would also be within easier reach of his family and friends at Plymouth. To return as headmaster, with the local respect this meant, was more than he could have hoped for quite so soon. But it was not that simple for his new young wife. Coming from London society to rural Cornwall must have been something of a shock, although Helston's leading families gave the young couple a warm welcome. In addition to acquiring a new husband, and a new home, the responsibilities of 'mothering' a spirited group of young boys was probably a major challenge for the young woman.

Prior to her most recent experience with young women training to be teachers, most being virtually her own age, Ellen was familiar only with the job of governessing with one or two charges at a time.[120] But she would have to rely strongly on Charles's previous experience amongst young boys, and also amongst the Cornish. The double chal-

----

[117]See Appendix ii for a brief summary of J W Parker's influence on Johns's publishing career.

[118]CRO B/Helston No 10, 6 April 1843.

[119]In 'Births and Marriages' of *The British Magazine* (1843) the marriage was announced between Ellen Julia Field of Bath and the Rev C A Johns, Headmaster of Helston Grammar School.

[120]See Appendix ii for Mrs Julia Field.

lenge must have seemed at least somewhat daunting to the new young bride. The couple, in exactly the same way as the Coleridges before them, would become in *loco parentis,* and Ellen's responsibility for the smooth running of a busy household, even with the help of servants, was not simple. Even as late as 1873, Charles complained in print about the poor public hygiene of the area, and the need for an improved system of drainage (*Week* p 49). And this would have been only one of the problems.

The two headmasters who had succeeded Coleridge at the school had not been successful in their posts, the first staying only three months and the second reducing the school to a very few pupils. Charles's work was cut out for him. The Schoolhouse, the cause of so many problems and much expense over the years, needed further repairs and improvements, some of which were carried out before Ellen and Charles arrived. When Charles Kingsley (junior) visited them in September, using the occasion of the annual school meeting to stay with Charles and Ellen, he wrote to Fanny Grenfell,[121] his fiancée, 'What do you mean when you said Mrs Johns's house must have plenty of <u>refinements</u> scattered about it? I hope you do not mean all those pretty artificial knick-knacks with which you, darling, and Charlotte and others make their rooms look so ladylike.'[122] Kingsley apparently had not noticed whether or not Ellen 'offended' unduly in that fashion.

Charles Kingsley had been ordained as curate of Eversley parish in Hampshire in the previous year, and his mission in September 1843 was not only to visit the Charles and Ellen in their new home but also to visit Fanny's close relatives in the area. Charles Johns's ready-made circle of friends and acquaintances amongst the Cornish gentry and further afield would have been reassuring to Ellen, despite the geographic distance between Chelsea and Helston. Cornwall, however, as ranked with other places in Britain, was usually found to be less class-conscious than other counties. Though there were the great families, these were both less patriarchal perhaps than elsewhere and often absent, maintaining their working homes in London and their parliamentary seats – of which there were many – from there as well.

---

[121]See biographical sketch of Frances (Fanny) Grenfell in Appendix II.

[122]Chitty, Susan (1974) *The Beast and the Monk* London: Hodder and Stoughton p 83.

Upon returning to Cornwall, Charles immediately re-connected with his former naturalist friends and joined them in their exhibiting and collecting activities. At the Annual Exhibition of the Royal Cornwall Polytechnic Society in 1843, it gave him great pleasure to submit a Collection of Mosses and to receive a first prize in the Natural History Section. It is also clear that his passion for exploring and rambling, and especially in the cause of 'botanizing,' had by no means diminished. Most often he would take boys from the school with him to places he had discovered years before, recalling expeditions he had made alone and also with his friend, the Reverend W S Hore.

At the annual school meeting in September, Charles preached 'a very clear and able sermon' on the advantages of a grammar-school education, and 40 attended the dinner at the Angel Inn. In his after-dinner speech, Charles said that because of the increasing number of pupils, he had engaged an assistant master, Mr G M D'Arcy Irvine.[123] All present were delighted with 'the prospect held out of Helston School recovering its former prosperity under its present able Head Master.' At the following day's ball the company danced from 9.30 till 4am.[124]

Earlier that same month Charles had been licensed by the Bishop to the curacy of St Bartholomew's Chapel, Porthleven. Previous headmasters, such as Coleridge, had been appointed curate of St Michael's, Helston, but that position was already filled by the Reverend Walter Blunt, a man who later caused much dissension in the town. As curate of Porthleven, Charles joined the clergy at the impressive funeral of the Reverend John Molesworth St Aubyn of Clowance that took place the following February, and he was in close contact with Canon John Rogers of Penrose, benefactor of St Bartholomew's.[125] Early the following year Squire Rogers offered 'a portion of ground adjoining the

---

[123]Later, headmaster of Napier Grammar School, Wellington, New Zealand. Full biographical information about TGHM D'Arcy-Irvine (b Dublin 1824-d 1894 Australia) on website of Kinder-Library, New Zealand, which also reveals that Johns employed him while he studied for his degree and later ordination at Trinity College, Dublin. Johns may have known him in Dublin.

[124]West Briton 13 October 1843 p 2f.

[125]In essence this was also the creation of a new parish, which was formally created in 1844 out of Sithney, after the Church building was completed in 1842. See Henderson, Charles, Cornish Church Guide (1925).

Helston Grammar School to the Corporation for 500 years,' which was gratefully accepted and enclosed.[126]

1844

As a recently ordained Anglican priest and a new headmaster, Charles found 1844 a difficult year. Helston parish church became the centre of an unholy row between Mr Blunt, the curate, and his parishioners. Blunt wished to introduce some of the new practices supported by the Anglo-Catholic movement (the 'Oxford Movement') led by Newman, Pusey and others, but his congregation were shocked by any change that suggested a move towards Romanism. This dispute was reported chiefly in the *West Briton*, the local paper that supported electoral reform and was more likely to be read by nonconformists than *The Royal Cornwall Gazette*.[127]

Mr Blunt so upset his parishioners and other clergy in the area that first the Bishop of Exeter and finally the Archbishop of Canterbury were forced to intervene, the Archbishop seeking to end the divisions nationally, caused by the Tractarian reforms. Charles had to tread very carefully through this controversy. The congregation at
St Michael's, still a chapel of
the parish church of Wen-
dron (until 1848), had greatly
diminished, but it is not clear
if his pupils were still attending
the church, as was the custom
under previous headmasters.
He wanted to keep on good
terms with the churchwarden,

Helston Parish Church

Frederick Hill Esq, who opposed Blunt's Anglo-Catholic practices, as three of Hill's sons were his pupils. However, as curate of St Bartholomew's, Porthleven, he did not want to offend the Squire, who was reported as having 'thought proper to give countenance to the Curate of Helston's indecent conduct by wearing a surplice . . . in the pulpit at Penzance' (*WB* 8 November 1844).

Perhaps because of these troubles there was no report of the 1844

---

[126]CRO B/Helston No 10, 7 February 1844.
[127]Entries in *West Briton* (8 Nov 1844-March 1845).

annual school meeting in the *West Briton* and only a short report
in the *Royal Cornwall Gazette*. However, in October the latter paper
announced the birth of a son 'to the lady of the Rev C A Johns's.'
Charles Henry Johns[128] was born on 13 October and brought great
joy to his parents at an uneasy time.

1845

Over the turn of the year Charles and Ellen and baby Henry travelled to
Plymouth to stay near their family. His good friend William Hore had
returned to Plymouth from curacies elsewhere and was living at home
with his mother and sisters at Trafalgar Place, a half a mile from Park
Street, where Charles's own parents remained. This offered the opportunity for the two to take up their walks and searches in the area again,
and one of these in late December took the companions on a specimen
hunt at Lydford about 25 miles away on the edge of Dartmoor. Hore
reported this trip in a note to *The Phytologist* in early January,[129] during
which he and Charles collected about 80 specimens of moss. 'Any musi-
cologist visiting this part of Devonshire in December, would be amply
rewarded by a day's stroll in Lydford woods, which are as beautiful as
any in the county . . . Either the Rev C A Johns, Grammar School, Hel-

OAK IN WISTMAN'S WOOD.

Oak in Wistman's Wood. From *Forest Trees of
Britain*, Vol 1, p 13.

ston, or myself, will be happy to supply any muscolo-
gist, to whom this moss in
fruit may be a desideratum,
with a specimen, as long as
our stock of duplicates ena-
bles us to do so.'

Another jaunt over the
holidays allowed the two
friends an investigation
of the trees that make up
the mysterious Wistman's
Wood on Dartmoor. Situ-

---

[128]In this text, because of the proliferation of Charles's persons in the Johns
circle, he is referred to as Henry only, as this was the name he was called. But in all
official documentation (Census and GRO registrations) he is designated Charles
Henry.

[129]'Discovery of *Bryum roseum* in fruit, at Lydford, Devon,' pp 53-4, *Phyt*
(1845), by the Rev W S Hore, MA, FLS.

ated about a mile above Two Bridges, on the left back of the river, Charles describes the trees, primarily oaks, as 'a colony of patriarchs in a wilderness.' A note, reporting on the nature of the 300 to 500 veteran trees in the wood, along with a great number of saplings, which delighted Charles and William, was offered by Johns in the same issue of *The Phytologist*.[130]

Charles had a lovely sense of humour, and one story retold by Caroline Fox, in her Diary for 1845, was illustrative of this. He enjoyed telling of his youthful fancies:

> *January 18:* Charles Johns, the Botanist, spent the morning with us. The earliest botanical fact concerning him is, that a biscuit was given him over which carraway [sic] seeds were sprinkled; he picked out the seeds, planted them, and waited, alas! Vainly, for a crop of biscuits!

The month of March brought the parish elections of the churchwardens. In Helston, Walter Blunt harangued his diminished flock, even jumping on the table in his passion, before abruptly leaving the meeting. Frederick Hill was re-elected as a warden, Blunt resigned his post and in August the Bishop appointed Charles Johns to the temporary curacy of St Michael's Church. This says much for the respect in which Johns was held, and moreover demonstrated both his political skill and the discretion with which he handled himself.

Meantime, the seeming chaos of the previous year had settled somewhat, and Charles could once more turn his attention to more cultural interests. On arrival back in Cornwall he had immediately returned to the status of subscribing member of the RCPS, joining his friends the Fox family, and Miss Elizabeth Warren. She received a 1st Bronze Medal for a Collection of Algae at the Annual Exhibition in September. Miss Warren was a foremost member of the Ladies Committee of the Polytechnic, and often a judge for the Natural History Section of the exhibitions.

In May, Charles joined William Hore again for a 'farewell botanical excursion' to Whitsand Bay, Cornwall, with their companion, Professor Thomas Edmondston, a few days before the latter was setting sail

---

[130]'Wistman's Wood and Anomodon curtipendulum' pp 54-5, *Phyt* (1845) by the Rev C A Johns, MA, FLS.

on the Californian expedition.[131] In his scientific note[132] following
this jaunt, Hore makes a point of commenting about Edmondston,
that 'His friends will be glad to learn that he quitted England [Ed.
Plymouth] in excellent health and spirits, anticipating with delight
an investigation into the botanical and zoological riches of an almost
unknown country.'[133]

Also published in the June issue of *The Phytologist*, was a long article which lays a trail that Charles followed in future. It is possibly not
too much to say that the paper, contributed by William Hore, was a
seed well-planted and an inspired prompt for Charles, who was also
a named part of the original expedition. Entitled 'A Day's Botanizing
on the Lizard,' the author promises to 'furnish an account of a day's
wanderings on the Lizard in June' and starts 'with my friend, the
Rev C A Johns, in a gig from Helston on the morning of the 11th for
Landewednack, the village adjacent to the Lizard lighthouses.' Adding 'six more days' into the excursion not three years later (1848)
Charles's own addition to the 'biography of Cornwall' in the form of
A Week at the Lizard, would be published. During the 1845 ramble
they also found particular plants and specimens near Cadgewith (sic)
that they had previously discovered for the first time in 1838 when
on a similar expedition together. And this is also the style that Charles
adopts in his later publication, by quoting previous expeditions and
pointing to spots where he had made discoveries before. By this time,
in any case, Charles was already hard at work on the various chapters
describing rambles in various types of terrain, and at different seasons,
which would make up his first major publication to appear the following year.

The annual school meeting in September showed that the school

---

[131]The topic of Letter 867, Darwin Correspondence Project, in which Charles
Darwin 'makes suggestions for Thomas Edmondston, naturalist on board the *HMS
Herald*, of places to visit and geological data to collect on proposed California expe-
dition.' 13 May [1845?]

[132]'Description of a species of *Orobanche* new to Great Britain, probably
Orobanche amethystea, *Thuillier' Phyt* ii pp 239-40 by W S Hore, June 27, 1845.

[133]Originally from Shetland, Edmondston had been appointed at age 19 to the
professorship of botany at Anderson's University, Glasgow (now U of Strathclyde)
and was a friend of the Hookers, who probably introduced him to Hore and Johns.
The following year (1846) he was accidentally shot dead in disembarking the ship
in Peru.

continued to grow. Charles recalled in his speech that 'on his first appointment, a little more than two years since, it consisted of three boarders and a few day boys. He had the great satisfaction of announcing that the boarders were increased to 26.'[134] Frederick Hill, whose three sons were pupils, complimented Mrs Johns on her care of the boys.[135] Richard Hichens, a very successful pupil, gained a place at Exeter College, Oxford. Charles was proving an able headmaster, and his wife an excellent housemother.

1846

This year was to introduce Charles Johns, the author, nationally in the field in which he wished to be known, the teaching of others about the natural world and the stories that adhered. This was what Charles enjoyed writing about most and the chapters of *Botanical Rambles* show the reasons for his popularity as he dealt with subjects that had been considered by some as serious, scientific and somewhat suspect, because it was delving too closely into God's creation. That which made Johns's work unique was not only his 'popularising' style, laced as it is with Christian gratitude for 'His bountiful gifts,' but his heartily expressed need to share the happiness of learning something.

Because of his association with J Parker & Son, Charles was introduced into the authors' ranks of the Society for Promoting Christian Knowledge, or SPCK. Though it is not known for certain, as no correspondence has emerged to confirm it, the original introduction to Parker and thence to the SPCK, for whom the Parker firm was publisher, may have been by Charles's older sister, Maria Jacob, who was already earning a living by writing in London (most of her work anonymous), or by Henry Carrington as a publisher of note in Bath. One of SPCK's specialties over the years was to provide knowledgeable scientific literature, written in an elementary manner, at prices which most of the populace could afford and that would benefit young people in schools. Having begun in 1698 as an organisation to sponsor

---

[134] *West Briton* 3 October 1845, p 2c.

[135] Not unlike Derwent Coleridge in his neglect in mentioning the huge contributions made by Mary to the success of St Mark's household supervision (Hainton, *Unknown Coleridge*, pp181-185), Ellen and her life as his wife or partner in the work is never mentioned by Johns himself. The general lack of documentation of women's roles is everywhere observed, and was undoubtedly considered part of the social code of discretion for married gentlewomen not to be seen to be working.

charity schools, they now seized the opportunity in their 'rambling' (walking) books to encourage the amateur and entertain the ordinary through spiritual writings emphasizing the importance of communing with nature. The hopeful outcome of such engaging reading was to inspire some converts to the Christian way of life.

While not the first exponent of the rambling genre, Charles was soon to provide some of the most entertaining examples available. With a natural exuberance and fearless attitude, he possessed the gift of expressing his zealousness in words. But he needed more illustrators for his intended projects, and a new friend met in Cornwall, Emily Stackhouse,[136] was to be foremost amongst these, alongside his sisters who continued to help him with drawings. This was the year that Emily Stackhouse received the 'Extra Prize' of a Second Bronze Medal at the RCPS Annual Exhibition, for her four volumes of botanical drawings, and it is clear that she and Charles were working together by this time.

'"Speak to the earth and it shall teach thee" is a precept He conveyed into my mind before I could read; and now that I can read and understand, I am thankful that this precept was but the stepping-stone to another, "Lift up your eyes on high, and behold who hath created these things"' (*Rambles* p 47).

The first chapter, 'The Meadow,' is addressed directly to a friend who has expressed surprise at the hours Charles has spent collecting, drying and mounting specimens of plants – surely a waste of his time? Charles's response is to take him on rambles, showing him the importance of grasses as pasture, the change in their root systems as they adapt to the soil, the spread of their seeds. Then Charles focuses on the daisy, whose central cup of florets are sheltered when it rains by the outer white petals closing over the yellow flowers, covering them like a tent. He conveys his wonder and delight in his exact description, and attributes all to God.

Charles sustains the same approach through each chapter and season as the writer rambles across field, wood, mountain and seashore. In the corn-field comes a vivid picture of the beauty of a field

---

[136]See biographical essay on Emily Stackhouse by Clifford Evans. Emily herself would also in later years add to the literature for ramblers when she published 'Rare Plants in the neighbourhood of Truro' as stray notes in the then absence of a 'Flora of Cornwall.'

of wheat or barley in June, with its poppies, wild geranium, scarlet pimpernel and flowering hawthorn, of which Charles says he would like to 'gather a branch, and to bury my face in its bunches of cool fragrant flowers.' Nothing dry and scientific here, as a lark sings and the breeze sends long waves across the fields. However, Charles the educator gives a scientific description of such things as the seed-pods of hairy bitter-cress or the stings of bees, wasps or viper, and refers to the medicinal use of plants and the need for a magnifying glass to see the 'most exquisite lacework' of mosses.

In 'The Mountain' Charles writes of a three-day excursion with a companion in the Scottish Highlands in the year before his marriage.[137] They had climbed Ben Lomond and Ben Voirlich, studying and gathering plants. Charles explains the radiation of heat, and why snow remains on mountain peaks. There are difficult climbs and descents, and long walks to Loch Katrine, scene of Walter Scott's *Lady of the Lake*. Returning from Stirling by coach to Edinburgh, they 'accompanied the Professor of Botany from the University through the splendid conservatories of the Botanic garden where, among tropical palms and ferns, we were able to draw forth from our cases living specimens of a plant, which happened to be the subject of the evening discussion, a humble native of the Scottish Alps *(Sibbaldia procumbens).*'

1847

Despite these successes both in the school and in Charles's growing reputation, Ellen was growing less content with life in Helston. It seemed to be generally known within the family that Charles was feeling restive in his post and was looking about, in places where he could mix more readily with his scientific colleagues. Henry Carrington, his brother-in-law, took his young son, Harry, with him to London. Writing to his wife Emily, Henry said that after visiting St Paul's and a trip on the Thames, they had been to tea with her brother, Bennett.

There, amidst the gossip, Bennett commented: 'There's no chance

---

[137]The date of this expedition, recalled later, was given in a letter written by Charles to Sir William Hooker, headed '11 Manchester Buildings June 21 1842.' His companion was W M Best (Note 105) and the professor of botany was Robert Graham, who had signed his application for the Linnean Society. These journeys away from London and his duties there may have been the source of the Committee's dissatisfaction with Johns's performance related to St Mark's College.

whatever of Charles being invited back as Chaplain at Whitelands –
he wouldn't recommend it anyway: a stink of a concern! Mrs Field
now declares she never wants Charles to come up to town. Ellen
writes a letter every post to her mother full of grievances about Helston, which keeps Mrs Field in a constant frizz.'[138]

Carrington continues with the reference that the Committee had
disliked Charles because of the way he conducted affairs at Manchester Buildings (Cannon Row), but that it seemed now that Charles
intended to come back to London on the merest chance of getting
employment. Charles had written to his brother Bennett saying that
if he hears of a good curacy he is to tell him. Carrington adds that
'to this curacy Mrs Field and Miss Snow will raise money and pupils
from Mrs Field's aristocratic friends for a splendid boarding school.'

Ellen's duties as the headmaster's wife had increased with the
growth of boarders at the Helston school. She had young Henry
to care for and by 1847 she was expecting their second child. The
rambling old schoolhouse, which had needed serious repairs to the
windows in 1845, was proving an unsatisfactory home in which to
raise a family. Charles was busy teaching or carrying out his duties as
curate of both Porthleven and Helston. The publication that year of
his *Examination Questions on the Pentateuch*, for the use of families,
national schools and the lower forms in Grammar Schools, showed
that his attentions were focused on his pupils. But he also spent much
of his time continuing his botanical and geological studies, especially
in his favourite haunts on the Lizard, leaving Ellen in Helston to write
those daily letters to her mother.

One happy occasion, when she and little Henry accompanied
Charles and his pupils to Loe Pool, was reported in *The Royal Cornwall Gazette* (4 June 1847). Canon Rogers invited the school to hold a
regatta (of model yachts) on the lake, where 'a breeze sufficiently fresh
to fill the canvas of the fairy craft' led to the two-and-a-half-year-old
Henry being announced as the winner of the third class, 'the *Ellen, C
H Johns*, built by Mr Enys.' Everyone present, including the Hills and
Mrs Glyn Grylls, then enjoyed a picnic in the woods, while music was
played by 'Helston's amateur band' from a boat on the Pool: 'merry
music borne across the wave.' Charles proposed a toast to Mr and Mrs
Rogers, thanking them for their hospitality.

---

[138]Letter dated 1847 in Emily Carrington's album.

Soon after that outing Charles was summoned to Plymouth, where his father had suffered a second serious stroke. From Plymouth Emily Carrington wrote on 14 June to her husband: 'We expect Charles by steamer and Bennett by coach from London. Poor papa's state of helplessness is truly trying to behold – still deprived of the use of both hands. The use of his left hand will, I fear, never be restored... May God support him.' Emily returned to Bath on 19 June, but writes, 'Julia is not strong and has a great deal to do and to cause her anxiety, and indeed there is much at home to trouble me.'

Their father had managed to do some sketches and watercolours with his left hand after his first stroke, but that was no longer possible. John ('Jack'), 18 and the youngest in the family, who was working as a bank clerk locally to help support the family financially, was greatly needed now, though whether he could adequately cope is doubtful: Carrington, in a letter to Emily writes, 'Don't worry about Jack. I'm sure he will turn out well.'

An intense quantity of work contributed to the major publication of that year, Volume I of Charles's imposing study, *Forest Trees of Britain* (Volume II did not appear until 1849), a large body of writing requiring many illustrations. Emily Stackhouse helped out with this volume as well. Two separate offerings to the scientific world appeared in *The Phytologist* in 1847 (see bibliography) and a contribution to Hooker's *London Journal of Botany*, based on excursions that Charles made in that summer.[139] These concentrated on Cornwall by making notes on Cornish plants, and special observations on the plants at 'Land's End,' the understood euphemism for the far west of Cornwall. In the second article he specifically mentions that his observations come from his diary entries made on a walking trip at Landewednack, near Helston from 3-9 July. That article recounts the occasion when he declared, 'If I throw my hat on the ground, wherever it lands there will be at least ten species of wild plant underneath,' a comment that Charles Darwin was to take up and quote.[140] One of the journal's readers was to reply 'he must have worn a large hat!' All of this and more would be gathered in one form and another into his next year's

---

[139]In the latter journal the topic was broader, 'Notes on British Plants,' but included a special section on 'Finds in Cornwall,' *LJB* pp 474-7.

[140]Letter in Johns's Autograph Collection. Also quoted in Bates & Scolding (2002).

publication celebrating his time spent on the Lizard.

Concern about his parents must have added weight to Charles's resolve to move from the comparative isolation of Cornwall, much as he loved it, to an area where he could earn more money and where Ellen would be happier. The birth of their second child was announced in T*he Royal Cornwall Gazette* in August 1847: 'At the School House, Helston, on Monday the 23rd inst, the wife of the Rev C A Johns, of a daughter.' Christened Anne Catherine (known as Katie by the family), she was not to spend long in Cornwall.

The school meeting that September was the last for Charles, although he made no mention of his intention to move. He spoke of the importance of classics and divinity and suggested that he was the first to introduce 'a systematic course of Biblical studies into a Grammar school.'[141] The Chairman, Canon Rogers, praised him saying that he devoted 'the hours of relaxation from sterner studies to scientific studies,' meaning, no doubt, Charles's continued pursuit of collecting wild flowers and mosses, and his geological interests in the area.

In the Annual Exhibition of the RCPS for that year in October, Charles had raised his subscription donation to the work of the organisation which he had supported strongly since its initiation, and had always encouraged his pupils to attend and participate. He also once again received a First Bronze Medal for his Collection of *Hepaticae*. The judges commented: 'It is probable that a Flora of Cornwall will shortly be published, under the auspices of one of our local societies; and this collection affords a gratifying proof, that, even in those departments of the vegetable kingdom which are least known and studied, there is a sufficiency of native talent and industrous [sic] research to render the forth-coming work worthy of public confidence and patronage.'[142] Charles acted as one of the judges in this final year of his membership, but for the School Productions (drawings) into which some of his pupils had contributed. Both Anna Maria and Caroline Fox were judges of this section with him. Miss Warren was again one of the Natural History judges.

---

[141] *Royal Cornwall Gazette* 1 October 1847 p 4b.

[142] *RCPS Annual Report*, p XVII. In fact, it was not until 1909 that a *Flora of Cornwall* was finally realised, though later to be continually referred to as 'soon coming about.' Though long dead before its publication, the names of both Emily Stackhouse and Charles Johns are met with frequently in its pages.

On 1 October, the Borough Council received a letter from Johns resigning the mastership of the Grammar School, which they accepted 'with sincere regret for the loss of his valuable services.'[143] This must have been a disappointment to them, but perhaps it was not unexpected, especially if Charles was experiencing similar difficulties to those of Coleridge before him. An intense period of farewells followed, alongside promises to return for scientific and friendly visits.

They returned to London with the children in mid-January of 1848, passing through Bath, briefly seeing Henry Carrington at the station by arrangement, and heading for their unknown new life. Though he returned several times thereafter to the Lizard area, usually synchronising his visits with the annual meetings of the Grammar School in September, but also for touring purposes, Charles and Ellen never resided in Cornwall again.[144]

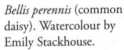

Bellis perennis (common daisy). Watercolour by Emily Stackhouse.

---

[143]CRO B/Helston No 11, 1 October 1847.

[144]Though the reviser of the CAJ entry in the DNB mentions that Johns returned briefly to Helston in 1863, there is no evidence or documentation for this assertion. That was the year Johns was searching for a suitable property for his new school (Winton House) and he could have toured the area with this thought in mind.

Title page of *A Week at the Lizard*, 1ˢᵗ edition, 1848.

12

A FAMILY OF WRITERS & ARTISTS: 1848

Charles and Ellen, with their two young children, moved into a house in Walpole Street, Chelsea, close to Ellen's mother at Whitelands and all the familiar places where they had first met. Other members of Charles's family were also living in London. Bennett Johns, still teaching at St Mark's Training College and lecturing at London University, was soon to become headmaster of Dulwich Junior School, following his ordination as deacon in 1846, and priest in 1848.[145] Bennett was also to become a frequently published author. [See Appendix ii for a summary of his work.]

Charles's elder sister, Maria Jacob, had been living in London for some years with her clergyman husband, John, who had at least a decade previously presented his former pupil to Trinity College, Dublin. Maria was contributing to the family income through writing for the publishing firm of Nathaniel Cooke and also for SPCK. John's health had not been good for some time, and indeed, he would die the following year. Inheriting the family's literary bent, she edited and largely wrote *The Lady's Almanac* as well as successfully publishing books for children. Her work is also outlined in Appendix ii.

Charles had begun his authorship in 1833 by publishing *Chronological Rhymes on English History* to help his pupils. *Flora Sacra* in 1840 completed his theological studies in Dublin, and in 1846 had come his most charming little book, *Botanical Rambles*, followed thereafter by a plethora of short rambling books, and books for children. During 1847, as he prepared to leave Helston, he had produced the scholastic *Examination Questions on the Pentateuch*, but rather more importantly for him in botanical terms, Volume 1 of *Forest Trees of*

---

[145] *Crockford's Clerical Directory* 1860 p 338. See Appendix ii for a summary of his work.

Britain appeared from SPCK's publishing arm. He was steadily at work on Volume II, which appeared in 1849. The first of these volumes, 373 pages in length, contained the reprint of an account of Wistman's Wood (Dartmoor) which Johns had written for *The Phytologist* (11 January 11 1845), showing clearly how he incorporated and re-used all his valuable findings in new work, gathering, sorting and re-arranging alongside new material.

The time and physical exertion of writing these tomes, small though some of them were, should not be underestimated. And, despite appearances to the contrary, financial rewards were not large. The most common contract with authors was to purchase the copyright for a work outright for a fixed sum, between approximately £50-£500, depending on length and the fame of the author, and then to negotiate separately when new editions were initiated. Fyfe[146] in her in-depth study of Christian publishing in Victorian Britain raises a range of issues relevant to the Johns's household from time and family management, the physical work of writing, and the payments expected and received.

'The ideal Christian writer was above the mercenary "trade" aspects of publishing, and pursued literature rather as a spiritual vocation. This was an extrapolation of the secular writer as a learned professional, in contrast to a "mere" tradesman's hack . . . like the secular professional, the Christian writer was presented as engaging in intellectual work, rather than the manual labour of a hack' (Fyfe, p 227). In Charles Johns's case, there was not only the intellectual and physical (hand-writing) work of organising and recording his materials, but of the manual and physical exertions of travelling and collecting his specimens. It is clear that Charles looked for every opportunity to provide work and employment for his family and some of his acquaintances, and they perhaps did the same for him in return.

'Unlike most professionals, writers worked at home, and this meant that time-management and self-discipline were essential for professional as well as part-time writers. But working in the home also had its advantages, and the presence of female helpers, doing

---

[146]Aileen Kennedy Fyfe (2000) 'Writing for Christ,' Chap 4 [in] 'Industrialised Conversion: The Religious Tract Society and Popular Science Publishing in Victorian Britain,' thesis submitted to Jesus College, Cambridge. On-line extracts, pp 170-228.

Cover of the small book *The Days, Months, and Seasons of the Year,
Explained to the Little People of England* by Maria Jacob, Charles's elder
sister. Painted in red, green and gold, it is an an eye-catching delight.

'March,' 'June' and 'October,' painted by Julia Johns. From *Monthly Gleanings from the
Field and Garden* by C.A. Johns (1859).

research, taking dictation or making fair copies, indicates that authorship was not always a solitary activity, pursued alone at the desk. It
could become a collective family activity' (Fyfe, p 227). The main
assistance sought by Charles for his books was expert illustration, and
this was readily available within his family circle, though the identification of individual drawings is not always possible. Anonymity and
the use of pen-names was more common
than not amongst female writers and artists
in the 19th century. Some monograms were
in use but these can be confusing where
two members of the family share the same
initials (Charles Alexander Johns and Anne
Catherine Johns being a case in point).
However, from independent sources it has
been possible to identify the several female
illustrators of Charles's texts as his artistic
sisters, his friend Emily Stackhouse from
Cornwall, and latterly his daughter, Anne
Catherine, all of whom achieved a professional standard of work in their art.

'*Common baywort, August*'.

'Common baywort'
Emily Stackhouse

Although Charles was now living near
to the Botanical Society of London's head-
quarters in Bedford Street and could visit its library and herbarium,
he did not remain actively involved in its activities after leaving Cornwall. Concentrating largely on his writing, he had little time for outside interests, although he certainly took the opportunity to visit the
Royal Botanic Gardens at Kew and to meet Sir William Hooker, who
had done so much to encourage his work as a botanist. A letter written in April 1848 refers to a visit to Kew with his Plymouth friend,
William Hore.

In between the two volumes of *Forest Trees of Britain* came the book
most prized in the far southwest. In the year 1848, the publication of
A Week at the Lizard was realised, a book of continuing fascination to
those living in and those visiting that beautiful area of Cornwall. This
was the book Charles most enjoyed writing, taking him to the places
where his ancestors had lived and worked, and allowing him to relive
his youthful delight in the cliffs, seas, flowers and mosses that he had
now left behind. He had tramped from Helston to St Keverne across
the wild Goonhilly Downs time and again, visiting his grandparents,

and he had walked the cliffs, explored the coves and talked with the farmers and fishermen who made their tough yet skilled living from land and sea. He had walked there with his friends, lived there with his family, and taken his pupils to amazing hidden places amongst the rocks and around the shores. Naturally he had friends there still, and he wanted to celebrate its interest and variety to others.

Charles writes as a friend, taking a visitor with him from Lizard-town to explore the coast, starting with the 'Lizard Lights.' The workings of the Lighthouse are explained, the geology of the rocks with their colours of greenish-black, orange and yellow is described, a story of a rescue from Bumble Rock included, followed by a most detailed picture of a fisherman's method of catching a small fish called a launce. As the chapter continues the reader learns about the formation of a cave called 'The Lion's Den,'[147] and the beauty of Househole (Housel) Bay. Druid rites are touched upon and the pilchard fishery vividly described with the enthusiasm of one who had been a part of the excited crowd of men and women greeting the boats returning with their loads of silver fish. The chapter ends with a visit to Landewednack church, where Charles's great-great-grandfather had been baptised some 175 years earlier.

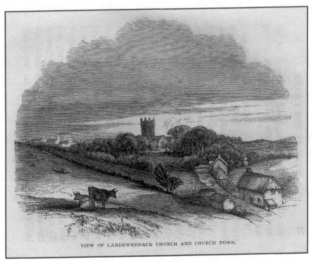

VIEW OF LANDEWEDNACK CHURCH AND CHURCH TOWN.

Engraving: Landewednack. From *A Week at the Lizard*, 1st ed., p 42.

---

[147]Also the subject of his publication 'On the Landslip at the Lizard' in *The London Journal of Botany*.

With youthful energy, Charles is always 'scrambling' up and down the cliffs, and continues writing with this mixture of fact and fascination with the power and beauty of the scenery, especially when he reaches his favourite place, Kynance Cove. He struggles to describe the awesome sight of a storm dashing the waves against the rocks, and then pictures a smooth sea like glass through which gleam the colours of sand, rocks and fish.

The book appeared in the early days of touring, when improving roads were encouraging those with leisure and money to explore the remoter parts of Britain, looking for 'picturesque' and 'romantic' landscapes to sketch and admire. One such visitor was Wilkie Collins, whose *Rambles beyond Railway* was published in 1851.[148] His was very much an outsider's view of Cornwall, dismissing Helston as a 'dull town' with an 'ugly church' and a 'barbarous carnival' [Furry Day]. The town's only value to Collins was as a gateway to the Lizard peninsula, where he felt a sense of superiority to the country people he met. For him the attraction of the scenery was romantic and gothic, the waves 'sounding as they first sounded when morning stars sang together.' He wrote: 'Each succeeding spot the traveller visited, was memorable for some mighty convulsion of Nature, or tragically associated with some gloomy story of shipwreck or death.' Kynance Cove was 'a palace of rocks' and he felt that his climb of Asparagus Rock was 'extreme in danger.' He gazed into the Devil's Bellow's, about which 'the rocks rose wild, jagged and precipitous,' and wrote: 'If ever the ghastly image of Dante's terrible *Vision* was realised on earth, it was realised here.' This was a very different approach from Charles's scientific appreciation and delight in the variety of God's creation, and the stories he could share to support his observations.

A Week at the Lizard was dedicated by Charles to 'His Royal Highness, Albert, Prince of Wales and Duke of Cornwall,' and dated 'Chelsea, April 24th, 1848.' The arms of the Royal Duchy with the 15 bezants and the motto 'One and All' appears above the dedication and on the title-page, which also carries a vignette of Mullion and a decorative floral border. Opposite is a full-page illustration of Kynance Cove from the 'Tar-Box.' There are over 70 illustrations, which, with the folded map and the appendix dealing with the geology and the botany of the area, make the book very attractive. The detailed black-

---

[148]Collins, W (1851) *Rambles beyond Railways* pp 92-3 London: Bentley.

DAWS' HUGO.—Entrance to Lions' Den.

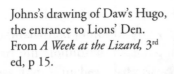

Johns's drawing of Daw's Hugo, the entrance to Lions' Den. From *A Week at the Lizard*, 3rd ed, p 15.

and-white illustrations in *A Week at the Lizard* were drawn by various hands, not all signed. Many of the coastal scenes and geological formations have J H Whimper printed below them and S Read's name appears below the Mullion vignette, while the illustrating of most botanical specimens is probably by Emily Stackhouse.[149]

Charles himself sketched, but did not consider himself skilled as an artist. However, when Whymper had no drawing from which to work, because the place being described was so isolated, it was Charles who had to make the initial images. His colophon signature appears on Daws' Hugo (p 15). On page 33 he refers to 'my companion's sketch-book,' for the scenes capture the homes and churches, the men and women, farm animals, boats and crab-pots, as well as the dramatic cliffs and seas. Whymper's name appears beneath a sketch of a launce and he probably produced the illustrations of all the fish and the splendid cormorant and Cornish chough. However, the botanical illustrations come from other artists. One is signed J J – either Julia or Jane Johns – and others unsigned were likely to have been by one or other of Charles's talented sisters. Ten of these beautiful drawings are signed with the copperplate initials 'E S,' those of Emily Stack-

---

[149] *West Briton*, Bequest notice 5 March 1870, mentions specifically her contributions to this Cornish book, and also *The Forest Trees of Great Britain* (1847-49).

house, friend of Charles and of great importance to his work.[150] This little book is the best attempt Charles ever made to exhibit his love for Cornwall, and to explain his own motivations in a form closest to autobiography.

Even his diary, often brief and elliptical as diaries often are, tells us little about his passion for nature. Of personal correspondence, we know nothing, and his opinions of people and political events are also a blank. In his religious thinking, he was known to be broad in his sympathies, with no time for the extremes in either direction. His appreciation of the natural world was consistently the basis for his love of the 'Creator' and his writings, in exhibit-ing the scope and depth of his interests and his intrepid tackling of the great outdoors, tell us most of what we know about the man. To accomplish the quantity and qual-ity of writing it all down in such detail, after living it in 'rough note form,' without the use of modern technologies, also illustrates the true nature of the scholarly person.

'Honeysuckle'
Emily Stackhouse

In departing Cornwall for pastures new, Charles took with him his memories of 'Fur-ry Day,' the colloquial name for Helston's Flora Day. For him it was not a 'barbarous carnival' that Collins described three years later, but a joyous and exhiliarating experience. Here he had danced over a period of almost twenty years, since he first arrived as assistant to Derwent. Here his ancestors had danced before him and here he had brought his brother and sisters from time to time to enjoy the festival. At the Furry his brother Bennet had first met his wife-to-be, Dellie, as he was prepar-ing his manuscript for publication.

> We must not quit Helston without briefly noticing a singular custom
> which has existed here from time immemorial. Annually, on the 8th
> of May, a party of men and boys go into the country at a very early
> hour in the morning, and return about seven o'clock, bearing green

---

[150]Clifford B Evans 'Forgotten Field' in *Country Life*, 6 July 1995, is an append-ed essay in this book. Also Ishteir, Ann B (1996) *Cultivating Women, Cultivating Science* Baltimore: John Hopkins University Press, 1996; *Bibliotheca Cornubiensis*, vol 2, p 681; *Lake's Parochial History*, vol.4, p. 91.

branches, and announcing in a very melancholy ditty, that "winter is gone, and that they have been to the merry green-wood to fetch home summer in its place." Having perambulated the town and accepted money from all who will give, they retire from the scene, and the town, for the remainder of the morning, is enlivened by the frequent arrival of carriages from the country and neighbouring towns, bearing visitors who intend to participate in the coming gaiety.

At one o'clock, a large party of ladies and gentlemen, wearing summer attire, and profusely decorated with flowers, assemble opposite the Town-hall, and preceded by a band of music, commence a peculiar kind of dance, called "the furry," first tripping on in a double row, and the, at a change in the tune, wheeling round in couples. These evolutions are not confined to the street; for, here and there, where the doors are thrown open, the dancers enter the houses, band and all, traverse the courts and gardens, and may presently be seen emerging by another doorway, if the house be furnished with two, otherwise by that at which they entered. In this way they traverse the whole town, presenting an appearance as gay as it is unusual, especially while winding through some of the exceedingly beautiful gardens for which the town is remarkable, and which, at this season, the laburnums and lilacs being in full flower, are arrayed in their most showy livery. Later in the day, other parties go through the same manoeuvres, and it is not till late at night that the at other times quiet little town returns to its propriety.

What is the origin of this singular custom is not known. In all probability it is a relic of very remote antiquity, and no slight confirmation of this opinion is afforded by the fact, that the air played while the dancing is going on is still traditional in Wales and Brittany, countries to which, as well as to Cornwall, our forefathers retired before their Saxon invaders.

From *A Week at the Lizard*, 2nd ed., pp 224-6

Echium vulgare (Viper's bug-loss). Emily Stackhouse

13

Beenham, Berkshire – A fresh start: 1848-55

It is not known specifically how Charles Johns heard of the need for a curate at St Mary's Church, Beenham, Berkshire. One possible source of information was through the Johns's family friend, Emily Stackhouse, who had strong family links with the Beenham church. Her great-great uncle, Thomas Stackhouse,[151] well-known for his religious publications, had been vicar there from 1733-52. Emily's family still had many connections in the area, and notice of their temporary need for help with the parish would reach Johns, if he was known to be looking.

Another and perhaps more probable source of information about the needs in Beenham may have come through Coleridge, Julia Field and their colleagues at St Mark's and Whitelands, because of the National School that sat beside St Mary's Church in Beenham and was the responsibility of the Vicar. In future years this would become the parish school for the village, but in 1848 it was administered through the network established by the National Society for the Promotion of Education of the Poor, in the Principle of the Established Church. This, of course, was also the founding body of St Mark's and Whitelands Colleges, and Charles's old employers. The vacancy would have been known about through these, since Charles and Ellen were temporarily staying in Chelsea until suitable work and home could be located. Charles's teaching experience, his growing reputa-

---

[151]Thomas Stackhouse (1677-1752) was a well-known theologian, whose great work was his *New History of the Holy Bible from the Beginning of the World to the Establishment of Christianity*. Stackhouse died at Beenham and remains the church's main claim to fame. The church building, as he and subsequently Charles Johns knew it, suffered from serious fire damage in 1794 and then again in 1856, only the tower surviving, after which it was largely rebuilt.

tion as author/botanist and Ellen's schoolhouse supervision were ideal for such an appointment.

The church of St Mary in Beenham, a village near Newbury, already had a young vicar, the Reverend William Bushnell, who had been appointed in 1842. Sadly, his health began to fail almost immediately and his living fell vacant while waiting for his younger brother Thomas to complete his education and take Holy Orders. Thomas Bushnell would then accede to the position of Vicar, hence the appointment was known to be an interim one in advance, or as the common expression was, 'keeping the seat warm.' Charles and Ellen Johns were happy to accept the temporary move to cover parish duties and oversee the National School run by the Parish, located next door.

The vicarage, constructed in 1825, was a large and attractive Georgian house, surrounded by an ample garden and a path through a copse led to the church.[152] Ellen was well pleased to settle with the two children into a comfortable, comparatively modern family home, and Charles no doubt delighted in the garden and copse, as well as having another parish and school in his charge. This was also a home that could welcome visitors with some ease, not a facility which Cornwall then offered, distant as it was.

Gardening for Children also appeared from SPCK's publishing houses in 1848, the Preface for which dates and places the author by October of that year in Beenham.[153] Demonstrating Johns's continuing interest in young people and their opportunity 'to see, and know, and consider, and understand' about God's creation, it was a big success, and sold out its first edition of 6,000 copies rapidly. By early June the following year, just six months on, a second edition was

---

[152]The Church where Charles conducted services burned down the year following his departure and was rebuilt in 1859, but the vicarage of 1825 still stands. In 1956 the vicarage and most of the land was sold to Lady Mary Keen, a professional garden designer and writer of many garden books. She maintained the garden, which contained mature specimen trees, old-fashioned roses and other interesting plants. [Information supplied by a parishioner and the Rev Canon Christine Redgrave, Rector.]

[153]Jane Brown, in her admirable work, *The Pursuit of Paradise* (p 275), lists this small book, *Gardening for Children*, edited by Charles, as a magazine following on from Jane Loudon's *My Own Garden* or *The Young Gardener's Yearbook* (1855), but to date we have been unable to locate such a format. However, many SPCK documents were issued later in parts or on cards, and this book may have received this treatment.

RUIN OF AN OLD OAK IN ALDERMASTON PARK, BERKS.

From *Forest Trees of Britain*, 1ˢᵗ ed, Vol II, p 436.

issued, and Charles prefaced the new one with the comment that the quick sale had convinced him 'that his little book made its appearance not before it was wanted.' Amongst his readers he found the seeds for the growing of 'nature lovers' and acknowledged the plaudits of the periodical press, hoping that the alterations will also meet with approval. The following year Volume II of *The Forest Trees of Britain* was published (1849), on which he had been working steadily since leaving Helston.

His sister Emily Carrington described her visit to Berkshire in her diary for 1850: 'Aug 22 – I am at Beenham! Charles waiting for us at Aldermaston and drove us home in the gig … Emily [her daughter] enjoyed herself playing with Katie and Henry and their dogs and riding on the Rocking Horse. It is a pleasant place, so "perfectly the country."'

Two days later she wrote: 'A lovely morning. The garden here very pleasant.' The next day was Saturday: 'Before breakfast again. Charles and the boys [from the school] gone to bathe. They are early risers here. Had a pleasant drive yesterday across a Common studded with furze and trees and enlivened with heath. The end of our journey a field perfectly gorgeous with heather and thyme. Never in my life saw anything so beautiful of the kind.'

Sunday was an especially busy day for Charles. 'Up early. After b'fast heard Emily and Henry say their catechism. He said it extremely well. Then the children spelt texts with their Box of Letters, only Katie was rather a hindrance. To Church at eleven. Charles said prayers and preached very impressively. Church again in the evening – Emily much pleased with putting together some Scripture Games.' These entries give a good picture of the Victorian family life enjoyed by Charles and Ellen at the time, with the children and three servants living in the roomy vicarage.

Every day, however, was for Charles and Ellen a busy day in term time, and from those days in Beenham came their ideas and plans of running a school of their own. Aside from his parish duties and his writing schedule, Charles also ran preparatory classes for residential and day pupils, providing board and lodging for up to eight young men, ages 11-19, at any given time. It seems that several pupils followed him very quickly from Cornwall, a tribute to his good reputation built at Helston. Others came from London and Kent, and from Bradfield nearby.

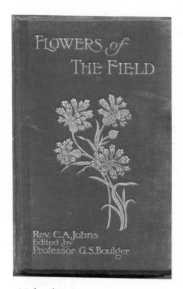

29th edition

During 1851 was published his best-known work, *Flowers of the Field*. This was the book that the ambitious schoolboy of Plymouth days had wanted to produce, following in the steps of his tutors, George Banks and John Jacob. Published in two volumes, it starts with an introduction explaining the terms used in the description of flowering plants and the Linnaean system of classification. Then follows the listed plants in their 'families,' each described in detail, given their native as well as their Latin name, and in many cases illustrated. Here Johns the schoolmaster writes for the amateur who wants to learn, 'to acquaint the lover of nature to an acquaintance with the common British plants.' His book was of special interest and delight because it included illustrations, many previous natural histories not having benefit of that kind of collaboration with an artist.

Flowers of the Field was re-issued at frequent intervals, virtually unchanged, until 1894, when Charles's son, Henry, added an appendix of 'Grasses' (including sedges) compiled from Bentham and

Hooker's *Handbook of British Flora.*[154] New editions followed with added material, revisions and coloured plates, and the work remained in print until 1949. The original illustrations, delicate and meticulously drawn, were printed from watercolours produced not only by Charles's sisters Emily and Julia, but also by Emily Stackhouse, whose monogram appears on 168 drawings, with many more identified as being distilled from her watercolours.[155] Four illustrations are signed by Charles himself, but many are unsigned. According to the family, Charles was paid £100 by SPCK for the first publication, but they doubted whether he received many further payments. This information has proved impossible to corroborate due to a large fire which destroyed much of the 19th-century correspondence archives of the SPCK, with whom Charles would have corresponded regularly about new commissions and contracts.

The year 1851 brought sadness as well as success to the Johns family. Emily Carrington recorded in her diary on 11 January that their father, Henry, in Plymouth, was 'suffering a good deal,' and four days later she wrote: 'Charles and Ellen came here last night from Cornwall.' They had visited Charles's parents in Plymouth on their return journey from a brief stay in Helston. Emily travelled to see her father later in the month, writing that he was 'certainly worse than I have seen him for a long time.' Henry Incledon Johns died on 20 February, aged 75, and was buried at Shaugh Prior. The service was taken by the Reverend Samuel Winter Pearse, vicar from 1808-65, who knew the whole family from before Charles's birth. Emily wrote that the burial at Shaugh was 'in compliance with his [her father's] earnest request in times past, and the brothers went together, a comfort I am sure to dear Mama.'

Henry (junior), Charles, Bennet and the youngest brother, Jack (John Jacob), accompanied their mother, Maria, to the funeral held in the beautiful moorland church of St Edward, and Henry was bur-

---

[154]George Bentham and Sir William Hooker had collaborated to produce this very popular handbook in 1858.

[155]Clifford Evans has completed a close analysis of illustrations from *Flowers of the Field* in its first edition of two volumes, in comparison with the bound volumes of more than 600 watercolours executed by Emily Stackhouse, in his possession for some years prior to the more recent sale to Mallett Fine Art, New York and London. From this study the heavy reliance upon her illustrations is conclusive, even though many are unsigned.

ied in the churchyard. The sisters were present as well. To mark their father's grave the family planted a rose tree.

The national census for the year 1851 was collected for the date of 30-31 March, and by that date the new school established by Ellen's mother, Julia Field, was in full flow at the newly-named Catherine Lodge (formerly Bath Lodge) in Trafalgar Square, London. With her colleague and business partner, Sarah Lowman, acting as headmistress, with two additional governesses and 20 girls between the ages of nine and 16, a well-functioning school had been put into operation in the previous year, with both day and boarding facilities offered. Also listed on the roster was Charles Henry Johns (age six), as 'grandson,' though this may simply have meant a holiday from Beenham. The family association with, and perhaps some shared ownership of, Catherine Lodge continued until well into the 1870s, when Katie Johns is found resident there before her marriage.

Early in 1852, national and West Country newspapers brought to the attention of the British public a tragedy that had widespread affect due to the number of souls lost in the shocking shipwreck and loss of *RMS Amazon*. A new steam packet, commissioned from Blackwall the previous year, set sail on her maiden voyage from Southampton in early January en route the West Indies, Gulf of Mexico and the

HOLLY BERRIES—WINTER OF 1845-6.

'Hollyberries'

Spanish Main. Some 60 miles west of the Isles of Scilly she was found to be on fire and from there the entire ship was consumed and the catastrophe ensued. No more than two of the several lifeboats could be reached and lifted down from their crutches. On board had been 162 men, women and children, 110 being crew and 52 passengers. Finally, with the help of *HMS Marsden* and the Dutch gallot *Hillechiena,* some 58 survivors were landed in Plymouth at separate times. Amongst the survivors was Lieutenant Charles Grylls of St Neot, Cornwall, the son of the vicar Rev Henry Grylls, a family well known to Charles Johns. Great celebrations with hundreds of local people turning out to welcome him home was a spark of joy in such dire circumstances, but another officer, the second mate of the *Amazon,* was a young man who was both a friend and former pupil of Johns. Compiling a permanent record of the national disaster for the SPCK, the publication forthcoming shortly thereafter, is dedicated 'To the Memory of Charles Henry Treweeke who with other officers of the *Amazon*, nobly sacrificed his life in discharge of his duty, this Narrative is inscribed by his friend and early tutor, The Compiler. February 13, 1852, Beenham, Berkshire.' Henry Treweeke, as he was known, was also a son of the manse, with his brother also a clergyman, and he had been a pupil of Johns and Coleridge, at Helston.

Three years later, in the summer of 1855, Emily Carrington recorded the death of their mother. Maria Johns died on 7 June and was buried beside her husband at Shaugh Prior in Devon. Following her death, the home at Park Street in Plymouth closed and the family's pivotal center in Devon was removed. The youngest son, Jack (John Jacob), remained unmarried, at least at that time, and moved from the bank in Plymouth on to Chester, Cheshire, where he served as a cashier for a railway company. At the age of 32 he embarked at Liverpool on the *City of New York*, to join his eldest brother, Henry (25 years his senior), in America. His hope was to obtain work as a writer for newspapers and journals or to continue with his accountancy in the new world. The family penchant and talent for writing and drawing ran through all their veins.

Charles and Bennett called at Bath on their return from their mother's funeral, to discuss with Emily and her family how they were to care for their two remaining spinster sisters. The youngest sister, Anne, had lived with the Carringtons since their marriage; now Julia was to live with Charles and Ellen at Beenham, and Jane to move to London with Bennett and Dellie. They also arranged for a tombstone to be erected over the grave, recording not only the deaths of Henry and Maria, but also of baby Bennett, who had died so many years before in 1819 at four months; of Sophia, who died in 1819 at the age of 10 years, and Elizabeth, who died in 1808 soon after birth. This was the end of Charles's youth; now he was the eldest of the family in England.

Callipers Hall, Chipperfield, near Kings Langley, Hertfordshire.

14

THE SCHOOL AT CALLIPERS HALL: 1855-63

By 1855 Charles and Ellen were facing another move. The vicar whose living they had been filling, the Rev William Bushnell, had died in 1853 and his brother, Thomas, was presented with the living. Charles, knowing that he was not to fill the position himself, had been considering other prospects for some time, and laying plans. The opportunity now arose for him to open his own boarding school for boys, where he could carry out the educational ideas and practices that he had been gathering over the years from his own schooldays, the Helston and the Beenham experiences. His educational work had always been with boys and young men, and there were no plans to change that pattern.

Meantime, there was also need for some refreshment. 'Entire relaxation away from home for a fortnight at least, joined to change of scene, change of air, and change of living, after many months' sedentary occupation, is a safer and more efficacious remedy for headache and languor than all the drugs in Apothecaries' Hall...so I turned my face towards France.' Though the book that would emerge from SPCK in 1859, *Rambles About Paris,* was written in the first person and based on a holiday in 1855, it is probable that when Charles turned his face to France, he also took his family with him.

. . . but it matters not in what part of Paris we may find ourselves when the need of refreshment overtakes us, we shall be pretty sure to fall in with a restaurant, where for a sum varying from two to four francs, we can procure, at a minute's notice, a satisfactory meal, consisting of fruit (melon is a universal favourite, meat of various kinds, fowl, fish, and wine . . . . Wherever we go, it is evident that a far larger proportion of Parisians than of Londoners board away from their own homes. This we discover, not simply from the number of guests, but from the numerous groups that one sees made up of a husband and wife, with perhaps two or three children.

It is equally probable that Ellen and the children did not do the long, exhausting walks around the city that Johns describes in admirable detail, throwing in anecdotes from history and comparative notes between the cities of London and Paris. Bringing his holiday to a close, the penultimate chapter announces the impending visit of Queen Victoria to France with the words, 'The Queen of England will make her entry into Paris on Saturday next, at about six o'clock in the evening . . . .' (*Moniteur*, 15 August 1855), his main comment being that 'however improbable it might have seemed a few years before, was by no means an unexpected one. It had been talked of, indeed, even before the emperor's visit to England . . . and considered as a natural consequence of it.' The steel engravings in this most interesting little book are beautiful and accomplished (49 in vignette form) but remain anonymous. None are signed and may have been selected from trade travel catalogues, or belong to the enormous stock of wood cuts and engravings collected in the archives of the publishing houses for use and re-use in their range of publications.

By 1856, the Johns family had moved to Callipers Hall, Chipperfield, a village close to Kings Langley in Hertfordshire. Callipers Hall is described in deeds of 1854 as a farmhouse[156] that must have belonged to a prosperous farmer.[157] A postcard of the house as it was before changes were made in 1911 shows a large three-storey house with an elegant Georgian façade. Charles made a number of alterations to transform the building from farmhouse to a preparatory school for boys, with boarding accommodation. The ample garden and grounds, however, were just what he needed for recreation and nature study.

The house was in the ecclesiastical parish of St Paul's Church, Chipperfield, the church itself being only 20 years old, having been constructed in 1837-38. The first incumbent was the Rev Henry Dennis, who was still officiating and welcomed Charles and his pupils, who attended the church regularly. Charles himself took occasional services. The vicar's health was failing and in the late 1850s he resigned, to

---

[156]Information received from the research by Mrs Mary Nobbs and her son, of the Kings Langley History Society.

[157]The owner of Callipers House before Charles was one Donald Mackay who died in December 1851, as revealed from his tombstone in the churchyard of St Paul's Church. His surviving wife, Cordelia, passed the property on to Johns.

be succeeded by the Rev Ralph Cumine Morton, who was also pleased to have the headmaster of Callipers Hall as an occasional assistant.

The school at Callipers Hall prospered, attracting parents who appreciated the education offered at the school by Johns, whose reputation as a naturalist and author reassured them of his ability to offer a stimulating and healthy environment for their sons. Indeed, he introduced a gymnasium and baths into Callipers, modern features offering better sanitation and a safer environment in inclement weather, and these attracted widespread interest and admiration.

The academic success of the school in preparing pupils for entry to public schools such as Harrow and Eton led to Arthur Evans (later Sir Arthur of Knossus fame) becoming a pupil at Callipers in the late 1850s. Arthur went from Callipers Hall to Harrow and then on to Oxford to study archaeology. Arthur's younger brothers, Lewis and Phillip, were also sent to Callipers, but were so unruly that Johns first wrote to their mother to complain and finally expelled Lewis, who went to another prep school in Sidmouth. Though not quick to anger, Charles was not a man who put up with bad behaviour.

Both Johns and his good friend, Charles Kingsley, returned to Cornwall on occasions to attend the September annual meetings of Helston Grammar School. In 1857 the *School Magazine* records: 'The Rev C A Johns BA, FLS, formerly Head Master, has recently presented a complete set of his works (*Flowers of the Field*, etc) to the School Library.'[158] These occasions were important to past pupils and teachers and there is mention of Alexander Johns of Carrickfergus, Ireland (Charles's uncle, see Appendix ii), presenting a Divinity Medal in 1852 and a maths prize in 1858, although he may not have attended in person. The family connections with Helston continued.

On a visit to Snowdon in Wales, Kingsley wrote that he collected plants for his daughter, Rose, and 'went birding' for his son, Maurice. He wrote to Charles at Callipers: 'Your bird-books are delightful; gladly would I throw up history to think of nothing but dicky-birds – but it must not be yet. Some day, ere I grow too old to think, I trust to be able to throw away all pursuits save natural history, and die with

---

[158] *Helston Grammar School Magazine 1857*. A copy is held by the Institute of Cornish Studies. The copy of *A Week at the Lizard*, held by the Cornish Studies Library, was a presentation copy, probably part of this gift to Helston Grammar School, with the compliments of the author.

my mind full of God's facts, instead of men's lies . . . .' Kingsley was made a Fellow of the Linnean Society in 1857, some 22 years after his friend Johns.

That summer was especially difficult for Ellen, as her mother, Julia Field, with whom she had always been especially close as an only child, died at the end of August, age 67. She is buried in the churchyard of St Paul's Church, Chipperfield, and was perhaps with them for some time prior to her death. Though she had owned Catherine Lodge School in London, it is assumed that Sarah Lowman was also a substantial partner, and continued as headmistress thereafter.

In the autumn term of that year, Johns welcomed, amongst other pupils, the 11-year-old Ernest Hartley Coleridge, Derwent and Mary's youngest child. This would be for a full year preparing Erny for the King's School, Sherborne, after which he then proceeded to Balliol. His year with Johns, however, cemented a friendship that flowered again when Erny came to assist Johns as a temporary teaching master at Winton House, Winchester, a few years later.

Ellen was once more busy caring for the boys who boarded at their school as well as looking after her own children, and in 1858 she was expecting their third child. At Easter of that year, Charles and his sister Julia were in Plymouth where they met Emily Carrington with her son, Harry, and daughter, young Emily. Emily wrote in her diary that Charles administered communion at the morning service and preached an excellent sermon in the evening. Ellen was not with Charles, and the next news was of a son, Frederick William, born on 15 August, about whom there were some concerns for his strength from the beginning.

Emily's diary records that Charles and Ellen came to stay near Bath in August and after a few days continued a planned journey to Dorchester. Later that month Emily wrote that she and her family met Charles, Ellen and the children at Helland (near Bodmin, Cornwall), but she does not mention the baby by name. By 13 November she wrote: 'No good news about little Freddy,' and the next day: 'This morning news came from Calliper's wh' put an end to all hopes and fears for dear little Freddy. He died on Sunday evening,' and was buried soon after in St Paul's churchyard near his maternal grandmother.

Part of Ellen's grieving for little Freddy found expression in a musical way. This was the year (1858) that their friend Charles Kingsley's

Emily Carrington.

poems, under the title of *Andromeda and other poems*, were published in October by Parker & Co of London, and in Boston by Tichnor and Fields. Aside from two that were written by Kingsley when he was a pupil at Helston in 1835, there was one which Kingsley had written at Eversley in 1848, entitled 'A Lament.'

> The merry merry lark was up and singing,
>   And the hare was out and feeding on the lea;
> And the merry merry bells below were ringing,
>   When my child's laugh rang through me.
>
> Now the hare is snared and dead beside the snow-yard,
>   And the lark beside the dreary winter sea;
> And the baby in his cradle in the churchyard
>   Sleeps sound till the bell brings me.

Ellen took Kingsley's words and composed the musical score for it. This was accepted for publication by music publishers D Davison & Co in London, and it became available to the public within the same year.

Henry Carrington returned from Chipperfield to Bath on 28

November, leaving his daughter to stay with Charles, Ellen and their family for some weeks. Towards the end of January in the new year, young Emily left Callipers to join Bennett and Dellie in London, where she attended the School for the Blind of which Bennett was now headmaster. Daughter Emily's eyesight was very poor, and her stay with first Charles and then Bennett was a means by which the Johns siblings continued to help to shoulder the trials of their wider family. Indeed, there was more sorrow to come.

Henry Carrington, Charles's life-long friend and brother-in-law, died suddenly on 5 February 1859, at the age of 53, and only 10 days after the birth of his 12th child. Emily named the new baby Charles Walter and asked Charles Johns to become the baby's godfather. (Bringing our story up to the present day, Charles's godson became the father of Molly Matthews, who carried out much early family research contributing to this book, and to whom the authors have dedicated it.)

Two years later, Ellen and Charles had another baby son of their own to care for, Edward Francis (Frank), born in Callipers Hall.[159] Charles, despite the daily work of tending to the school, continued to write and edit his work, adding significantly to his publication list. Working steadily on both revisions for new editions and initiating fresh texts, he also found time for magazine articles and columns. Admittedly, many of the smaller items were taken from his larger work, but nevertheless required careful selection and crafting to make them attractive. His publishing schedule was busy and productive in the late 1850s, four new publications appearing in 1859 alone and three in 1860.

British Birds in their Haunts was the culmination of Charles's previous work on birds, some of which had appeared in small books on animals for children, along with stories. First published in 1862, the book continued to be produced until the 25th edition in 1948.

---

[159]Many years later, Frank (as he was generally known) contributed to a 1937 church magazine of St Paul's, Chipperfield, recording that he was baptised in the church by his father, the Reverend C A Johns, on 27 May 1861, after his birth in April. He continued: 'My father only took duty occasionally at Chipperfield, but he started Callipers Hall the Preparatory School which in 1863 he transferred to Winton House, Winchester. Besides *Flowers of the Field*, he also wrote *British Birds in their Haunts* and several other books on Natural History. He was a great friend of Charles Kingsley.'

Although edited and revised, with the addition of coloured and black-and-white illustrations, Charles's voice is ever present in his close observations and sympathetic descriptions of birds, common and less well-known. He conceived of it as an extension to that 'milestone in ornithological literature' by William Yarrell in the *History of British Birds* (1837-43). He explained:

> The present volume contains an account, more or less detailed, of all the birds figured in the second edition of Yarrell (1845), as well as of some few which have been observed since the date of that publication. And in order that the reader may be presented with a catalogue completed up to the present date, June 1862, of all birds having any claim to be considered British, the following supplemental list is added, specifying the names of recently observed birds not described in the body of the work, the seasons and places of their appearance, and references to the works which contain a detailed account of their capture and history.

He makes a list of 14 additions and then continues with:

> If the above additions be allowed, the number of British Birds will be:

> Resident all the year 140
> Summer visitors 63
> Winter visitors 48
> Capricious visitors 110
>   Total 361

Within the text, after giving the scientific details of each bird, Charles continues with a personal description of its characteristic movements, song and nest-making, adding lines from poems, legends, anecdotes, indeed anything that might encourage his readers to look more closely at the birds that surround them. In addition, presumably on the basis of careful research and much observation in different geographical locations in the British Isles and Europe, he records where the birds have been observed and by whom and when. The sheer gathering of evidence from every part of the world and from previous writers and illustrators, from Pliny to the present, is impressive, even if the then habit of collecting specimens by shooting them may seem against our present-day standards of ecological behaviour.

The Chaffinch is a smart, lively, active bird, always in a bustle, flitting here and there incessantly and staying long nowhere, always wearing a holiday look, so trim and spruce is he, and rattling through his song with wondrous volubility.

By contrast, the barn owl's 'phantom-like' flight is described as like 'a sheet of silver paper wafted along by the wind, so lightly and noiselessly did it pass on.'

He writes with affection of the familiar robin and blue tit, contrasting the latter with the great tit: 'Though much smaller than his relative, the Tomtit is equally brave and pugnacious, and is even more quarrelsome.' When defending its nest, 'the bird, instead of endeavouring to escape, retains its place and makes an unpleasant hissing noise, and if this be not enough to deter the intruder, pecks his finger with great vigour. Hence it has received the popular name of "Billy Biter."'

The glossary includes a fascinating list of 'Common and Provincial Names,' such as 'Charlie Miftie' for the Wheatear,' 'Hadji' for the Swift, 'Flopwing' for the Lapwing and 'Huckmuck' for the Longtailed Tit. The Cormorant's nickname was 'The Isle of Wight Parson,' and the Pied Wagtail, the 'Washerwoman.' Charles believed that it was important that all these dialect names should be recorded.

In describing the Song Thrush he writes of its love of summer fruits, not always to the pleasure of gardener or farmer, but 'the wise man will prefer the scarecrow to the gun, the protecting net to that which captures.' Referring to two adjoining estates in Yorkshire he writes: 'On one the gardener shoots blackbirds and thrushes in fruit time. On the other they are protected. The latter yields always more fruit than the former.' However, Charles accepted the sport of shooting game-birds as part of the life of the countryside.

He also showed no criticism of caged birds, even when writing of a bird as large as the Chough. Of special significance to Cornwall, it is described as 'the Red-legged Crow' or 'the Cornish Chough,' building its nests in inaccessible cliffs. Charles wrote that it was then becoming less common in Devon and Cornwall, 'though it lingers on in the latter county.' He must have watched it often when walking the cliffs of the Lizard, and also have seen it in captivity, when it was 'inquisitive, intrusive, captious in temper, disposed to become attached to those who treat it well, fond of attracting notice; in a word, it surpasses in intelligence most other tribes of birds . . . .'

THE COMMON KESTREL (p. 22).

THE HEN-HARRIER
(p. 41).

MONTAGU'S HARRIER
(p. 42).

THE MARSH-HARRIER
(p. 39).

[*Frontispiece*].

PLATE I.

Frontispiece drawn by Wolf, engraved by Whymper, from
British Birds in their Haunts, 12th ed., 1911.

Winton House, Winchester, Hampshire, July 1867.

15

WINTON HOUSE, WINCHESTER, HAMPSHIRE

After *British Birds in their Haunts*, the time was approaching when Charles felt that he should move on from Callipers Hall to a larger building in a more popular and accessible area. During 1863 Charles arranged for the move of both his family and the school from the rural village of Chipperfield to the ancient cathedral city of Winchester, a great change in surroundings and prestige. Charles needed to prepare the new premises for his pupils to settle at Winton House; Ellen was looking forward to returning to life in a city once more.

Charles Johns's own enthusiasm for the observation of natural wonders was certainly shared by his children. When the family arrived in Winchester, Henry was 19 years old, Katie 16, and Frank only two. Henry had progressed from Callipers Hall to Rugby and was now an undergraduate at Oxford, the university that his father had so longed to attend at the same age. But Charles had no time for personal regrets as he opened the new school of Winton House to his pupils.

> We looked upon that school of his as a palace of delight to which we were sometimes invited; not only for its scientific atmosphere, but because it was luxurious and full of new things. I can see now that he was a pioneer in school matters. There were out-of-door and indoor gymnastics, bathrooms which people came miles to see, in the days when bathrooms were a new kind of freak. In fact there was always something new and startling.

These words come from the memoirs of Charles Walter Carrington, Emily and Henry's 12th and youngest child, who was Charles Johns's nephew and godson. He is writing of Winton House, which Johns was determined to make the best in the city, with a broad curriculum and teaching of the highest standard. At Callipers he had already established a good reputation for sending pupils to Eton, Harrow and other public schools. Winton House would now provide a convenient school for day-boys from Winchester as well as boarders, many of whom might progress to Winchester College.

Winton House stood on the northern outskirts of the city, just off the Andover Road. Photographs taken a few years after the school opened in 1863 show a large two-storey house with additional taller buildings at the back. Large bay windows rise on either side of steps leading to the entrance doors and the house stands on a terraced drive with steps down to the lawn below, surrounded by trees and shrubs. Concurrent with the writing of this book, the whole site of the school and its subsequent extensions is up for planned re-development, as a modern housing estate.

Other photographs taken in the summer show boys playing croquet and cricket.[160] In one photograph, an older man, perhaps Charles, has a tripod with a camera set up before him.[161]

The school grew and was successful. According to a past Helston pupil, W F Collier, often quoted in this little book, 'It was of such good repute that it was difficult, and it took some time to get a boy into it' (*Cornish Magazine*, p 118). Some of the letters in the Autograph Collection (Appendix v) vividly confirm the difficulty and trouble that some parents took in attempting to obtain places for their children. Charles Carrington continues in his memoirs to give an interesting picture of his uncle's character and interests at this stage in his life.

'He was a stalwart, rather aggressive person, with great powers of observation, organisation and perseverance.' However, 'he was not in the least the pedant, or the "learned man," but had a genial, sometimes almost rollicking vein. I remember his showing us how to dance a hornpipe, and attempting a frog dance in our dining-room.' Aggression in this context was not a negative, but indicated a thrusting and open personality, a passionate and forthcoming person – always forthright, rather than defensive.

Charles kept in close touch with his now widowed sister, Emily. Charles Carrington writes that on his uncle's frequent visits to the family in Bath, he 'always brought new and exciting things with him. To go with him for walks was a delight, because he stopped every

---

[160]Hampshire Record Office, Ref 12M61/21 (loose page) AD 1128/3.
[161]Photograph in Emily Carrington's album.

minute to investigate something we had never noticed, and generally discovered something new. He had a stormy side and we were sometimes afraid of him, but not often. He used to have a sovereign or half a sovereign for the younger children. We liked him. I dwell on him because he filled us with healthy enthusiasm and really tried to do so.' Here was an excellent teacher with wide interests in natural science that he carried into the schoolroom in Winton House.

His nephew continues:

He was interested in other things besides Botany and Ornithology. He tried to take in all Biology – insects, beetles, forminifera, in fact everything that came in his way. He had an astronomical observatory with a good 8 inch reflector; microscopes of the newest type.' A special gift that his godson received was 'a really beautiful achromatic telescope by Berthon, Vicar of Romsey, one of his (Charles's) close friends – Berthon, who invented the collapsible lifeboat and other things. This telescope was set up for me on a stone pillar in our garden, and was the occasion of my spending hours, weeks, in astronomising. I adjusted it myself to the latitude etc., and with sufficient success to be able to find any bright star by daylight.

The close friend of Johns's that Charles Carrington remembered best was Charles Kingsley, by now a well-known and controversial author[162] as well as the Professor of Modern History at Cambridge (elected 1860 and resigned 1869) and tutor to the Prince of Wales. Kingsley dined at Winton House when Walter was there, and the boy noticed 'how he monopolised the conversation at dinner,' and 'also a lecture of which I remember nothing except: "Yo-yo-you people of Winchester are living in the ac-ac-accumulated filth of ages" – the enormous emphasis his stammer enabled him to put on the important word. He was quite above my reach. I remember Mrs Kingsley [Frances 'Fanny' Grenfell] much better.'

---

[162]Kingsley's bibliography is large and will not be reprinted here. It is of some interest, however, due to the publishers (also named Hypatia) of this monograph, that he was the author of the extraordinary and dramatic novel, *Hypatia, or New Foes with an Old Face* (1853), depicting the major initial crisis of Christianity against the Neo-Platonist philosophers and humanists. Basically *Hypatia* was a fictional attack on the high-church leanings of the Victorian era, as best represented by Cardinal Newman and the Tractarians.

Above: Charles Kingsley. Engraved by
Jeens, from photograph c 1876. *Right:*
Fanny Kingsley and Grenville, c 1867.

The friendship between the two families was of great importance
to Charles Johns and to the standing of his school, helping him significantly and personally in the social life of Winchester. Grenville
Kingsley, born in 1858 to Fanny and Charles at Eversley, was supposed to be delicate and was much cosseted (often said to have been
'spoiled') by his mother. In 1867 he was sent to Winton House, 'the
young gentleman's academy that Kingsley's old master, the Reverend
C A Johns had recently established in Winchester . . . .' The place was
said to have a waiting list of hundreds and father and son went to
inspect it together. Kingsley wrote to Fanny: 'Nothing can have gone
better than our day. I left Grenville playing with the boys by himself,
and I ran in the sack race. He was happy and good and quite well. The
place is delightful – high and healthy – and the arrangements for the
boys perfect. They are a nice looking set – rosy and jolly. Mrs Johns is
like a mother to them all.'[163]

Grenville Kingsley, alas, only stayed for a few days before running
home to mother in Eversley, causing his father to write to Johns to
apologise.

---

[163]Chitty *op cit* p 251.

I cannot express my gratitude to you and Mrs Johns and your dear girl [Katie] for all your trouble about my little renegade. I am quite sure this is merely the first struggle of a child who has never met his equals, and been much petted and spoilt. But he is perfectly hardy, strong, and bold, not really sly because he has never been bullied – and quite shrewd – not to say clever, as I suspect him to be. My own belief is that if we can only keep right the liver which he inherits from both parents, he will be a fine frank forward lad, and a credit to us both.

Your kindness meanwhile is very great. You seem to understand that he is a chick only half out of the egg, who needs a little help in self-deliverance. (Aboyne Castle, Aberdeenshire, September 27 [1867].)[164]

The boy returned to the school, leaving, eventually, with low marks. Kingsley wrote to Johns in 1874 to tell him that, after having a tutor, he and Fanny intended sending Grenville to Harrow (*Kingsley Letters* Vol 2 p 289).[165]

A nature rambling group, Winton House c 1870 (perhaps 'The Goslings'?).

---

[164]Reprinted from Thorp, Margaret F (1969), p 106.

[165]The 'spoiled' Grenville was only to live to the age of 40, dying in 1898, having left England for Australia in some kind of impulsive chase, and was destined after Kingsley's death to drain the family fortunes away from his mother, Fanny. See Lundberg, and Chitty.

The historic city of Winchester was growing and thriving when Charles opened his school in 1863. The population was increasing and new civic institutions were being built. There were a number of private schools for both boys and girls in the city as well as the Winchester Central Boys School and Central Girls School. Only the year before, a diocesan training college had been built, which would have reminded Charles of his own time as a master at St Mark's in London. The training college provided certificated teachers for schools in the city, especially the Anglican National Schools, and possibly Winton House.

The most prestigious school of the area, Winchester College, also saw revival under its headmaster, Dr George Ridding.[166] In 1863, the year that Johns arrived, Ridding returned to Winchester, becoming second master at the college under the Rev George Moberly, later Bishop of Salisbury. Four years later, Ridding became headmaster. There he broadened the curriculum to include English literature and modern history, and personally paid for new playing-fields. It was said that 'not a term passed without some new development or modern improvement.' This was a man after Charles Johns's heart, and they appreciated each other's work, both educationally and socially.[167]

The Winchester Conservative Land Society was led by another influential associate and close friend of the Johns family, Isaac Warner, head of a firm of family solicitors. This Society developed the southern slopes of the Western Downs, building new roads and houses, but the problems of drainage and sewage were ever present in Winchester and it is doubtful whether even these new houses possessed bathrooms. No wonder Winton House was admired.

Isaac Warner's son, Frederick, also became a companion and friend, and was like Charles a Fellow of the Linnean Society, sharing in Charles's love of botany. In 1869-70, both were deeply involved in the setting up of the first Winchester Scientific and Literary Society, with Johns as its first president and Fred Warner as the honorary secretary, first of the Botany Section, and two years later, of the whole

---

[166]Born in 1828, Ridding was the son of a Winchester College master, growing up there and attending the school as a pupil. At Balliol College, Oxford, he was ordained and gained a DD, staying at Oxford as a Fellow and tutor of Exeter College from 1852-63.

[167]Information researched by Dr D E Allen.

Society. Charles was also made a godfather of Fred Warner's son, George Johns Shatton Warner, as later mentioned in Johns's will.

The spur for the founding of the new scientific and literary organisation may well have come from Charles Kingsley, who was then standing down from his Regius Professorship at Cambridge. In 1869 he was made a canon of Chester Cathedral, spending three months in residence there. During that time he started 'a botanical class for middle class young men' that was very popular, leading them in a walk with a field lecture each week (*Kingsley Letters* Vol 2 p 241). For this purpose he employed Johns's *Flowers of the Field* as a text. He also founded the Chester Society of Natural Science. This was also at the time when Grenville Kingsley was a pupil at Winton House and there was steady contact between the families. Kingsley would have encouraged Johns in the setting up of the Winchester Society, which was referred to under a variety of titles, including 'The Hampshire Scientific Society' and 'The Winchester Natural History Society.' Reports of their proceedings together with programme cards show that the Society continued until 1938-39, ending with the disruption of World War II.[168]

Charles Johns was elected the first president of the Society in 1870, and its first report mentions that on the 17 January of that year 'a conversazione' was held at Winton House 'by the kind hospitality of the President.' Charles and Ellen must have been pleased to open their home for such an occasion, playing a full part in Winchester society and showing the many features of scientific and botanical interest that lay within for the benefit of their pupils. This was one of two such functions during the year and there were also seven meetings and three 'general excursions.'

The annual report includes: 'Abstracts of Papers and Lists of Plants,' and the latter is still of interest to local botanists. It is headed 'List of flowering plants, ferns, etc., found within seven miles from Winchester,' reflecting the activities of the Botanical Section of the Society. It was probably written by Fred Warner, who had intended to write a Flora of Hampshire himself, but when Mr F Townsend, a more competent botanist with more leisure, appeared on the scene, Fred generously handed him his data. This contributed later to Townsend's *Flora of Hampshire with the Isle of Wight*, published in 1884.

---

[168] *Ibid.*

Henry Johns, the eldest son, was entered as a member of the Winchester Scientific Society in 1870 with the letters BA, FRAS (Fellow of the Royal Astronomical Society) after his name. This may explain the splendid observatory that had been fitted out at Winton House. Henry remained at home acting as an assistant master in the school, until after his father's death. He contributed papers to the Society, such as *Notes on the Map of the Gold Coast*,[169] and the following year he was elected to the Committee. Frank, too, although only nine years old when the Society was founded, is recorded as an early member and enjoyed joining the outings with his father and brother. The membership of the Society totalled 105 by 1872, and the average attendance at the monthly meetings was 26, plus visitors, mostly female. Early members from Winton House also included H T G Moncrieffe, who was an assistant master at the school.

Charles Kingsley delivered a lecture for the Winchester Society the following year, described as a 'masterly review of the Bio-geology of Hampshire – its plants, reptiles etc. and glances at the European and Atlantic flora,' and ending with theology (*Kingsley Letters* Vol 2, p 241). Kingsley had encouraged Johns to be a co-founder of the Lecture Society of Winchester and was one of those who gave courses of lectures on various topics. It seems that both men were also involved in founding reading prizes (performance or public speaking) at Cambridge University, though the offer to do the same at Oxford had not been accepted there. (This may have been due to the protracted dissension promoted by Kingsley in his opposition to the Tractarians.) Kingsley agreed to present the silver medal to the best reader at the Winchester Diocesan Training College. Both were concerned that future teachers and ministers should be able to read (speak) well before audiences and congregations.[170]

Ernest Hartley Coleridge (called Erny by the family) was teaching as a temporary assistant master at Winton House from January of 1871. In March Derwent came down from Hanwell to Winchester for the day, to talk with Johns about the boy's prospects. 'Ernest wished to start his own private school for teenage boys, relying partly on Johns's recommendation – a scheme which Derwent and Mary viewed with considerable anxiety, in view of Ernest's very limited means and their

---

[169]Advertised in the *Hampshire Chronicle* of 18 July1874.
[170]*Hampshire Chronicle* 4 July 1874 p 4d.

Katie Johns *(left)* and Mary St Leger Kingsley, with
German tutor in the garden at Winton House.
Grenville is in forefront, c 1867. (HRO)

own shortage of money.' Charles Johns, however, gave Erny glowing
references, and Derwent expressed this as 'he earned golden opinions'
from his old second master.[171] Between them, the two colleagues were
to set the boy up in his own school and on his future path as a teacher.
From Winton House, Erny moved on in September the same year to
his own small tutorial school at Pickhurst, Chiddingfold, Surrey, with
his sister Christabel as housekeeper.

Because we have no personal papers from the family period of
Charles Johns's life, it is not known the extent to which Katie was a
participant in the teaching programme of the school. But Charles,
close as he was to his sisters, and mindful of the need of more women
to provide themselves with a livelihood, would have been well aware
of the need for women's education. The common pattern, of course,
was for the sons to receive formal education outside the home, and
the daughters to be educated privately. Ellen was an educated woman,

---

[171]Letter from Derwent Coleridge to Moultrie, 24 March 1871, as quoted in
Hainton and Hainton, *The Unknown Coleridge*, pp 277-8, from Coleridge MSS,
University of Texas.

a former governess, and had, before her marriage, assisted her mother as a teacher of young women in London. Equally, Katie's maternal grandmother, Julia Field, following her headship at Whitelands College, had set up Catherine Lodge School for Girls. It is doubtful that Katie's educational opportunities were limited in any way, and, aside from her strongly spiritual nature, it is known that her main inspiration and interest was art and illustration. Readers of *Home Walks and Holiday Rambles* (1863) would have been particularly impressed by Katie's illustrations for her father's book and the beauty of her personal monogram in signature. Her pen-and-ink drawings of people are particularly fine. By the end of the decade, by which time she had provided illustrations for the Goslings' magazine, *The Barnacle*, she had been asked by Charles Kingsley to contribute illustrations to his natural history stories for boys, *Madam How & Lady Why*.[172]

Left: Charles Kingsley's drawing in the Johns family autograph collection.
Right: Katie Johns's finished illustration for *Madam How & Lady Why*.

Of the several other societies in Winchester at this time, Charles supported the Society of the School of Art, which was under the supervision of the City Corporation, with the town clerk as its sec-

---

[172]Subtitled *First Lessons in Earth Lore for Children*, the first book edition (1870) is dedicated 'To my son Grenville Arthur, and to his school-fellows at Winton House.' For further information about Katie as illustrator, see entries in Appendix ii.

retary. He recognised fully the importance of art to his father and sisters, and the skill of those who illustrated his books. In this respect, he would certainly have recalled the contributions made to his work by his friend, Emily Stackhouse, who had died in 1870, quite aside from the talents of his daughter Katie.

One further society that Johns may have had some part in founding was the Winchester College Natural History Society.[173] Apparently the suggestion for the formation of the society was made in a letter to the school magazine, *The Wykehamist*, in

'Winter Fishing in Norfolk,' Katie Johns's illustration for *Home Walks and Holiday Rambles*.

October 1869, but the writer remained anonymous. The society was formed with the Reverend Dr Ridding, the headmaster, as its first president, and held its first meeting in the spring of 1870. Charles Johns attended the December meeting of that year to present a paper on 'The fall of the leaf.' The following October it was reported that 'The president stated that Mr Johns, the celebrated botanist, and other gentlemen of the town belonging to the Winchester Society, had offered to bring down their microscopes and other instruments, and to spend an evening with members in the Moberly Library.' A similar visit was repeated in March 1873, and the following October Johns attended the meeting, contributing information about seedlings of *Primula cortusiodes* and *Delphinium nudicaule*.

In December of that year Charles was elected as an honorary member of the Natural History Society at the college. He was present at the February and March meetings of 1874, exhibiting and talking about Blue Gum Trees at the first and reading a paper on 'Trapdoor spiders and harvesting ants' at the second. He seemed to be almost

---

[173]Information provided by Winchester College Archivist, Miss S Foster in her letter of 22 April 2004.

as fully involved in the college society as he was with his Winchester Society, continuing his friendships with members of staff as well as with George Ridding.

Behind this busy schedule of meetings, talks, papers and exhibitions, not to mention the teaching and administration of his school, lay Charles's continued delight in walking and exploring the countryside that surrounded Winchester. He led or joined the society's excursions, gathering examples or specimens of plants, butterflies, birds, insects etc, all material for his continuing research. One of his favourite and more relaxing pastimes, however, was fishing, perhaps in Isaac Walton's river, the Itchen, not far from Winton House.[174]

Charles's writing at this time was chiefly concerned with the short articles and papers he presented at meetings, and preparation for new editions of his most popular books. There was a second edition of *British Birds in their Haunts,* in 1869, illustrated by Wolff, as well as a further edition of *Forest Trees,* and Charles was writing books for children, such as his *Child's First Book of Geography,* published in 1872. However, the book that had always given him special pleasure was *A Week at the Lizard.* A second edition had been authorised by the SPCK in October 1862, with various additions and changes. By 1873 a third edition was wanted, which meant that Charles could return to his beloved Cornwall once again. He could not have known at this stage that this would be his final visit.

In August, accompanied by his son Henry, Cornwall Simeon[175] and E L Berthon,[176] he went on 'a ramble around the coast,' leading to the discovery of much new information, including many important botanical additions, listed in Appendix 1 of the book. Charles acknowledges the additional information that his companions provided and mentions, by name, various helpers.[177] James Cunnack, the Helston bookseller and botanist, supplied new records of plants, and Lord Falmouth gave a list of 30 shipwrecks between Mullion and

---

[174]*Hampshire Chronicle* 4 July 1874 p 4d.

[175]A barrister friend of Johns who was the County Treasurer of Hampshire and a fellow naturalist. He was the author of *Stray notes on fishing and natural history* (1860), Cambridge: Macmillan.

[176]See Appendix ii for biographical information on the Rev Berthon.

[177]Other than those mentioned in the text above, are the Rev E G Harvey, Mr Richard Davey, Mr F V Hill, Mr G A Howitt, Mr H Fox and Mr J H Fox.

Gunwalloe. The Rev Philip Vyvyan Robinson of Landewednack also contributed to the book, in which the Direct Spanish Cable to Bilbao is mentioned, as well as the opening of the Lizard Signals Station in April 1872, which became Lloyds Signal Station, closing nearly a hundred years later. Johns also describes the changes to the 'Lion's Den' since 1848 and 1863, and writes that the two rock arches at Kynance Cove, shown in the frontispiece of the earlier editions, had been washed away.[178] A particular pleasure that this visit afforded Charles was 'to shake hands with Samson Hill and Samuel Stevens, the only two survivors of the "Cornish Giants" who formed my crew on the occasion of my "Day at Sea" in 1847,' as described in the first edition. To a large extent this was a walk down memory lane for Charles, and his excitement and delight with the Lizard and its people is well expressed.

Charles, at the age of 61, was an active man, with every expectation of a number of years ahead to continue his writing, research and his school. Winton House was flourishing and attracting parents such as Mr and Mrs R H White of Boulge Hall. In a letter to Mr White, written in December 1873, Charles writes:

My terms, 150 guineas per annum, include Board, Education in the Classics, French, Arithmetic, Geography, Natural Science, Gymnastics, Drilling, (Washing), Drawing. German, Music, and Dancing (if required) are extra.

He also mentions that, to avoid the sending of baskets from home, he provides each boy with 'as much fruit as is good for him' for an extra 10/- a term, and that occasional excursions in summer cost about 15/- or less. The Whites' son, Eaton, joined the school the following term.[179]

[178]Coombe, D E (1970) 'Which Week at the Lizard?' *Journal of the Society of Bibliography Natural History* 5 (4), April issue. An article written for the Lizard Field Club, based on comparing editions of Johns's book, by a member of the Botany School, University of Cambridge.

[179]Suffolk Record Office, White (Boulge) MSS F/49/1-16, letter dated 28 December 1973.

Emily Carrington's poem and drawings for her brother in the
Carrington family album, 1874.

16

'A HOME I'D SEEK IN SOME BRIGHT STAR . . .'

By Easter of 1874 Charles was suffering the symptoms of his final illness, cancer of the liver. The third edition of *A Week at the Lizard* was published about this time, and Charles sent copies to a few of his friends and family, writing an inscription in each himself. In late spring he wrote his will, dated 9 May 1874, making his son, Charles Henry Johns Esq, and Frederick Isaac Warner his executors.

The previous autumn, his daughter, Katie, had married the Rev Henry Lloyd[180] at Chelsea, where her parents had married before her, but it appears that she continued to help in the care of the pupils at Winton House for some time after their marriage. In a letter dated 24 June 1874 she wrote to Mrs R H White, thanking her for her sympathy for them all, as Charles was so ill. Katie described his last days:

> My dear Father still lingers, though one can scarcely call it now being alive as he is mostly unconscious, and has eaten nothing for six days. He can only take a few drops of champagne or water occasionally. Until yesterday he has been perfectly conscious and clear headed, and God has mercifully given him the most beautiful peace and calm so that he could talk of the end more quietly than any of us; indeed has been longing to be at rest. He has been so wonderfully patient, never complaining, and full of kind thoughts for everyone. [181]

Charles died on 28 June 1874. The shock of his death was great, and not only for his family. One obituary mentions his 'painful illness,' when Ellen and their children were faced with the knowledge that the man whose enthusiasm and capabilities had built up their home, the school and their place in Winchester society would not

---

[180]GRO. See Appendix for biographical information.
[181]SRO Correspondence.

be with them. The shock is also shown in the reaction of friends and in the obituaries of local and wider publications. Kingsley wrote to Ellen: 'I had planned to bring home for him a collection of U S Lepidoptera. At least I can hope to meet hereafter somewhere that brave, able and beloved spirit to whom I have owed so much on earth.'[182]

The SPCK headed its obituary 'Death of an Eminent Botanist,' referring to his educational achievements and the popularity of his books on natural history, including 'those written specially for children.' *The Proceedings of the Linnean Society* wrote similarly.[183] Local papers reported with more personal accounts of the character and gifts of the man. The Winchester and Hampshire Scientific and Literary Society held its fifth annual meeting in the Masonic Hall, when the Hon Sec Mr F I Warner reported 'anxiety as to the future of our Society' after the loss of 'their late President, the Reverend C A Johns, whose wide and keen sympathies were combined with a rare simplicity and geniality of disposition, and with a judicious tenderness in his dealings with others which eminently fitted him for his position amongst us.' Excelling in one special branch of natural science, 'he took an active and discriminating interest in all, and was thus fully capable of appreciating the work of others, and of drawing the attention of the Society to objects of interest beyond his own special field of investigation.' The report ended, '. . . the very existence of the Society is in itself a testimony to his strong persuasion of its possible usefulness and value to the community.'[184]

The Hampshire Advertiser of 4 July wrote, too, of the friends and contacts he had made through his 'educational establishment in which the sons of the aristocracy and gentry were trained,'[185] and felt that 'our Literary and Scientific Society' would remain 'as a memorial of a most valuable and estimable citizen. The Society we have named, and society in its wider sense, have lost a friend, and the scientific circle will have a great difficulty in replacing him in the presidential chair.'

The fullest tribute appeared in *The Hampshire Chronicle* on 4 July

---

[182]Chitty *op cit* p 293.

[183]*Proceedings of the Linnean Society of London 1874-1875* pp lii-liii.

[184]Undated obituary supplied by Molly Matthews.

[185]Hampshire Record Office 12M61/26 is an album (1870) made up by Charles and, perhaps, Ellen, showing photographs of various associates and friends, including Lord Anson, the Kingsleys, Lyells, Powles and others.

1874. This followed his career up to his arrival at Winton House, describing how, once settled, 'he threw himself, with all his natural energy, into the educational work of the city.' After helping to found the Hants Scientific and Literary Society, he was 'the perfection of a president.' As well as encouraging the younger members and being 'wide and liberal in his tastes,' the report praises his abilities: 'Mr Johns never appeared to better advantage than when describing any flower, or insect, or subject of natural history that had been laid, perchance, upon the table at the night of the meeting.'

This paper alone referred to Johns's Christian beliefs: 'He disliked all religious controversy and never willingly engaged in it. His sympathies in this respect were broad.' However, 'his strong masculine good sense led him to regret the meaningless puerilities of a certain school in our Church.' This is likely to be a reference to the Oxford Movement, that had caused so much discussion and dissension when Johns was headmaster of Helston Grammar School, and the Tractarian controversies in which Kingsley had been so deeply engaged.

The Hampshire Chronicle's report ends with an account of the funeral and burial of Charles, held at West Hill Cemetery, which took place on 2 July. The service was conducted by the Rev E Firmstone and Rev E L Berthon of Romsey, who both shared Johns's love of nature. Mr Firmstone, MA, FRAS, was in the chair at the Scientific and Literary Society's meeting held on 18 July, when the society lamented the loss of their late president and sent their condolences to Mrs Johns and the family. Attending at the grave were Dr Ridding, C Collier, G Richardson, G Beckwith and Mr Griffiths, representatives of the College Scientific Society. Messrs Pamplin, Savage, Sheppard, Reynolds and Dr Earle represented the Hampshire Scientific Socety; and Dr Richards, F I Warner, Cornwall Simeon and Dr Butler are also named. 'Many others to whom the deceased was dear were around the grave' and the throwing of flowers into the grave was felt to be especially fitting.

As well as Ellen, the children and Julia, several other members of the family may have been present, though there is no list to confirm this. Bennett was still living in London, working as chaplain and secretary to the School for the Indigent Blind in St George's Fields and writing many books, religious and secular. He, with Jane and perhaps Maria, probably travelled to Winchester. Emily Carrington, one of Charles much loved sisters, had moved, after Henry's death, to a smaller home in Bath, where she and her sister Anne, with the help of her daughters, Mary and Edith,[186] had set up a small school. They were unlikely to have been able to attend the funeral as a group, but one or more would have attended on behalf of them all.

Charles's will, written in May, was proved on 12 August 'by oath of Ellen Julia Johns, widow.'[187] Ellen was bequeathed £100 to be paid as soon as possible after Charles's death, and also all his books, except those in the school library, all pictures, prints, ornaments, wines, liquors, other household stores and his effects. After other bequests were made, the rest of his estate was left to Ellen for her lifetime, and after her death, the school and its contents were to be shared equally by the three children.

Individually, Charles left the Observatory at Winton House with all its instruments etc. to Henry, and also a silver salver presented to Charles by Lord Houghton MP,[188] one of his silver cups and his silver snuff box. To Katie he left the other silver salver, one of his silver cups and his silver inkstand. Frank, only 13 years old, was left his father's gold watch and chain, a silver cup, a gold pencil case and Charles's signet ring, all to be given to him on his 18th birthday. Charles also left £100 to each of his unmarried sisters, Julia, Jane and Anne, and £25 to his godson, George Johns Shatton Warner, all 'free of legacy duty.' The rest of the will is concerned with the use of sufficient money held in stocks and shares or other property to be spent in providing a good education for Frank, who had begun his studies at Rugby.

The written legacy

It is clear that Johns continued his personal journal writing from at least 1842, if not before, though the primary evidence for this time-

---

[186]Edith Carrington's own large bibliography of nature books for children, from which she was able in future to earn her living, sustaining a large home in Bristol, appears to have received much inspiration from the subjects explored by her uncle, Charles Johns.

[187]HRO Ref M364, Vol 28 p 32.

[188]Richard Monckton Milnes, 1st Baron Houghton (1809-1885) English poet and politician (MP Con Pontefract, Yorkshire). He was a patron of literature, secured a pension for Tennyson, helped make Emerson known in Britain, and supported many other authors. Milnes was a constant suitor (refused) and supporter-friend of Florence Nightingale, along with her primary supporter, statesman Sidney Herbert.

taking activity becomes his publications, rather than extant handwritten diaries such as the one that the Cornwall Records Office holds today. These must be located somewhere, as yet unfound, and it is hoped that they will come to light in future. The prodigious amount of detail included in the works that Johns published with SPCK in diary format has to be seen in the perspective of edited versions of fuller notes, written and kept for long periods by the author himself. From these works, his personality and good humour emerge, but very little else, other than his passion for nature and his acceptance of God as the 'first great cause.' His record-keeping on specimens, habitats, and the geographical characteristics related to his travels are such that the reader feels the warmth of immediacy upon beginning to read, and wants to know more of his opinions on the personalities and politics of the day. About his personal life in his family and amongst his parishioners, we know little of an intimate nature. Emily and his other sisters clearly loved and respected him and his talents, and he in return was always readily available to them.

His fame, such as it is today, lies with his publication of *Flowers of the Field*, which can be found on many shelves where there remains a quantity of Victorian books. *British Birds in their Haunts* also continued in print up to 1948, but Charles's own favourite, *A Week at the Lizard*, remains of significance, especially in Cornwall. This became the final book upon which he worked in 1873, in preparing the third edition published shortly before his death, as previously mentioned.

In 1992, a facsimile of the 1848 edition was produced in paperback by Llanerch Publishers, Felinfach. Six years later, to mark the 150th anniversary of the book's first publication, a weekend course was organised by the Workers Education Association in Cornwall. A group of about 15 people, led by Patrick Sargent and Dr Paul Gainey, took a field trip around the Lizard, seeking out the plants mentioned by Johns and revisiting some of his favourite haunts.

One of these favourites was undoubtedly Mullion Cove, and a closing excerpt is appropriate.

Mullion Island serves as a natural breakwater to Mullion Cove, into which we shortly descend by a steep declivity. If, as it has been conjectured with much plausibility, the names of places on this coast are of Phoenician origin, the name Mullion may well be derived from a word cognate with the Persian for "smooth," for although it is too much to say that it is always a safe harbour, yet it often happens that the sea is in a very tempestuous state all around, except under the lee of the island; so that it is at least possible that some ancient mariner may have given the name to the only spot on the coast in which he could take refuge from a storm with any chance of security. the Pacific Ocean itself has no better title to its name....

Making our way to the beach between the seine-boats, hauled up beyond the reach of the surf, and in the fishing-season having all their stores on board ready for instant use, we find ourselves in one of the most romantic coves on the coast. Mullion Cove should be visited about midday on the second or third day after new or full moon. The tide is then low, and several interesting spots may be inspected which at other times are inaccessible. the rocks on both sides are very beautiful; that on the left is perforated by a natural archway many yards long, leading to an open part of the shore, which near the base of the cliff is covered with huge blocks of stone, and further out is composed of firm sand. No time should be lost in traversing this and rounding a projecting mass of serpentine, for on the other side of it lies the entrance to by far the most impos-ing of those caves on the coast which are accessible from the land. There can be no doubt that at some very distant period it was filled up by a lode of soft steatite, which has since been worn away by the action of the sea. It is now a huge chink between two sombre rocks, the entrance being partially blocked up by a smooth black pillar curved like the cutwater of a ship. It is a striking object when seen externally, yet the view from within is yet more so – impenetrable gloom above – brilliant light streaming in through the fissures, but revealing nothing behind – the smoothest of all possible sands – lit-tle pools of crystal water, so still that not even a sunbeam is seen to dance on them – richly dark rocks, so polished as to reflect the light with a splendour scarcely to be endured – the blue sea with its curled edging of snow-white lace – St Michael's Mount, the fabled "tower in the sea" in the extreme distance....

The first time that I explored this cavern was in company with a large party of holiday schoolboys, who can scarcely have forgotten how when we first discovered it, we regretted that we had not brought candles with us, and how one of the party volunteered to run to the village, a mile off, to procure some, and with what rapture he was descried with his bundle in his hand, and how eagerly every one crowded round for his share of the prize. But even the light of eighteen candles was insufficient to penetrate the gloom, or to give a distinct view of so much as the roof; though the ringing echo of the "three cheers for the boy that brought the candles" made up for the lack of adventure in the course of exploring.

Another visit was in the November of 1844, when the number of lights was reduced to two, hardly enough to save us from stumbling over the rocks. The floor was then strewed with apples sodden in water, which had been washed from a vessel that had recently been wrecked near the Land's End. As we approached the extremity of the cave we were compelled to retrace our steps as hastily as possible by the sudden rising of myriads of flies, which had probably taken up their winter quarters in a spot inaccessible by the tide, but, disturbed by the sudden glare, swarmed around us and threatened to extinguish our candles and take refuge in our eyes and mouths.

My last visit was paid in August, 1873, in the company of three friends, two of whom were familiar with most of the picturesque scenery of Southern Europe. Though prepared by my description to see something exceedingly grand, they were lost in admiration, and urged on me the propriety of recommending all future tourists not to leave the neighbourhood without paying a visit to one of the most remarkable objects on the coast, the most picturesque cave in England.'

(pp 139-142, *A Week at the Lizard*)

As one of the many Victorian parsons who felt that the pursuit of knowledge and understanding of the flora and fauna of the natural world was part of the revelation of their Creator, Johns was particularly skilled in communicating his research and making natural history popular for the amateur. Nature Study was an important part of primary education from 1870 to the mid-20th century, gradually becoming incorporated in General Science, and separated into biology, physics and chemistry in secondary schools. The amazing scientific and technological achievements of the 20th century, the splitting of the atom, the discovery of DNA, the landing on the moon and the increasing exploration of the universe, led some scientists to feel in control of the planet and perhaps dismissive of the studies of tiny mosses and rare plants in the far west of Cornwall. Nonetheless, as we move well into the new millennium, much that has never been exploited or understood previously may come into their own time, be they rats tails, stem cells, new processes, and new worlds in the galaxies.

This renewed attention to the natural world attracts the interest of young and old and one can feel sure that Charles Johns and his son, Frank, if living today, would be actively involved as environmentalists and investigators. In his youth Charles[189] wrote: 'People very frequently ask what is the use of botany?' He would have a rational scientific answer to make in our present environmental state, but the underlying reason for all his research and writing was his wonder and delight in the intricacy and beauty of the plants and creatures that he studied. For him this was 'the desire which I believe to be implanted by God in the hearts of all men, to inquire into and understand something of the works of nature.'

Could Magic arm me with the shaft of Light
Or had I but the pinions of a Door
If I could soar aloft with Eagle's flight
And revel fearless in the expanse above –

Could the fleet Swallow with his untired wing
Call me to sport with him, with him to rove –
Thinkst thou I'd seek the land of lasting Spring
Of cloudless skies – the ever-blooming grove?

Ah! no – a Home I'd seek in some bright Star
Where livelier scenes of livelier life I'd prove;
With anxious eye I'd soar this Earth afar
And watch the pilgrimage of all I love.

CAJ June 4, 1834 *(Diary)*
An untitled poem written at Helston, Cornwall

[189] *Botanical Rambles* (1846) Ch 2 p 15 London: SPCK.

Emily Stackhouse
(1811-1870)

A BOTANIST WHO PAINTED:
EMILY STACKHOUSE (1811-1870)

By Clifford Evans

The countryside of 19th-century Cornwall was a flourishing patch-work of varied habitat groups, ranging from the sub-tropical vegetation of the Isles of Scilly to the windswept hills of Dartmoor in West Devon. Although certain areas were significantly ravaged by tin mines and clay works, an attentive botanist of the day could be richly rewarded with numerous discoveries in the nooks and cran-nies of this dramatic landscape. With the era of Romanticism in full bloom throughout Great Britain bringing with it a greater awareness and appreciation of the surrounding flora, a new pastime was created known as the countryside 'ramble.'

Enjoyed by the village vicar, squire and school mistress alike, ram-bling attracted nearly everyone with a penchant for the out-of-doors. For many of those gifted individuals who possessed the ability to commit their findings to paper, whether by the pen or brush, ram-bling became a highly important exercise. Miss Emily Stackhouse was just one of those individuals and she was also one of many ladies who ventured into various scientific endeavours to pursue a never-ending quest for knowledge. Delighting in their discoveries, but rarely com-municating them to the outside, these ladies, unheralded and solitary, rambled about England painting, collecting, and cataloguing; a true expression of individual freedom as they knew it. Exploration was at their doorstep and Botany was the preferred discipline. Ranging from the armchair amateur to the muddy-booted savant, they were the backbone of early British taxonomy. Miss Stackhouse took her work quite seriously, traipsing through the relative tranquillity of the fields and pastures around her home, journeying overland to the seashore, and thence slopping about various bogs and other 'watery places,' as she was fond of inscribing on her watercolours.

The Stackhouse family inhabited many parts of Cornwall, from the Trehane estate near Truro, to the Pendarves estate near Camborne, and Acton Castle near Perranuthnoe. Displaced family centers included the Acton Scott Estate in Shropshire and How Caple near Hereford. As the clergy claimed many a livelihood amongst the Stackhouse descendants, those branches lived in Beenham (Berkshire), St. Mellion (Cornwall), Horton cum Studley (Oxfordshire), Enniscorthy (Ireland), and as far afield as Australia. A branch just outside of Cornwall, in the market town of Modbury, Devon, was the home of Reverend William Stackhouse and his wife, Sarah, and the birthplace of Emily Stackhouse.

Born on the 15th of July in 1811, Emily Stackhouse was the fifth of six children of the family. Although his father was the owner of the Stackhouse family estate of Trehane, Cornwall, William Stackhouse III found it necessary to travel to Devon in order to find an appointment in the ministry for himself. As were many of his ancestors, William was educated at Eton and then Trinity College, Oxford. The Provost and College of the Blessed Virgin Mary of Eton were the patrons of the 14th-century church in Modbury and it was from them that William received the living of the church and the Old Vicarage as their residence.

Virtually nothing is known of the formative years of Emily. We do know that both her immediate and extended family could have provided any number of seeds for growth. From eminent botanists and geologists, to artists and even colour men and brush makers, they were all familiar with the distinguished Stackhouse family. Botany seemed to run throughout the family and so it is more than likely that William and Sarah possessed a reasonable collection of botanical books. William's uncle, John Stackhouse, was the author of *Nereis Britannica* and also aided William Withering in his publication *Arrangement of British Plants*. From inscriptions on several of Emily's watercolours, we know that she was able to refer to *English Botany* by Sowerby and Smith and the later Sowerby Supplement to this monumental work.

William Stackhouse was later to become a member and judge of the Royal Horticultural Society of Cornwall and was known to have a direct interest in botany, contributing by exchange to the herbariums of other collectors. This usually meant that he would have also possessed a herbarium to which the children would have access. These collections, generally of dried grasses and mosses, were the source of inspiration for more that one budding naturalist.

Schooling in pre-Victorian Britain was usually reserved for the boys, with the girls either receiving instruction in their own home or one of a close relation. Records indicate that Emily's older sister, Charlotte, had lived for some time with her second cousin, Frances Knight Stackhouse-Acton, and it is likely that Emily did the same. Frances was an accomplished botanist and botanical artist and her father, T A Knight, was the author of the beautifully illustrated book, *Pomona Herefordiensis*. Charlotte later became a most accomplished watercolourist with a specialty in painting fruit. There were many opportunities for the study of watercolour technique in the Modbury area as well. With the town's proximity to Plymouth, any number of drawing instructors were available including Henry Incledon Johns, whose son Charles Alexander was to play such an important role in Emily's later life.

Unfortunately, these formative years were visited by the all too common tragedies of the day. Epidemics were frequent in these not wholly hospitable times, with cholera, typhoid and tuberculosis lurking behind every arriving ship in this sea-faring nation; Emily began life with only a two-in-five chance of surviving until adulthood. She lost her brother to cholera at Eton in 1824, and her younger sister, Anne, died at the vicarage in 1830. That year of 1830 was also to be a dramatic year for the family as the "Trehane" Stackhouse, the father of William III, passed away, leaving his vast estate and the finest Queen Anne mansion in Cornwall to his son. It was to be four years before the family formally took up residence in William's birthplace, but in 1834, the first date on any of Emily's collection of watercolours, the family had moved to Trehane. Though it is not supposed that they would have occasion to make immediate acquaintance, this was also the year following Charles Johns's own move to Cornwall to take up his teaching assistant's post at Helston. Emily is not mentioned in the diary of Charles Johns in these early years, and it not thought that they were introduced until they met at the Royal Polytechnic Society in the mid 1840s.

The home in Cornwall
This vast estate, just a few miles from Truro and near to the village of Probus, consisted of well over 4,000 acres including numerous tenanted farms, and was always passed on as the privilege of the first-born son. Trehane offered to William and his family security of a kind only enjoyed by the landed gentry of the day. It secured the well-being of the family, allowed ample funds for travel with a well-staffed

family coach, and it was here that Emily's dreams of botanical study became a reality. Virtually every habitat was available to her right on her doorstep. From the ponds of Tregeagle to the bogs of Bodrean, the woods of Trehane and the fertile soil of Nankilly, there were quarries, orchards, streams, mills, and gardens galore.

Trehane dated back in parts to 1288 and had developed over the centuries into a substantial holding. Originally referred to as the 'old town,' it may have been a small hamlet in bygone days, and is listed as 'Trehan' on the Jonathan Speed map of Cornwall circa 1630. The home farm of Trehane Barton possessed as its centrepiece a magnificent Queen Anne residence, built in 1700-03, by John Williams for his new bride, Catherine Courtenay, a descendant of the great knights of old in Devon. Many architectural elements were featured including a fine Adams staircase and a plastered ceiling created by an Italian sculptor who ornamented it with the signs of the zodiac, the first known usage in England.

Through various marriages and subsequent deaths, the house and holdings had passed to William Stackhouse I in 1738 and thence down to his great-grandson. The Stackhouse family itself is thought to have originated in North Yorkshire in the village of Stackhouse. As is usually the case in this circumstance, it is believed that they either lent their name to the village through their settlement in the area, or they simply took their name from the village. William I was from County Durham and had travelled to Cornwall via Oxford and then to the living of St Erme, adjacent to Trehane.

The circle of naturalists

Among the first watercolours from this early period (1834-36), several were completed in and around Norwich and it would appear that Emily wasted no time in beginning her numerous journeys which would take her throughout England and Ireland. The Stackhouse family previously had maintained friendships with such prominent botanists as Sir Joseph Banks and Sir James Edward Smith (botanist and founder of the Linnean Society). Dawson Turner was also numbered as one in the inner circle, and it is believed that Emily stayed with him and his artist wife, Mary Dawson Turner (née Palgrave), and his daughters during her visit to Norfolk. Within closer proximity were her cousin, William Rashleigh Esq. of Menabilly, and her closer neighbours, the Hawkins family of Trewithen.

The Rashleigh family seat of Menabilly is located near the village of Fowey in an area of Cornwall now and forever immortalized in the novels of Daphne du Maurier, particularly the Manor House in which the Rashleigh family lived, or Manderley, as it is known in her books. William Rashleigh was the Member of Parliament for his district and was also well acquainted with Queen Victoria. He was a first-rate amateur scientist and contributed to a diverse range of books from Sowerby and Smith's *English Botany* to Yarrell's *History of British Fishes* to Johnstone and Croall's *Nature-Printed British Sea-Weeds*. William Rashleigh was married to Emily's aunt, and as Fowey was only 20 miles distant from Tre-hane, she made many visits to this most con-genial household.

Menabilly

John (1761-1841)[190] and Mary Esther Hawkins (1778-1861) were much closer at nearby Trewithen, with-in easy walking distance and were both able and experienced naturalists as well as artists. Mary's father was Humphrey Waldo Sibthorp (1744-1815), who had been Shawardian Professor of Botany at Oxford. Her half-brother, John Sibthorp (1758-1796), the Professor of Botany following his father, had been associated with the famous botanical artists Ferdinand and Franz Bauer, whom he had been instrumental in bringing to London. John Hawkins had accompanied his friend Sibthorpe (1794-95) on his epic voyage of plant collecting which ultimately formed the basis of the *Flora Graeca* (3,000 species from Troy, Athens, Zakinthos and the central Pelopon-nese), and after the latter's death, had married Mary Sibthorp. Hence the people around the naturalist painter in the 1830s, Emily, and

[190]John Hawkins FRS was born at Trewithen, Cornwall, in 1761, and was a keen geologist. He was one of the first vice presidents of the Royal Geological Soci-ety of Cornwall, with a special interest in Cornish mining and mineral collecting. He died at Trewithen (registered as Truro) in 1841, after which his wife moved back to their other family home, Bignor Park, near Petworth, Sussex. He corresponded with the geologist Gideon Mantell, and was a close friend of Cornishman Davies Gilbert, the celebrated president of the Royal Society.

her family, were distinguished and knowledgeable about the natural world she also loved. They were all members of the philosophical, horticultural and scientific societies, locally and nationally, and it was natural that she would engage herself in like manner.

William Stackhouse appears to have taken to livestock and cultivation as much as his daughter Emily took to the rough borders, bogs and woodland. The family grew acres and acres of cabbages, turnips, and potatoes as well as providing rye, barley and other corn for milling and feed. Sheep and cattle were numerous with pigs and oxen rounding out the livestock. In reviewing the farm ledger from 1834 to 1861, visits were made to market in Truro every week and most of the entries appear to be in Emily's hand. With such a pastoral life beckoning, Emily Stackhouse was to produce well over 600 delicately coloured watercolours and several collections of mosses, grasses and flowers. In addition to these accomplishments, she made significant contributions to the *Hortus Siccus* of the Royal Horticultural Society and her writings enriched the *Journal of the Royal Institution of Cornwall*.

Her watercolours themselves speak of a supreme dedication to detail and a phenomenal accuracy of colour. Usually sketching an outline in pencil, Emily would then use what must have been the finest paints available as their outstanding staying power and light-fast qualities are echoed by the technique with which they have been applied. Her paper of choice was produced by Whatman, both regular and Turkey Mill, cut to approximately 12x10 inches and various smaller sizes. These appear to have been carefully chosen with annual watermarks when she would embark upon one of her numerous excursions. She occasionally used various enhancement techniques that included applying varnish to simulate the sheen found on some leaves or petals, and mixing gouache or gum arabic into her paints to give a three-dimensional texture to the flower stamens.

After completion of the watercolour, Emily would carefully inscribe the Latin and English names of the plant on the bottom corners in her usual cursive stroke. Most pieces also have the location and month listed either in pen or pencil, with some humour interjected from time to time with comments such as 'partout' (everywhere), 'do you not know it,' or 'where is it not.' The appropriate Linnaean taxonomy was usually listed on the reverse.

The image depth achieved in her plants shows that she must have truly painted from nature. There is no stylization present and she certainly had a remarkable sense of line in order to commit such perfect poses to paper in an extremely unforgiving medium. Some images seem quite literally ready to pirouette off the page as might a Degas ballerina. These are not depictions reminiscent of a flower sitting in a glass on the writing bureau.

Exhibiting

The 14th Annual Royal Cornwall Polytechnic Society Exhibition took place in Falmouth during 1846 and a group of four albums of Emily's watercolours were entered in the Natural History competition. The collection was awarded a Bronze medal and reviewed in the *Royal Cornwall Gazette* in which they wrote, '. . . four volumes of beautiful botanical drawings . . . .'[191] The judges of the exhibition were somewhat critical of the placement of the watercolours in the Natural History category, perhaps they should have been entered in the 'Amateur artist' sections. They were deemed to not be a satisfactory entry in the Natural History section, but, of course, they didn't know that they were dealing with someone who considered herself neither an artist, nor an amateur: Emily Stackhouse was a botanist – who painted.

During these highly important years from the mid-1840s into the 1850s, Emily formed many lasting relationships with several of the local botanists. Primarily this was due to her involvement and interest in the Royal Cornwall Polytechnic Society (RCPS) to which later she became a subscribing member. Through the RCPS she met two knowledgeable and influential ladies, Elizabeth Andrew Warren (1786-1864) and Isabella Gifford (c1823-1891). Miss Warren, a founding member of the Polytechnic and an honorary member of the Royal Horticultural Society, was also a close friend of Reverend Johns and Sir William Hooker.[192] It may very well have been she who first introduced Charles to Emily. Miss Gifford published at least one botanical book on seaweeds, *The Marine Botanist* (1853), and was

---

[191] RCPS Proceedings for the year 1846.

[192] In 1843, Elizabeth Andrew Warren, algologist, published *A Botanical Chart for the use of Schools* dedicated to Sir William Hooker. This was the same year that Charles Johns returned to Helston as headmaster, and he may have employed it for Helston Grammar School. There are three volumes of her collections at the Royal Institution of Cornwall (National Archives).

in several of the local organisations as well, exchanging specimens with William Henry Harvey, the Irish authority on algae, and Hooker, as did Miss Warren. Both of these ladies, along with the Rev Mr Hore, another friend of Charles Johns, and (Mr) Stackhouse (Emily's father), are acknowledged as contributors to Harvey's *Phycologia Britannica* (Vol 1).

Sometime during this period, possibly as early as 1843 but certainly before 1846, Emily came into contact with the Rev Charles Alexander Johns, now headmaster of Helston Grammar School and also a member of the Polytechnic Society. At some point around the time of Emily's first exhibition in Falmouth Charles must have seen her watercolours, and these met with his warm approval. Due directly to her association with Charles, her botanical watercolours were soon to become some of the most reproduced drawings of plants in the history of publishing, though often not acknowledged as such, nor known about in published sources to date.

The first true rambling book written by Charles was *Botanical Rambles,* published in 1846, and it made him almost immediately well known. This was later issued in four parts following the seasons of the year. A number of the illustrations of leaves, blossoms, and nuts or fruit in these volumes are by Emily, and therefore he must have known her and her work at least a year in advance of the publication.

The next title and perhaps the consummate rambling book, *A Week at the Lizard,* was issued in 1848. The botanical information on this windswept peninsula was included in the appendix and virtually all of the botanical illustrations are woodcuts taken from Emily's watercolours, some with her characteristic ES monogram, but many simply lifted anonymously.[193] Other wood engravings, mainly of people in various scenes, are engraved by Whimper and all are signed. Charles's *magnum opus* was *Flowers of the Field.* Considered by many to be the bible of the amateur botanist, this book was first published in a two-volume set in 1853. Well over 200 of the book's illustrations have come from the anonymous hand of Miss Emily Stackhouse.

---

[193]Her drawings and paintings were used as the templates for engravings to be made from, by Whimper's company or other engravers. The provenance is known from comparing the originals to the plates made for the books, for which a complete table has been produced (C Evans Collection).

Another grouping of paintings by Emily was entered at the RCPS in 1853 with the same prize results although a more eloquent statement by the judges was made this time. It read: '. . . two volumes of Flowers, in water colours, painted from Nature, and beautifully executed, belonged rather to the department of the fine arts; but as they had been submitted to the judges in the natural history department they had awarded to the exhibitor a second bronze medal, the more willingly, as the art of preserving an exact representation of a rare or new plant, whose colours would soon fade, is highly useful and important.' By this juncture, Charles and Ellen and their family had moved on to live and work in Beenham, Berkshire, another stronghold of the Stackhouse family. It is believed that Emily paid visits to them there, and was a good friend to the family.

The saga of the illustrations did not end with the writings of C A Johns nor by the relatively early deaths of either Charles (1874) or Emily (1870). The woodcuts that were used to illustrate all of these books were then placed in further rambling and botanical books by later authors employed by the SPCK. From their series on Natural History Rambles ranging from *The Woodlands, Lane and Field*, to *The Seashore* and then to other botanical subjects such as M C Cooke's *Freaks of Plant Life*, it is estimated that the watercolours of Emily Stackhouse have been used to partially illustrate at least 15 and perhaps over 30 publications issued in the period from 1870 to 1890. However, despite her tremendous accomplishment as one of the great anonymous illustrators, Emily attained other heights far more dear to her heart.

The ensuing years brought the first signs of a decline in the usually brilliant detail of Emily's botanical drawings as her eyesight obviously began to fail towards the end of the 1850s. During this period her watercolours took on an almost soft-focus, impressionistic quality and concluded with her last dated work done in Newquay during August 1859. A few others probably date from or just after this time, as they all bear the hallmarks of this later style. The colouration is just as robust as in any of her earlier work, but the superb detailing gives way to a hazy quality. After this period, Emily began to concentrate more on herbarium collections, and these, like the watercolours before them, were successfully entered into competitions at the Royal Polytechnic Annual Exhibitions. One of these collections, a large grouping of Indian grasses that had been forwarded to her by her nephew stationed in the 27th Inneskilling Regiment, was duly classified by Emily and later donated to the British Museum of Natural History in South Kensington.

The first indication of any severe health difficulties is contained in several letters from Emily to William Wilson, who was a noted expert on mosses and the author of *Bryologia Britannica.* Shortly after this correspondence, Emily and her sister Louisa purchased a Georgian terraced house in Truro near to the Royal Infirmary and moved out of Trehane. It was also in this same year of 1861 that William Stackhouse passed away at the age of 88, leaving the estate to his first-born child, Sarah. However, Sarah and her husband declined the inheritance and passed it on to their son, Emily's correspondent from India. The surviving Stackhouse daughters, Sarah, Charlotte, Louisa and Emily, erected a monumental stained glass window in the church in Probus in memory of their father. Captain William Stackhouse Church Pinwill gladly resigned his commission in India and returned to England. Although not a farmer himself, the estate continued to prosper through the excellent lettings that Pinwill arranged with local families. This provided him with ample time for gardening, which reached its zenith with his receipt of the Victoria Medal of Honour from the Royal Horticultural Society in 1914.

Despite attacks of apoplexy, the move to Truro allowed Emily to continue exercising her considerable talents in the field of botany. She began by firstly having her collection of 629 drawings bound into three volumes by one of the finest bookbinders in Great Britain, Zaehnsdorf of London, now a part of the Asprey Group. In 1864, they completed the project leaving many blank pages interspersed throughout the books presumably because Emily felt that there was more work to be done on certain species. This is possibly a definite sign of her continued optimism in the face of failing health.

In this same year of 1864, Charles's and Emily's great friend, Elizabeth Warren, passed away, and it was on that occasion that Emily first contributed to the *Journal of the Royal Institution of Cornwall* with a memorial tribute. Part of Isabella Gifford's tribute to Elizabeth is included in the Appendix two of Charles's friends and colleagues. In 1867 two articles were published in this *Journal,* 'Musci, Natives of Cornwall,' in which Emily described and classified the various mosses of the area, and her own attempt at a rambling story, 'Rare Plants in the neighbourhood of Truro,' which takes the reader on a botanical

Engraving: Probus Church, where Emily Stackhouse
is buried. Published in 1824 by Simpkin & Marshall,
London.

search around some of the roads and byways around Truro. Emily
was later acknowledged to have collected and classified virtually every
British moss, and her 'Rare Plants' article listed *Rubus Radula*, the first
such mention of this plant occurring in Cornwall.

The last few years of her life were not kind to this gentle lady, and it
is not known to what extent she and Charles remained in close touch.
Always in revising his texts, there was occasion for selecting new illustrations, but this would also have been part of the 19th-century bonfire
that destroyed SPCK's archives of correspondence. A severe attack of
apoplexy brought on paralysis for Emily in 1869 and she lingered on
for another year before a final episode took her life on the 1st of March
1870. She was buried in her family corner of the Probus churchyard
beneath a verdant canopy of her beloved mosses.

The plight of the talented and intelligent woman in the 19th century is almost impossible for us to imagine today. Many of Emily's
watercolours pre-date the accredited discovery of various species in
Cornwall by as much as 45 years and several of these were included in her two exhibitions at the Royal Polytechnic Society in 1846
and 1853. She was always beset with 'second' place status in most
of the exhibitions she entered. It is difficult to comprehend how a
volume of delicate watercolours that possessed her amazing red pop-

py as its centerpiece could have been surpassed in the medal awards. Most women exhibitors were referred to simply as 'a lady amateur' in the discussions of prizes awarded with the men all receiving proper named acknowledgments. Only gentlemen served on the village and town committees, whereas women subscribers were represented by one committee – the Ladies Committee – listing women from all over the county in one.

This same social attitude continued with the various organisations to which she belonged. The Royal Institution of Cornwall had Emily and other prominent lady botanists in regular attendance at their annual meetings, and even though their *Journal* is at great pains to note individually by name all of the gentlemen present, the lady members are lumped into their customary terminal anonym '. . . a large number of ladies.' However, they do redress the pathetic situation a bit in their tribute to lost members which reads, '. . . Miss Emily Stackhouse enriched our journal, from time to time, with admirable contributions relating to a branch of science seldom treated of in its pages, but which she had long studied with singular zeal and success.'

Many conjectures about this remarkable woman will remain educated guesses at best and much will simply never be known. The magnificent Queen Anne mansion of Trehane literally burnt to the ground in 1946, the victim of a torch that was being used to re-lead the gutters and roof. The flame apparently reached in through a crack in a slate tile and ignited one of the rafters underneath. This smouldered away in the attic un-noticed throughout the day. When the fire took hold in the evening, the villagers in the town of Probus thought it was one of the many bonfires that were seen throughout the countryside due to the clearing up of the fields after World War II. The alarm finally reached the village, but it was too late. It is known from family sources that the house and attic were filled with papers and memorabilia. Fortunately, the three volumes of watercolours which can be clearly seen in a turn-of-the-century photograph of the drawing room had already been removed to the homes of various Stackhouse descendants.

Therefore, the legacy of Emily Stackhouse is represented by these 629 delicately crafted watercolours. Whether a simple blade of Sedge or a bouquet of Henbane, each plant received the fullest possible attention. Her travels took her the length and breadth of

England with several overseas excursions to Ireland and the Isles of Scilly. Unacknowledged, she provided numerous illustrations to C A Johns's 'little books,' as she so-called them in a letter to Sir William Hooker,[194] and a vast array of other SPCK publications, thus making her one of the great unheralded illustrators of her time.

But then, such was the humble nature of this lady, a quiet and solitary figure, developing a superb technique for preserving and seeking out the natural beauty around her, and at the same time, amassing great local knowledge, which, had it been shared or communicated, would have secured her a place amongst the foremost discoverers of plant species in Cornwall. Miss Emily Stackhouse, a great naturalist in her own time, awaits recognition as an equally great botanical artist in ours.

---

[194]Archives, Royal Botanic Gardens, Kew: Hooker's correspondence. Correspondence from Emily Stackhouse can also be found in the Botany Library, Natural History Museum, London in the William Wilson Correspondence (main author) 1799-1871 (MSS WIL 1).

APPENDICES

APPENDIX I: THE JOHNS FAMILY TREES

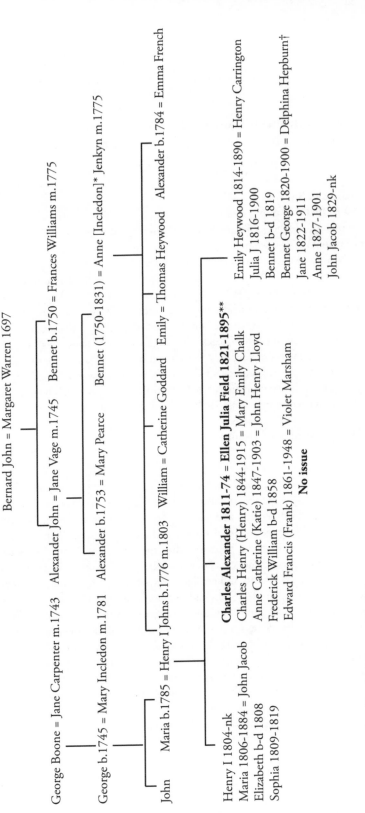

Bernard John = Margaret Warren 1697

George Boone = Jane Carpenter m.1743   Alexander John = Jane Vage m.1745   Bennet b.1750 = Frances Williams m.1775

George b.1745 = Mary Incledon m.1781   Alexander b.1753 = Mary Pearce   Bennet (1750-1831) = Anne [Incledon]* Jenkyn m.1775

John   Maria b.1785 = Henry I Johns b.1776 m.1803   William = Catherine Goddard   Emily = Thomas Heywood   Alexander b.1784 = Emma French

Henry I 1804-nk   **Charles Alexander 1811-74 = Ellen Julia Field 1821-1895****   Emily Heywood 1814-1890 = Henry Carrington
Maria 1806-1884 = John Jacob   Charles Henry (Henry) 1844-1915 = Mary Emily Chalk   Julia J 1816-1900
Elizabeth b-d 1808   Anne Catherine (Katie) 1847-1903 = John Henry Lloyd   Bennet b-d 1819
Sophia 1809-1819   Frederick William b-d 1858   Bennet George 1820-1900 = Delphina Hepburn†
                                            Edward Francis (Frank) 1861-1948 = Violet Marsham   Jane 1822-1911
                                                              No issue   Anne 1827-1901
                                                                                                   John Jacob 1829-nk

*Her mother, Elizabeth, was an Incledon.
**Ellen Julia Field was the only child of Julia Burk(e) (1789-1857) and James Field of Bath, Somerset
     (c1780-1822), his second marriage from which he had older issue.
†Bennet George remarried after his first wife's death.

George Banks FLS
(fl. 1820s-1830s) d March, 1840

This early mentor of Charles Johns, was a silversmith and engraver, and excited the interest of young Charles when he lectured on botanical subjects in Devonport, the site of his home and his business. He was the author of *An Introduction to the Study of English Botany* (1823). Davey in his *Flora of Cornwall* (1909) referred to Banks as projecting, 'under the title of *The Plymouth and Devonport Flora*, what promised to be an important contribution to the botany of the two westernmost counties, but the venture was probably too big a tax on the author's pocket, and after the issue of eight monthly parts at one shilling each, nothing further was done. In all sixty-two plants, some of them accompanied by well-drawn coloured plates were treated: the following thirteen were first records for Cornwall.' It was through Banks, that Johns was to receive communications from Sir William J Hooker, to which he responded with enthusiasm over many years. [See John Jacob LLD following.]

Notes: Davey; Desmond; Freeman

The Rev Edward Lyon Berthon (1813-1899)
English inventor and friend of Charles Johns

Having also studied in Dublin (medicine in the early 1830s, that he abandoned upon marriage in 1834) Berthon and Johns had much more in common. Both were clergy, Berthon holding the living of Romsey, when Johns was at Winton House, Winchester. It is there that it is supposed they first met. Both were keen natural historians and members of the local societies relating. Whereas Johns's avocation was botany, Berthon's was boats and mechanical science. His first experiments were with the screw propeller in the 1830s, and in Cambridge where he was studying in 1841 he produced a registration (of water flow, speed) instrument for boats known as the Berthon Log. The collapsible boat for which he is best known to the public (as a rescue craft) was invented in 1851, and resulted in the creation of the Berthon Boat Works at Romsey, supplying craft of various dimensions internationally. Of special interest to Johns was Berthon's construction of astronomical telescopes and the design of the Romsey Observatory. An unusual feature of Winton House was its astronomical observatory, which greatly inspired the interest of Henry Johns. In 1873 Berthon accompanied Johns on his walking tour of Cornwall with friend Cornwall Simeon and Henry, from which *A Week at the Lizard* was revised (3rd edition). Berthon officiated at the funeral of Charles Johns in 1874. He not only outlived Charles by a quarter of a century, but also survived Ellen Johns.

Notes: Cambridge University Alumni; *DNB*; *A Week at the Lizard* (3rd edition, p x); CAJ obituaries

Henry Edmund Carrington (1806-1859)
Brother-in-law to Charles Johns

Charles's main benefactor outside the immediate family, Henry had been a lifelong friend. Henry's father, Nicholas Toms Carrington (1777-1830) always known as 'N T,' was well known in Plymouth as a journalist, teacher and poet ('The Poet of Dartmoor').[196] Two years before Charles was born, N T set up a private academy at Plymouth Dock, which 'he conducted without intermission until six months before his death' (*DNB*). His eldest son Henry, of five sons and three daughters, though born when his father was teaching previously in Kent, had spent his boyhood in Plymouth. The two families remained close friends, and Henry had loved and courted Charles's sister Emily Heywood, for many years. N T Carrington was an important exemplar to Charles Johns, of a man who lived by his writings and publications, and from taking students into his academy, and probably had a substantial hand in Charles's early education. His son, Henry, as described in the text, was a crucial support to Charles Johns at University.

After their marriage in Bath Abbey, Henry and Emily lived at Lyncombe and Widcombe, near Bath, and also in Bath itself at several locations during their married life. Henry was the owner of a printing works, a publisher and also the proprietor and editor of the *Bath Chronicle*. Charles's first book, *Flora Sacra*, was printed by Henry, on commission of J Parker, Strand, and it is probable that Carrington introduced Charles to this publisher, who also became a close friend and publisher to Charles Kingsley. Carrington's wealth at death was computed at £14,000, measured today in relation to average earnings of several millions of pounds. The couple also assumed responsibility for the bringing up of Anne Johns, the youngest daughter, to alleviate the Johns family purse in Plymouth. One of their daughters, Edith Carrington, became a novelist and prolific children's story writer, earning her living through her pen. His youngest son, C W Carrington, namesake for Charles and his godson, later became the Dean of Christchurch Cathedral, New Zealand. Charles Walter was the father of Molly Matthews, to whom this book is dedicated, and his grandson, Philip Carrington (1892-1975) was Archbishop of Canada and Metropolitan of Quebec, in the Church of England. Family trees for the Carrington, Johns and Incledon intermarriages are included in Matthews's book, *Your Family History* (revised edition, 1982).

Notes: C M Matthews; Family correspondence & knowledge; printing records; Census

Derwent Coleridge (1800-1883)
Headmaster, mentor and friend to Charles Johns

---

[196]Please note: In the *DNB* and therefore introduced elsewhere on the internet and in documents and books is a reference to N T as being <u>Noel</u> Thomas. This is incorrect. [C M Matthews; Family information]

Charles may have met Derwent Coleridge in Plymouth and learned something of his unusual background. Derwent, younger son of the poet and philosopher Samuel Taylor Coleridge, came down from St John's College, Cambridge, in 1824 with an undistinguished BA pass. His father, a man of genius and a brilliant conversationalist, was not a responsible or very reliable parent and had drifted away from his family. Derwent had only been able to go to Cambridge through the financial help of his father's friends (especially Robert Southey) and while there he realised that his gifts and interests were in classics and languages rather than mathematics, which at St John's was the only path to an Honours degree. He had a passion for languages, not only the classics, but according to Dean Stanley: 'He could read Cervantes and Alfieri as easily as Racine and Schiller, and was well acquainted with Hungarian and Welsh… He could also read not only Arabic and Coptic, but Zulu and Hawaian.' He neglected his other studies, instead spending much of his time discussing poetry, philosophy and politics with his friends, William Praed, Thomas Babington Macaulay, F D Maurice and John Moultrie, as well as with his cousin, Henry Nelson Coleridge. This group of brilliant young men were developing the ideas of Christian socialism, but Derwent's intellectual questioning led to a loss of religious faith and he set aside the idea of entering the church. He desperately needed a job to enable him to support himself and pay off the many early debts he had accumulated.

Derwent's distinguished friends, who were to be a great help to him throughout his life, came to his rescue. John Heywood Macaulay, cousin of T B Macaulay the historian, was Master of the new Proprietary Classical and Mathematical School, which opened in Plymouth in 1822 (when Charles Johns was only 11). He offered Derwent the post of Third Assistant Master, which he gratefully accepted. This school was the same Plymouth New Grammar School where Henry Incledon Johns began teaching, after the bank failures, as Professor of Drawing in 1825. It was here in Plymouth also that Derwent met Mary Pridham, the daughter of another banker in the city

Derwent's love for this beautiful dark-haired girl of 17, led him to return to Cambridge to read for Orders and in 1826 he was ordained deacon in Exeter Cathedral. He expected to be appointed curate of the parishes of Kenwyn and Kea, near Truro in Cornwall, where the Vicar was his cousin, James Duke Coleridge. However, J D urged Derwent to apply for the Mastership of Helston Grammar School instead. He knew that his cousin was constantly in debt and felt that the position in Helston would give him the opportunity to be his own master, build up the school and, hopefully, his finances. Derwent accepted the school and the Lectureship (curacy) of St Michael's Church and in January 1827 moved to Helston to begin his duties. In July he was ordained priest at Exeter and licensed by the Bishop to the free endowed school of Helston. By the end of the year he was able to marry his beloved Mary.

Derwent began his cure of Helston (1827-1841) by visiting all the parishioners of St Michael's in Helston itself, and of its mother church at Wendron (the home parish of the John(s) clan of families), discovering and helping those who were sick or in need. He then tackled the school, which he described as 'horribly neglected.' The earliest schoolroom had been built at the bottom of Coinagehall Street, Helston's wide main street that led down to the site of an old castle, all traces of which had disappeared long ago. This schoolroom was re-built in 1610 and again towards the end of the 18th century; now Derwent arranged for improvements to both the building and the playground. As for pupils, these seemed to have disappeared and he began his teaching with only two: James Henwood, aged 13, son of a surgeon apothecary, and John Vivian, eight, son of Mr Vivian of Nansloe, a manor house on the outskirts of Helston, whom Derwent described as 'a nice genteel little boy.' (Hainton)

The Coleridges made Charles Johns most welcome, treating him as one of the family, which now included their son, Derwent Moultrie. Emily (1835-1836, in Cornwall) was named for their Helston friend Emily Trevenen. Their daughter, Christabel Rose (1843-1921) and son Ernest Hartley (1846-1920) were both born in London, after Derwent had taken the headship of St Mark's College. From that early time in Cornwall, their family lives intermingled. It was Christabel, who would later become the biographer of her distant cousin, the novelist Charlotte Mary Yonge, the latter a part of the same literary circles as the Johns family in Winchester (friend and correspondent of Ellen Johns; see Autograph Collection). Erny later became an Assistant Master at Winton House under Charles Johns, as referred in the text, and thereafter a poet and educationalist. Derwent and Charles were jointly instrumental in setting Erny up to run his own preparatory school.

Notes: DNB; Journals of Caroline Fox, Barclay Fox; Hainton; Dare; New York Times obituary 1883; Autograph Collection; BL

De la Beche, Sir Henry Thomas (1796-1855)
Geologist and cartographer engaged in establishing the Ordinance Survey, and potential employer of Charles Johns
Caroline Fox, in her diary, describes Henry de la Beche as 'a very entertaining person, his manners rather French, his conversation spirited and full of illustrative anecdote' (1836). This refers to an occasion when he and his daughter Bessie went to luncheon with the Fox family. It is probably also the occasion when Charles Johns walked with him to St Keverne and de la Beche met his grandfather, Mr Boone. Pym makes an editorial note (p 5) to the Fox diary, that de la Beche established the School of Mines (in Cornwall) and was knighted in 1848. He was a long-time member and sometime officer of the Royal Cornwall Polytechnic Society, of which Charles was also a member. See Autograph Collection for letter from De la Beche to Johns.

Notes: DNB; Journal of Caroline Fox; CAJ Diary (CRO); Autograph Collection

Mrs Julia Burke Field (1791-1857)
Mother of Ellen Julia Johns, mother-in-law to Charles Johns, and residential matron at Whitelands College, Chelsea
Born in Galway, Ireland, Julia Burke, Mrs Field, is described in various places, for unknown reasons, as a 'Scottish widow' (there is some mention of lineal descent from Robert the Bruce). She was herself a daughter of the Anglo-Irish noble house of Clanricarde, the Burkes of Ower, Co Galway, and part of a large landed family. She married, as his second wife, James Field of Bath. He was an organist and

a music teacher, son of Thomas Field, in a large musical family of Bath, Somerset, and may have been the organist at Bath Abbey. James died the year after Ellen was born. *Pigot's Directory of Somerset* (1822) indicates that Mrs Field established a ladies boarding and day school, at Kingsmead Terrace, near other members of his family who were also professors and teachers of music. Census data indicates that Julia Field may have become Matron of an asylum school for girls in Frome Selwood, Somerset prior to removing to London. Her daughter Ellen from her late teens worked as a governess to the Samuel Evans family, wealthy cotton mill owners in Darley Abbey, Derby (*1841 England Census*).

The joint post at Whitelands College in Chelsea brought mother and daughter together in their teaching capacities. Julia Field continued in her work there following Charles Johns's marriage to Ellen, until in 1851 she set up Catherine Lodge School for Girls in Trafalgar Square, as the owner-proprietor, with Miss Sarah Lowman as Headmistress. Julia died at Callipers House, Chipperfield, Hertfordshire (the Johns's home and school at that time) and is buried in the churchyard of the parish. In the *1871 Census*, her granddaughter, Anne Catherine (Katie) Johns was listed as a 'visitor' at Catherine Lodge, this well-attended school in London, and may have been staying there while working or studying. Miss Lowman remained as Principal.

Notes: *Burke's Peerage* (1862); Census data & GRO; Seed (2005); Family correspondence & knowledge; *Pigot's* (1822)

The Rev William Strong Hore (1807-1882)
Friend and naturalist

Slightly older than Charles Johns, Hore was born at Stonehouse, Plymouth, receiving his BA at Cambridge in 1830. It is not known when the two first met, though they may have known each other from school days. It could also have been through shared botanical interests and lessons with George Banks, or while Hore was a curate in Stoke Damerel, Plymouth and a clergy-friend of the Rev John Jacob. Following that curacy he moved to Norwich, which also features largely as an area throughout Johns's writings. Johns often identifies his friends anonymously as 'my companion,' and it is likely that Hore was a constant one of these. Hore was also for some years the Vicar of St Clement's Oxford (1850-55), and then in later years returned to Devon, where he was Vicar of Shebbear (1855) near Torrington. In both the 1830s and the 1840s, the two shared several walking tours in and around Cornwall and Devon as recorded in scientific notes of their discoveries, and in Johns's books.

Like Johns, he exchanged specimens with other collectors nationally (letter from Hooker to Johns, mentions Hore, as listed in Autograph Collection) and published findings, sometimes with Johns in *The Phytologist*. The British Association meeting (for the first time in Plymouth) of 1841 featured a paper by Hore entitled 'A List of Plants found in Devonshire and Cornwall not mentioned by Jones in the *Flora Devoniensis*.' It contained first published references to some plants found in Cornwall. He is also credited with the discovery of *Trifolium molinerii*. [Summary information found in Davey's *Flora of Cornwall*.] In a number of published references to his own work and in letters to botanical magazines, Johns mentions Hore as his companion and friend in locating species and specimens. For example in *Brit-*

ish Birds in their Haunts, he reports being informed by the Rev W S Hore (p 503) that an instance of the Garganey breeding in the Broads of Norfolk has occurred within his own experience.

Notes: Desmond; Darwin Letter Project (Letter no. 13870); Letters at Kew; F H Davey (*Flora of Cornwall*) 1909; *The Phytologist* Vol II, 1845

Benjamin Charles Incledon aka Charles B Incledon (1764-1826)
Second cousin for whom Charles was named
Son of Mr Incledon, Surgeon of St Keverne, Cornwall on The Lizard, which Charles Johns was to make better known through his book, *A Week at the Lizard* (1848). It is believed that Charles was Incledon's namesake, and it is interesting to note that the name of Incledon is well preserved in the family lineages, sprinkled through several generations. He was a cousin of both of Charles Johns's parents, who themselves both came from local and St Keverne families. Incledon died in Worcester, after a very successful career at Covent Garden and elsewhere, as an actor-singer, though no actor of consequence. A large bibliography about him is listed on p 263, Vol 1 in Boase and Courtney (1874) *Bibliotheca Cornubiensis*. 'Incledon, The Singer' and sub-noted as 'The British National Singer' as called by His Majesty King George III, is a chapter, pp 89-111, in Tregellas, Walter H Vol II, *Cornish Worthies: Sketches of Some Eminent Cornish Men and Families*.

The family may have died out in Cornwall by the mid 1850s, by which time Jemima Incledon, a cousin of Charles died, but Boase notes in *Collectanea Cornubiensia*, that this appears to be untrue. A descendant tree for the Incledon family has been traced as a result of the researches of C M Matthews (Molly) in her book *Your Family History* (1976), p 55 into the ancestry of her grandmother, Emily Heywood Johns, Charles's younger sister. At time of writing there are no Incledons in the telephone directories in Cornwall though the family still survives in Devon.

Notes: C M Matthews, Family knowledge; Autograph Collection; Boase & Courtney; Tregellas

Rev Dr John Jacob LLD (1796-1849)
Clergyman-educator, naturalist and brother-in-law to Charles Johns
London-born Dr Jacob married Maria, the eldest sister of Charles, and was instrumental both in Charles's early education at school, and acknowledged as presenter for his studies at Dublin. (*Trinity College Register*). Jacob's living in Devonport was in the gift of the St Aubyn family, who were main property and land owners in Stoke Damerel where Devonport was situated, and he acted as Vicar to the St Aubyn Chapel, Chapel Street and Headmaster of the Devonport Grammar School. His *West Devon and Cornwall Flora* dedicated to Sir J St Aubyn of St Michael's Mount was published in 18 parts (discontinued in 1837) by Longman (London), and is noted in the *Bibliotheca Cornubiensis*, Vol 1, p 264. A more elaborated entry of his contribution to Cornish botanical studies is included in the Introduction, p xli, of F H Davey's *The Flora of Cornwall*. He is listed with botanical references by R Desmond. Other publications included *A Selection from the New Version of the Psalms of David* (1831) Devonport: W Byers, and *A Letter to the Marquess of*

Lansdowne, on the Government Plan of Education (1839) Devonport [printed]. John Jacob died in London in the early months of 1849, leaving Maria and all the family much saddened, and especially Charles who had received so much help from his brother-in-law.

Notes: Family knowledge; Davey (*Flora of Cornwall*); *Trinity College Register*; BL Catalogue; Boase & Courtney; Death registration: PRO, Vol 1, p 329, Jul, Aug, Sept 1849, St Pancras

---

The family of Johns of Devonport, Stoke Damerel and Greater Plymouth:

[Separate notes not listed for the following, as all information obtained from family knowledge, correspondence, census and GRO data, and extensive internet and library searches. No family or personal correspondence has yet been located, and none of the family are represented within the Autograph Collection in Appendix v, with the exception of Charles Johns himself and his family as recipients. Letters from Johns to Sir William Hooker are located at Kew Archives in the Hooker correspondence.]

Alexander Johns (c1780-c1860) and William (1784-c1862)
Brothers of Henry Incledon Johns and uncles to Charles

Charles Johns had strong links with Ireland through his uncles, Alexander and William Johns. Both having been born in Cornwall, they grew up in Plymouth, and returned infrequently to visit from Ireland where they latterly made their permanent homes in Carrickfergus and Belfast. Alexander had been placed also by his father, Bennett Johns, in a bank in Dublin, Ireland, just as Henry Incledon, his older brother, had been settled in the bank in Devonport, and like his brother William was also a solicitor.

Alexander, while working in Dublin, met and married Emma French of the Anglo-Norman family of French who had settled and were prominent landowners and politicians in Galway (her grandfather was a Bishop of Limerick and Elphin of the protestant establishment). By 1816 Alexander was Ordnance Storekeeper at Carrickfergus Castle, near Belfast, remaining there until 1834.[197] He was then appointed the first Manager of the Carrickfergus Branch of the Northern Bank of Ireland. Later he was also a founder of the Johns-Elliot partnership of solicitors in Belfast. Ultimately he was a Director of the Belfast Banking Company. Fifteen children were born to them, several dying in infancy. However, there were four sons named Bennett, William, Alexander and Thomas Digby, cousins for Charles to know and to mix with during his Dublin years. William was studying at Trin-

---

[197]Family information given by Harold Gross and Molly Matthews. Further research is added from Vernon Clegg, Belfast, to honour the donors of the Pillar of Agriculture and the David window of the Belfast Cathedral (2007). The persistent use of the same names throughout all branches of the family is both a help and hindrance in trying to chase any single one of them, at any given period, and latterly immigration of some in all the descendant families to the new world spread the same names even further.

ity College from 1834 (Irish Bar 1841) and (Cousin) Alexander, aged only 14, entered in 1837, soon after Charles, who was 10 years older than that at his own entrance in 1836. It is believed that Uncle Alexander also contributed financially to his nephew's education in Dublin, and possibly both uncles assisted.

William, a prosperous solicitor, also lived in Carrickfergus, his wife Catherine Goddard having been born there, the daughter of Robert Goddard. William's children included Maria Noy Johns (1828-1916), and much later another Henry Incledon Johns (1860-1924) amongst at least five children (census records are sketchy). H I Johns became a partner in the law firm of Johns, Hewitt, and Johns, Belfast, and succeeded his uncle, Alexander, as a Director of the Belfast Banking Company.

Alexander, especially, kept in close touch with Henry and Maria, and took a keen interest in his nephew and namesake, Charles Alexander, and his ambitions. The brothers were all leading churchmen in the Church of Ireland and the Church of England respectively, taking responsible positions within Diocesan and General Synod activity.

Henry Incledon Johns (1776-1851)
Father of Charles Johns

Henry was born at Helston, Cornwall, the eldest son of Bennett John and his wife Ann Incledon Jenkyn. Much later in the Preface to his *Poems Addressed by a Father to his Children* 1832, Henry described his early life. One of his poems, extracted from the volume above, entitled 'Sonnet on Human Life' is included in Wright's anthology of *West-Country Poets*. He wrote that he was painfully shy as a young man, and enjoyed walking on his own, exploring the beauty of the countryside around the Three Towns[198]: Dock (becoming Devonport), Stonehouse, and Plymouth, the area to which his family had moved from West Cornwall after his earliest years.

He loved to draw and paint and to study the work of artists, and took a few lessons from a local teacher. He read a great deal, especially poetry, but on his father's insistence, he also became a competent mathematician and accepted his father's decision that he should enter the bank. At the age of 17, he was engaged as a junior clerk, working his way reluctantly toward full partnership. Never fully abandoning his creative pursuits, he assisted T H Williams with the research for his book *Picturesque Excursions in Devonshire and Cornwall*, published in 1804.

When he became co-partner in the Dock Bank, also known as Shiells-Johns (Devonport), he suffered great anxiety, finding that the bank was already in difficulty because of the bad feeling between earlier previous partners.[199] Henry found it impossible to be on good terms with Mr Shiells, who dominated the younger man, refusing to speak to him if he disagreed with any course of action. Henry gradually gave up the struggle, although he knew that there were serious faults in the bank's practices; with his growing family, he did not feel bold enough to leave

---

[198]The Three Towns became officially known as Plymouth in 1914.

[199]Previous partners had been Mr J Carpenter and the widow Mrs St Aubyn, who withdrew in 1818. See www.plymouthdata.info (*The Encyclopaedia of Plymouth History*).

his position. He did accept the management of some of the charitable institutions of the town, which he believed to be worthwhile, but he frequently suffered from bouts of depression. Both of his younger brothers in Ireland met with much greater worldly success, and this may have added significantly to his sense of futility, and impending ill health.

The crisis of October 1825 arrived and, as he wrote in his Preface, 'in a few hours, the fabric, which long hours of misapplied toil and anxiety had laboured to sustain, was levelled with the dust!' He lost his social position and many of his group of business associates and acquaintances deserted him. His partner died only a few days after the bank closed, which left Henry alone to deny any criminal responsibility for the bank's failure. Nevertheless, he felt deep regret for the sufferings that his clients and customers experienced. And many of these same sufferings, he was to share.

Maria Incledon Boone Johns (1786-1855)
Mother of Charles Johns

Maria Johns was of strong Cornish stock, and survived 12 pregnancies; nine of the children grew to adulthood. The enormous reversal of fortune for the family in the bank failure of 1825, must also have taken a toll on Maria's outlook on life, perhaps bringing to the fore the same adaptation capability as for her husband, but there is little information about her in family papers. Correspondence within the family records does show high regard for their 'dear mother' and particular concern for her welfare following their father's death in 1851. Always one or more of the children and later their spouses remained with her at home until her death, and all of the family visited with frequency. After her death, the unmarried sisters went to live with their brothers' families, and then later with each other as the family diminished.

The siblings of Charles Johns

1. **Henry Incledon Johns (1804-nk)** Named after his father, Henry was also a teacher from the age of 21, but remained living at home and contributing to the family purse as a school teacher until after his father's death in 1851, when he emigrated to the USA becoming a journalist for a New York newspaper, thought to have been the *New York Herald* (established and edited by the famed James Gordon Bennett Sr.) However, this information remains unsubstantiated.

2. **Maria Johns Jacob (1806-1884)** Her parents' first-born daughter, she was named after her mother. After the change of the family's fortunes in 1825, she assisted her mother in looking after Charles and the younger children, until her marriage to John Jacob (see entry), the Vicar of the church they all attended. From family records, it is clear that John Jacob and Maria moved to London from Stoke Damerel sometime early in the 1840s and Maria took up a career of writing stories for young people, and for journals, magazines, and annuals. There is no doubt that her prolific writing output aided and influenced Charles in his own efforts.

Maria may have been responsible for recruiting Charles Johns to the notice of SPCK, as she also wrote various short stories for the SPCK, as early as 1843: *Mar-*

tha Brown, *The Cottage Bible*, *The Cottage in the Wood*, and *Scripture Quadrupeds*, on the animals mentioned in the Bible. *The Conceited Pig* (1851- John & Chas Mozley) was another publication. She is thought to have been the Editor/Author (anonymous) of *The Ladies Almanack* for some period of time. The family holds two copies (1851, and 1853), which are described rather like '*Mrs Beeton's Book of Household Management*, i.e., full of useful facts and hints/recipes/etc. but also giving a calendar for the year with a wealth of historical dates and anniversaries.' Inscribed to her sister, Jane, 'from the authoress,' it was a publication of *The Ladies Newspaper* (part of the Cooke-Ingram empire of related acquisitions contributing to *The Illustrated London News*.)[200] Other publications were *Days, Months and Seasons of the Year, explained to the little people of England* (1853) by Maria Jacob[201], authoress of *Prince Arthur's Alphabet* (c1850), *Wonders of the Sea-shore*, all published by Nathaniel Cooke in the series 'Flowers From the Garden of Knowledge.' Hugely successful was her *Illustrated London Spelling Book* (originally published by W S Johnson), with 'upwards of half a million sold.' The dating of this book is inexact, but the hundredth thousand copy was published in the year 1854, a tattered copy of which is in our Johns Archive. In 1871 she was admitted to Salisbury Matron's College as widow of Reverend Jacob and at her death, ten years after Charles, she was buried in the Salisbury Cathedral Cloister, aged 79.

3. **Elizabeth Johns (1808)** died in infancy.

4. **Sophia Johns (1809-1819)** died at 10 years old, cause unknown.

5. **Charles Alexander Johns (1811-1874)** The subject of this monograph.

6. **Emily Heywood Johns Carrington (1814-1890)** Emily married Henry Carrington in 1841, becoming the mother of a large and illustrious family, and the keeper of the family memories through the making of scrapbooks and the filing of records. In her own right, she was a talented artist, a considerable poet, and latterly also a teacher. See the following entry in 'illustrators.' The couple began married life in Lyncombe & Widcombe, Bath, later moving to Swainswick Lodge, Lansdown. After her husband's death (1859, see Henry Carrington), Emily was left an exceptionally wealthy woman, but with an immensely large family to support. Her two eldest sons were at Cambridge and Oxford respectively, one to follow in his father's footsteps as a journalist, and the other to become an educator. At least two became clergymen. Her sister Anne remained beside her to help with the younger children. Emily was the grandmother of Molly Carrington Matthews (1908-2008), the author and historian to whom this book is dedicated. Emily opened a school at Walcot St Swithins, with the assistance of one of her sons and Anne. In latter years she retired to Rock House, Alphington, Exeter. At her death in Bedminster, where she was staying with her daughter Edith, her wealth had dwindled to £111, the modern day equivalent of approximately £49,000. Her published poetry, signed as EHC, appears in at least two of Johns's books, *Monthly Wild Flowers*, and *Monthly*

---

[200]See 'The Early History of The Illustrated London News,' The World's First Illustrated Newspaper On-line: www.iln.org.uk, which also features an excellent summary of the engraver's art.

[201]Republished recently (2007-8, but undated) by Kessinger Publishing's Rare Reprints. [www.kessinger.net]

Gleanings (both published c1860). No separately listed publications are in British Library Catalogues, though family information indicates that her poems were published with frequency in newspapers and journals.

7. **Julia Johns (1816-1900)** Julia is the daughter who remained at home through thick and thin, caring for her father, and then her mother, while also helping to bring up her younger brothers and sisters. She and Emily, both talented artists, worked as teachers of drawing and took commissions for artwork, also painting and illustrating in pen-and-ink for Charles's publications. After her parents had both died, Julia joined Charles and his family in Chipperfield, and continued with them at Winton House, Winchester. One of signed contributions to Charles Johns's books is identified as the joint working (with W Dickes) on the illustrations for *Monthly Gleanings from the Field and Garden* (nd, c1860), where the signature to the left side of the floral arrangements pictured is consistently 'J Johns del' ['she/he drew it']. After Charles's death she joined her older sister, Maria Jacobs, to live at the Liberty of the Close, Salisbury Cathedral, qualified to gain entrance as the sister of a clergyman (Charles) and also sister of a widow of the clergy. When Maria died in 1884, Anne joined Julia and they were admitted to No. 2, St Paul's Homes at Fisherton Anger, now a part of Salisbury city, where she died.

8. **Bennett Johns (1819)** died in infancy.

9. **Bennett George Johns (1820-1900)** Later, The Reverend. Family records relate that he met his wife-to-be, Delphina Sophia Hepburn, at the Flora Dance in Helston, Cornwall (1847), during Charles's last year as Headmaster at the Grammar School. Bennett, following Charles's example, had attended Dublin University, gaining a Master of Arts degree. While training as a priest, he was strongly influenced by the High Church movement and felt called to become a celibate. Seeking to retreat from worldly London where he was living as a curate and working as head of practice schools at St Mark's College, he travelled to Cornwall to stay with his brother and spend time in meditation. The family story, recorded by Emily's grandson, Philip Carrington, later Archbishop of Canada, continues: '...But he had forgotten the Helston Furry, the prehistoric folk dance on May 8th... He found himself linked with a "wild Scotch girl," Delphina Hepburn (a "mad Hebburn" – for so it was pronounced) and within a week they were married.'[202]

By 1851, Bennett Johns was lecturing at King's College, London, and the following year, he was appointed chaplain, secretary, and treasurer to the London

---

[202]Here family legend somehow leads away from the truth because their marriage certificate records that Bennett George Johns, bachelor and clerk in orders, residing at St Giles, Camberwell, married Delphina Sophia Hepburn, spinster of St Pancras, on the 7 September 1848. However, there is no doubt that they fell in love on Flora Day and perhaps became betrothed very soon after. Charles must have been surprised at the magical effect of Helston's special day. 'Dellie,' as she was known in the family was born in Jersey, Channel Islands in 1825/6 and died in Southwark in the autumn of 1870. There is no basis, as yet found, for the suggestion of a Scottish link; this is a similar charge as that made about the Irish Mrs Julia (Burk) Field.

School for the Blind, a post which he held for 32 years. True to the literary tradition of the Johns Family, he wrote and published several well-reviewed books including: *The Elements of Geography* (1851), *A Short & Simple History of England* (1851) *Sermons to the Blind*, and *Blind People: Their Works and Ways* (1867). The latter book, as well as *Outlines of Roman History* and *The Book of Poetry*, are available as reprints from www.kessinger.net, like one of Maria's and two of Charles Johns's. He was a frequent contributor to periodicals ('By the Seashore; or, A Few Words on Seaweeds' *Boys Own Paper*, v 6, #283, 1884, being one example) and for forty years he reviewed books for *The Morning Post*...he had many friends in London among whom were the bishops, canons, and dean of St Paul's Cathedral. He belonged to the Savage Club and the Authors' Club. He was on the Royal Commission for the Blind, and was often invited to civic dinners. A fine preacher, he put church work first in his life. In appearance he was very like Lord Tennyson, for whom he was mistaken on two occasions...A very handsome man, he was a distinctive figure in a crowd, with his blue eyes and black hair...Friends dropped in, various authors and artists, Charles Dickens among them. There was reading aloud every evening and music quartettes. He had a lovely tenor voice...' (Words of Bennett's daughter, Dellie, as reported in Philip Carrington's family memoirs)

10. **Jane Johns (1822-1911)** Jane, two years younger than Bennett, had travelled up from Plymouth to London, representing her parents at her brother Bennett's wedding in 1848, and joining other family members there. She was close to Bennett and later was to live with him, Dellie and their family. In 1881 Jane and Anne lived together at Partis College in the Batheaston section of Bath where Jane was supported on an annuity given by the clergy family at Broad Clyst, Devon for whom she acted as governess. Anne, described only as a 'gentlewoman,' lived with her on her own means. This was the period when together they ran a small school, with their widowed sister Emily.

11. **Anne Johns (1827-1901)** At the age of 14, Anne went to live with her sister Emily and her husband, Henry Carrington, near Bath from the time of the birth of their first child. This arrangement alleviated expense for the Johns family in Plymouth, and also meant that she could help her sister (who was 13 years her senior) in bringing up the many Carrington children who would arrive. Later she assisted in running the small school in Bath with Emily and Jane. In the production of *Monthly Gleanings from the Field and Garden*, it is believed that Anne Johns was responsible for the drawings incorporated in the floral frames (worked with W Dickes) facing the poems of her sister, Emily (EHC).

12. **John Jacob Johns (1829-nk)** Known as 'Jack,' and named for his brother-in-law, Dr John Jacob. His first employment was as a bank clerk in Plymouth, but after his mother's death he left Plymouth to work as a Cashier to a Railway Company, lodging meantime in Chester, Cheshire. In March 1862, at the age of 32, he sailed from Liverpool on the *City of New York* to join his brother in the newspaper trade in America.

The children of The Rev Charles A and Ellen J Johns

In Ellen's rather sad, short will, written in 1890, many years after Charles's death, she leaves half her books and music to Henry, and her clothes and jewellery to 'my daughter Anne Catherine Lloyd,' and to each of the three children she leaves £50 '(if possible).' She stated: 'My affairs at this date are so entangled and embarrassed that I cannot see my way to apportioning any more money to my elder children, who have, in fact, by their past actions, reduced me to my present state of poverty.' The rest of her possessions she leaves to 'my beloved and ever dutiful and loving son, Edward Francis Johns.' She lived on until 1895, remaining there with her son Frank until her death at Winton House.

Perhaps some light on Ellen's cryptic references can be shown in the brief biographical summaries that follow. Charles must have expected that Henry would take over the running of Winton House after his death, with Katie remaining there for at least a short period, before her husband's curacy would take them elsewhere. In fact, it appears clear that both of the older children moved in separate directions, perfectly worthy in their own terms, but less likely to have gained their mother's approval. And it was young Frank who was prepared to take up his father's work.

1. **Charles Henry Johns aka Henry (1844-1915)** Henry was the eldest child, born in Helston, Cornwall, on 13 October 1844, in the year following Johns's return as Headmaster to Helston Grammar School. His early schooling was with his parents and his grandmother, Julia Field at Chelsea (*1851 Census*), and later at their school, Callipers Hall in Hertfordshire. However, to widen the breadth of his lessons in a different environment he was sent to Rugby at age 16, under the headmaster, Charles A Anstey before matriculating at Oriel College, Oxford in 1863, though there is no extant record of a degree taken. He became a Fellow of the Royal Astronomical Society. Working under his father thereafter as an Assistant Master, he taught mathematics, natural sciences, and astronomy. A strong avocation was music, inherited perhaps from his mother and her musical antecedents in Bath, and shared with his younger brother Frank. In records of the Hampshire Scientific Society, he is referred to as Henry Johns, B A, but it is not known where and when he completed a degree.

Unknown also is the reason why Henry made his decision to leave Winton House, after his father's death, as he would have been the probable choice as a future Head. According to the report of the Winchester Scientific and Literary Society by 1879, Henry had moved on from Winton House to teach in Biggleswade. Another headmaster was appointed.[203] In 1881, he was teaching in Broadwater, Sussex, and living in lodgings in nearby Worthing.

In 1886, at the age of 42, Henry married Mary Emily Chalk (b 1837), the co-proprietress with her sister Ellen Chalk, of the Althorpe House Seminary for young ladies in Lydney, Gloucestershire, which their widowed mother, Mary, had established in the late 1860s. Mary Emily, born in Batheaston, Somerset, had been a governess previously, and both of the sisters were schoolmistresses. Together, the sisters and Henry moved their school to Waverley Grove, Hendon (part of Barnet, and now a London borough). Henry was then teaching science, maths, and music, and his wife teaching general studies along with administration. Upon or before her

---

[203]W F Rawnsley is listed as Head at Winton House in the *1884 Winchester Directory*.

sister's death in 1898, the couple moved to Folkestone, Kent, where Henry and his wife continued teaching. His death is registered at Sevenoaks, Kent, at the age of 71. There were no children.

His only known publication, other than notes in the *HSS Newsletter* is the 90-page Appendix on 'Grasses' which was added to his father's most famous publication, *Flowers of the Field* in 1892 (28th edition).

Notes: British Library Cat; D E Allen: HSS records; Census 1851-1901

2. **Anne Catherine Johns aka Katie (1846-1903)** Katie was born in Helston, Cornwall, in September 1847, but stayed only a few months. The family moved on to live at Beenham, Berkshire, her schooling at home with her parents from that time. Her mother's experience as a governess to the Evans family of Derbyshire will have prepared her well for teaching her children at home. (See entries amongst 'illustrators' following for a brief summary of Katie's contribution to Johns's books, and other magazines and journals.) The Autograph Collection confirms in its various replies that Katie regularly worked on her art and illustration, and put forward illustrated stories to magazines of the time.

The year before her father's death she married a Portsmouth naval curate (RN), John Henry Lloyd (b1846) who was the son of the Vicar of Aldham, Suffolk. Lloyd was made deacon in 1871 and ordained priest in 1872, having served as a curate of St Michael's, Lichfield. In 1874, he became a Chaplain in the Royal Navy, serving on *HMS St Vincent* at Portsmouth, Katie remaining at home.

By 1881, the couple had moved to Wormleighton, Warwickshire, where he was the Curate-in-Charge. The living there had been given to William Harrison in 1878, the husband of Mary St Leger Kingsley, who would later become rector of Clovelly, Devon. It is believed that the Lloyds, through friendship links, had taken over the day-to-day parish work in Warwickshire, while looking for a more permanent living of their own. By 1889, Lloyd was made Vicar of Fotheringhay, Northamptonshire, but it appears he and Katie had parted by that time.

From 1889-90 she had become Matron in Charge of Mrs Annie Besant's residential women's home and Working Women's Club set up that year to aid the 'match girls' following their successful strike in 1888 against Bryant and May. Located at 193 Bow Road, across the street from Bow Church, Tower Hamlets, this well-built and well-fitted home, with library and meeting rooms became the Working Women's Club of the East End of London.

Besant calls her Mrs Kitty Lloyd, and found in her 'a devoted Theosophist' who worked herself to exhaustion, managing the feeding of up to 150 working poor each day. After four years, her health (always a problem due to a weak heart) broke down under the strain of the work and failing financial support for the project. The Club was closed and sold and Katie/Kitty was sent first to Ceylon and then to Benares, where she ended her days as the much-loved Matron of the Central Hindu College Boarding House, sharing a home with Mrs Besant and other teachers.

Her obituary notes that 'She had a genius for dealing with boys, and they became at home with her at once as did all young people...daily some came to her to read English.' Mrs Besant and many other revered scholars, teachers and pupils attended her funeral pyre on the same evening of her death, and her ashes were scattered on the Ganges. She was a known contributor of historical and religious articles to a number of journals and newsletters, as both a writer and an illustrator.

Notes: Census; Dr Charlotte Mitchell (UCL); J Courtney [in] Nelson & Vallone; Nethercot (1960) *The First Five Lives of Annie Besant;* Dr Joy Dixon (2003); Central Archives of the Theosophical Society of India, Adyar; *The Theosophist,* 1890-4 intermittent notices of the Working Women's Club-Bow, 1901: Benares, 'Lecture on the Royal Library of Nineveh,' *Theosophical Review Magazine;* 1903: Obituary.

3. **Frederick William (1858)** Died in infancy.

4. **Frank (Edward Francis) (1861-1948)** Referred to later as Dr Johns. Frank Johns was certainly the ideal successor to his father at Winton House. Following Charles's death, Ellen moved temporarily to Bradfield near their old home at Beenham, to make a home for Frank while he was attending Bradfield College, prior to entering Oxford. He had left Harrow to complete his preparations for entering Oxford, where he gained a classical exhibition to Exeter College, and was Abbott scholar a year later. A violinist of talent, he also became President of the University Musical Club, and returned to Winton House with an MA, becoming Headmaster in 1887.

Accounts from past pupils at the school show that his father's delight in the study of nature was continued, as well as his belief that 'the most important part of a boy's education is the development of his character, and this depends more upon out of school activities than upon the work done in Form.' Frank was a keen lepidopterist and encouraged his pupils to join his field trips and add to his collection of butterflies. 'A fine way to disappear into the blue yonder...'wrote one later pupil (A R White 1932-39). Frank inherited his father's comprehensive enthusiasm for exploring and recording the natural world, which he passed on to future generations of pupils, who held him in high regard. Well after his mother's death, he married in 1910 the Hon Violet Mary Marsham (b 1872, daughter of the Rev John Marsham, a son of the 3rd Earl of Romney) and there were no children. In the *1901 Census* she appears as a Visitor at Winton House, Winchester and is stated to be a Hospital Sick Nurse.

Prior to the 1937 publication by Margaret Thorp of her book on Charles Kingsley, Edward made letters available to her from the Kingsleys to his parents. As yet, the whereabouts of these personal letters is not known. Just months before his death as reviewed in the *Hampshire Observer* (20 March 1948) he published a booklet entitled *"Let the Twig Follow Its Bent": Recalling Charles Kingsley.* He died on 23 September 1948 and was buried in West Hill cemetery, Winchester, his name carved on the Celtic Cross above those of his parents. Winton House, evacuated during the Second World War, combined with another prep school becoming Dunchurch Winton Hall and was re-located to Warwickshire, near Rugby. This school finally closed in 1993.

Notes: Census; family information; Thorp; HRO: Winton House records.

The Kingsley family

Charles Kingsley (1819-1875)
Friend, clergyman, novelist and social reformer

A friendship that began in Helston and increased during the rest of Charles Johns's life was with Charles Kingsley, his mother and father (The Rev Charles Kingsley Sr) and family and later, his wife Fanny (née Grenfell) and their children. Two pupils who joined the Helston school in 1833 when Charles Johns was Second Master were Charles and Herbert Kingsley. Their father, the Reverend Charles Kingsley, Vicar of Clovelly, had provided a private tutor for his sons until, in 1831, they were sent to a preparatory school in Clifton, Bristol.[204] The Headmaster, the Reverend John Knight, there described the boy Charles Kingsley (junior) as 'affectionate, gentle and fond of quiet,' and as 'a passionate lover of natural history.'[205]

His stutter must at times have caused his shyness and made his parents take extra care over their choice of the next school for the boys. Despite talk of Eton and Rugby, Emily Trevenen[206] of Helston, a friend of the Kingsleys as well as of the Coleridges, recommended Helston Grammar School as a place where pupils were given a certain freedom to follow their own interests as well as receiving an excellent classical education. Derwent Coleridge had a strong dislike of systematising or organising education. 'To build up the intellectual man is the purpose of education,' he believed;[207] first the memory was to be strengthened and then judgement developed, and boys were to search out the meanings of words for themselves, not just be told them. These ideas were to influence Charles Johns strongly in his future as a Headmaster. They also suited young Charles Kingsley, who had already begun writing poems and poetic prose. By 1833, he and Herbert had joined the other boarders in Coleridge's household.[208]

The other siblings of Charles Kingsley (1819-1875) were as follows: Herbert (1820-34) died at Helston; Gerald (1821-44) died in naval accident; Louisa Mary (1823-4) died in infancy; George Henry (1826-92); Charlotte (Mrs John Mill Chanter, 1828-82) and Henry (1830-76). In all there were seven children, though

---

[204]A third son, Henry Kingsley (1830-76) was not yet old enough for schooling, though Charles Johns met him at home with his family. Henry would become a novelist of greater achievement, in some ways, than Charles Kingsley was destined to be, however he remained overshadowed by CK throughout his life.

[205]*Charles Kingsley: His Letters and Memories of his Life,* edited by his wife (1877), 2nd ed, vol 1, p 20. London: Henry S King & Co.

[206]'Emily Trevenen 1786-1856 and Her Influence on Education in Helston,' Appendix A by Ann Trevenen Jenkin, pp 137-145 (with portrait) in Dare (1996) *The Unknown Founder, The Story of Helston Grammar School.* See entry in Appendix ii.

[207]Hainton, *op cit,* p 145

[208]According to Kingsley's schoolfriend, Richard Cowley Powles, 'For all his good qualities, Charles [K] was not popular as a schoolboy. He knew too much and his mind was generally on a higher level than ours.' (*Kingsley Letters,* p 25). However, Kingsley and Powles were to develop a lasting friendship that began at Helston School.

the *Dictionary of National Biography* indicates five only, and several sources have confused dates, according to R B Martin (p 21), because of early errors made in a preface by Mary Kingsley (about her father, Gerald). Charles Johns was known to, and familiar with all of these except Louisa Mary. And in future years, the children of both Charles Kingsley and Charles Johns were to know each other intimately. In the Preface to *Charles Kingsley (1819-1875)*, published in 1937 by the Princeton University Press, the publication of the PhD dissertation of Margaret Farrand Thorp, the distinguished critic and journalist, she mentions the 'interesting collection of letters' written to Charles and Ellen Johns by Mr and Mrs Kingsley, that was put at her disposal by Edward F Johns. On p 106 (1969 edition, Octagon Books) Thorp reprints one of these letters, as an example: 'Kingsley and Johns were close friends all their lives and the letters they exchanged about Grenville might serve as models for parent-teacher correspondence.'

Later, while living at Beenham the Johns family lived near the Kingsleys at Eversley and visited with frequency. It is around this time that Kingsley revived his own long-time interest in natural history prior to becoming Regius Professor of Modern History at Cambridge in 1860 deciding that he would like to be, as Johns had been for so long, a member of the Linnean Society, with FLS after his name. Johns's bird books were of particular interest and delight to Kingsley aside from *Flowers of the Field* that Kingsley used for botanical instruction classes for youths in Chester.

Notes: See bibliography for books consulted about Charles Kingsley and his family.

Francis (Fanny) Eliza Grenfell Kingsley (1814-1891)
(Mrs Charles Kingsley)

Fanny's full name was Francis Eliza Grenfell and she was a member of the well-established and widely connected Cornish family of Grenfells. She was the daughter of Pascoe Grenfell, MP (1761-1838), son of Pascoe Grenfell of Marazion and his wife Mary Tremenheere, and his second wife Georgiana St Leger (d 1818). The Grenfell family inter-married with several great families of Cornwall and of Britain, one sister, Charlotte, married (unhappily) to the famed historian and scholar, James Anthony Froude (author of the *Nemesis of Faith*), Emily to Lord Sydney Godolphin Osborne, Caroline to J A Warre, Henrietta to Robert Myrtens Bird and yet another, Marianne, to Baron Wolverton. Fanny was a contemporary and friend of Emily Borlase Bolitho of Penzance and the niece of Lydia Grenfell (1775-1829) of Marazi-

on, Cornwall, the subject of a prize-winning biography by Barbara Eaton (2005) *Letters to Lydia 'beloved Persis'* published by Hypatia Publications previously. Fanny first met Charles Kingsley in 1839, marrying finally despite family opposition in May 1844, before moving to his curacy, which became his living in Eversley, Hampshire. Fanny's niece, Georgina Grenfell, later married Professor Max Müller, Taylorian Professor of Modern European Languages at Cambridge, and close friend to Charles Kingsley. Fanny added several letters and signatures to the Johns Autograph Collection between approximately 1866-1870, with some undated.

Notes: Bolitho; Chitty; Eaton; Kingsley (*Letters & Memories*); Autograph Collection

Mary St Leger Kingsley (1852-1931)
Later Mary Harrison, aka Lucas Malet

The daughter of Charles Kingsley and his wife Frances, who married the Reverend William Harrison, her father's curate and assistant at Eversley in 1876. Rose, Maurice, Mary St Leger and Katie Johns and her siblings became acquainted through the close friendship of their parents. Harrison's presence in Eversley from 1869 allowed Kingsley to take up a Canon's position at Chester, and to travel extensively in America and Europe. From 1878-83, after Charles Johns's death, Harrison served as the Vicar at Wormleighton, with the Reverend John Henry Lloyd (see Katie Johns) acting as his Curate-in-Charge.

Harrison and Mary St Leger moved on in 1883 to the living at Clovelly, Devon (in the gift of the Lord of Clovelly Manor), where Charles Kingsley Sr had been the Vicar many years before. The *nom de plume* of Lucas Malet, was a combination of family names, Lucas being 'the maiden name of my father's mother and Miss Malet her aunt, hence her father's great aunt,' and probably chosen to avoid connection with her father's famous reputation. Her first novel was *Mrs. Lorimer: A Sketch in Black and White* (1882), centred on illness, self-sacrifice (of the heroine), rebellion and death, and foreshadows much of the frustration and distress that appeared not only in her future work, but also in her life. The couple separated finally in 1891, Harrison dying in Brighton in 1897 of tuberculosis. Her better-known novels are *The Far Horizon* (Gutenberg on-line text) and *The History of Sir Richard Calmady*. Her photograph together with Katie Johns is found in this book.

Notes: Chitty; Lundberg; HRO

John William Parker (1792-1870)

Having turned around the fortunes of the Cambridge University Press while in the employe of the London printer William Clowes, John Parker set up for himself as a publisher at 445 Strand, London in 1832. Immediately he was chosen to be an official publisher of the Society for Promoting Christian Knowledge (SPCK). In that capacity he also instituted the *Saturday Magazine*, a penny-per-copy journal aimed at the poorer classes. By the time his son, also John William Parker (1820-1860) after his Cambridge degree, had joined the firm alongside his brother Frederick, the elder Parker had already published two of Johns's works, the *Flora Sacra* and *Short Sermons for Children*. Thereafter, and for the rest of its existence, as a 'bastion of liberal Christianity and eventually of Christian socialism' (DR Dean, *DNB*), J W Parker & Son were not only to publish for SPCK, but for an impressive array of the intelligentsia of the time, John Stuart Mill, F D Maurice, Sir Arthur Helps, and Charles Kingsley (*Hypatia* and *Yeast*), Carlyle, Ruskin and Tennyson.

Johns's work fitted well into the framework set up by Parker to make available books to lower-income households, and to inexpensive editions for children and their teachers, and all of Johns's major works were published for the SPCK. In 1863 the Parker firm was bought by Longmans, and correspondence within the Johns Autograph Collection indicates that their publishing relationship continued thereafter. Printing strip-lines are the following: John W Parker (London: 1832-1843) also signed J Parker, Strand; John W Parker and Sons (London: 1843-1848); John W Parker and Son (London: 1848-1860) and Parker, Son, and Bourn (London: 1860-1863).

Notes: Dean [in] Anderson & Rose; *DNB*; Victor; Autograph Collection

Richard Cowley Powles (1820-1901)

Another pupil of Charles Johns at Helston, who became the school chum of Charles Kingsley's, and his 'earliest friend' (CK, *Letters*, page 7 for a lengthy and much quoted description of CK as a youth). Powles was to become a Fellow of Exeter College, Oxford, but was forced to give up his Fellowship due to marriage. In 1850 he purchased 9 Eliot Place, Blackheath, on the outskirts of London, from the Rev George Brown Francis Potticary who had been running a school there since 1831.

An inspired teacher and person of great character as well, Powles, also an Anglican clergyman, developed the school into a flourishing establishment, remaining there until 1865 when he moved to become Headmaster of St Neot's Preparatory School, Eversley. Powles at Eversley, like Johns at Winton, also received Kingsley's son, Maurice, as a pupil and with his cricket eleven from Wixenford-Eversley, features in scrapbook photographs held in the Hampshire Records Office, about school life at Winchester. Hence the educational and friendly connections between Johns and Powles continued throughout their lives from the time they met as teacher and pupil at Helston. Surviving by a quarter of a century both of his Helston friends, Kingsley and Johns, Powles died at Chichester, Sussex.

Notes: Hainton; Kingsley; HRO

Cornwall Simeon (1820-1880)

A good friend of Charles Johns in Winchester, Cornwall Simeon was a solicitor with a great interest in natural history. By the time that Johns had opened Winton House, Simeon had already written and published *Stray Notes on Fishing & Natural History*, published by Macmillan, Cambridge in 1860. The third son of Sir Richard Godin Simeon (2nd Bart) of St John's, Isle of Wight, he had been a barrister-at-law in Lincoln's Inn (1845) after Christ Church, Oxford. As part of the Canterbury Association, from 1851, he supported the establishment of a Church of England colony in Lyttelton, New Zealand, by purchasing land in the Christchurch district, and lived there for a brief time. Returning to England, he married Mary Evans in 1861, settling in Winchester. Much later, his fourth son, like Johns's nephew Charles Carrington, was to serve amongst the clergy back in New Zealand. Simeon's grandfather was Sir John Simeon (1st Bart) and his uncle the Rev Charles Simeon, the famed evangelical cleric. Cornwall Simeon abandoned private legal practice, to become the County Treasurer for Hampshire, and was a member of the Hampshire Literary & Scientific Society with Johns. In 1873, Simeon accompanied Charles, son Henry, Berthon (see entry) on the walking tour of Cornwall, to update material for the third edition of *A Week at the Lizard*.

Elizabeth Andrew Warren (1786-1864)
Friend of Charles A. Johns and Emily Stackhouse

The following is a short excerpt from the 'Memorial of Miss Warren of Flushing, Cornwall,' a close friend and possibly a distant relation of the Johns family (*RCPS Annual Report* 1864, pp 11-14), as rendered by Isabella Gifford. Emily Stackhouse also wrote an obituary for Miss Warren in the *Journal of the Royal Institution of Cornwall* (RIC), Oct. 1865, p xviii.

> 'The late Miss Warren of Flushing, was a zealous member of the Polytechnic Society [later RCPS] from its very commencement, and an ardent follower of the science of botany....Miss Warren...explored the shores of her native county, and, in so doing, discovered a fine species – *Kallymenia Dubyi* – until then, unknown on the English shores. In the Society's Report for 1849, she published a full list of all the marine algae found by her on the Falmouth shores previous to that year, with remarks on their variety, &c. Her name will survive, in connection with these plants, in the *Schizosiphon Warreniae*, a small alga, discovered on rocks at Maenporth, near Falmouth, by Dr Caspary, and named by him in her honour....The Botanical Chart, which she published for the use of schools, and dedicated to Sir William Hooker, contains as great an amount of information respecting the properties of the different classes of plants, as could possibly be condensed into a publication of that nature.'

Later this was plagiarized without reference by Frederick Hanham MBCSL, Bath, 1846, and meant to be considered as his own, as referenced by Gifford.] Johns would have used this chart at Helston Grammar School, and served with Elizabeth Warren on judging exhibitions at the RCPS. They were both correspondents of Sir William Hooker over many years.

Notes: Davey (*Flora of Cornwall*); Desmond; RCPS; RIC; Autograph Collection (Wm Hooker letter)

Illustrators of Johns's works

Emily Heywood (Johns) Carrington & Julia Johns
[See entry in family, Charles's sisters]

The closest to Charles in age, and with Julia, the closest of friends as children and then throughout their lives, both sisters inherited and developed the family's literary and artistic skills. It was to these skills that the whole of the family turned for financial support when their father became progressively ill, and Emily took over Henry's tutoring of private pupils, and drew and painted from home, as a source of income. Charles, knowing that he had 'the finest of sisters' keeping the family together, could always rely on Emily to be able to draw the plants that he found and brought home from earliest times throughout his writing career. Imogen Thomas, g-great niece of

Charles, wrote (2007) 'My mother was told by her father [Charles Walter Johns, godson to Johns] that his mother, Emily, had done many of the illustrations for *Flowers of the Field*. My mother always understood that the unsigned ones were her work. She was a very competent artist as well as a frequently published poet.'

Of the 507 line drawings in *Flowers of the Field*, 165 are signed ES [Emily Stackhouse], 310 are unattributed, and the remaining 33 have a variety of initials. Many of the unattributed drawings would undoubtedly have been executed by Emily and Julia. Emily also contributed 12 of her poems to Charles's 1860 collation, *Monthly Wild Flowers* (See Dickes and Bibliography). In *Monthly Gleanings from the Field and Garden*, 24 of her poems, half on wildflowers and half on garden flowers are also seen. In these little books the drawings of the seasonal bouquets of wild and garden flowers are drawn by Julia.

William Dickes (1815-1892)

Dickes was apprenticed first to wood engraver Robert Branston and then attended the Royal Academy Schools, winning a number of prizes. He engraved on wood and copper before beginning as a colour printer in 1849. A prolific printer, he worked extensively for the SPCK, and a wide range of journals. His early (1840) major commission to illustrate W. H. Lizars *Naturalist's Library*, and later Charles Kingsley's *Glaucus, or The Wonders of the Shore*, for which he did the Frontispiece and 12 coloured plates, made him the obvious choice of illustrator for cards and other small books produced later in Charles Johns's writing career. These would have been commissioned not by Charles Johns directly but by the SPCK on contract with him. His inscription appears on all the floral frames employed for *Monthly Wild Flowers*, and the following monthly collations that Johns wrote together with his sister Emily Heywood Carrington.

Elizabeth Noel Gwatkin (1846-1941)

Miss Gwatkin's illustrations for *Flowers of the Field* were first employed posthumously for Johns's work, and Routledge commissioned them from the 1907 edition forward until 1949, when the book went out of print. She dedicated her immense quantity of work for this book to the memory of 'James Thomas Gwatkin, her father, who for many years was a member of the Brighton Natural History Society, once its president, and for some years its Honorary Librarian' [her words]. She died in Headley, Hampshire, at the age of 96.

Anne Catherine (Katie) Johns
[See entry in family, Charles's daughter]

For Katie, as for many well-educated and middle-class women, the 'age of the New Woman' was upon them, a time when it became incumbent upon them to consider employment and supporting themselves. Katie, it seems, was interested in education, art and latterly converted to theosophy, through which she became a teacher. The novelist Charlotte Mary Yonge, a friend of the Johns family and cousin of the Coleridge family, formed the Gosling Society (1859-1877)[209] to encourage young

---

[209] *'Charlotte Yonge: The Goslings 1859-1877*, Charlotte Yonge's essay society

women to read and write essays. Primarily this was an exercise in early women's education, and the members came from the narrow social circle of clergy and gentry families, mostly spread out in rural areas isolated from London. At any particular time there appears to have been ten or so members, each identified by the name of a bird. Often the girls were related to one another, and the membership fluctuated naturally. Katie (Kittiwake) helped with the circulation of group's magazine, *The Barnacle*, and was valued highly for her artistic ability. Julia Courtney comments about Katie's work: 'Kittiwake's skill as an illustrator surpassed that of any other contributor; her miniature watercolours reach a professional standard. Their deep, rich colouring is particularly striking. There are also pen-and-ink sketches, including one of "the young artist" herself at work, the only contemporary portrait of an individual Gosling. She is wearing a flat hat, snood, and full-skirted dress ending just above the ankle, and she looks about sixteen (or eighteen at most).'[210]

Of particular relevance to Charles Johns's books are her illustrations employed for *Home Walks and Holiday Rambles* (1863). It is also known from reference to the Johns's Autograph Collection (see Appendix v), that she was responsible for some of the first edition illustrations to Charles Kingsley's *Madam How and Lady Why* (1868-9, published first in *Good Words for young people*), in both serial and book formats. It is clear that she kept up her drawing throughout life, and provided a drawing of Mrs Besant's new meeting room at Blavatsky Lodge, to the national newspapers in 1890.

Notes: Courtney [in] Nelson & Vallone; correspondence (2007): Dr C Mitchell, UCL; A H Nethercoat; Autograph Collection letters

Samuel Read (ca 1819-1883)

Born at Needham Market, near Ipswich, he was apprenticed in the office of an architect. In 1841 he came to London and drew on wood with Mr Whymper. This apprenticeship connected him with the *Illustrated London News*, by 1844 when he also illustrated *Zoological Studies* for the SPCK. These connections made him an obvious choice as another illustrator for the works of Charles Johns. He studied watercolour painting with W C Smith and became an accomplished painter (elected OWS, 1880). With that newspaper for more than forty years, he was the first special artist sent abroad by such a journal, going in 1853 to Constantinople, just prior to the outbreak of the Crimean War. In 1857 he was elected an associate and in 1880 a full member of the Old Water-Colour Society. His specialisation was the drawing of interiors and exteriors of churches and cathedrals. He died at Sidmouth.

Notes: Dictionary of Painters and Engravers, Biographical and Critical by Michael Bry-

---

for teenage girls and young women': www.dur.ac.uk/c.e.schultze/context/goslings. html. with direct contact to Dr Charlotte Mitchell, Department of English, University College, London. See also Julia Courtney's essay, n 156.

[210]Julia Courtney (1994) 'The Barnacle: A Manuscript Magazine of the 1860s' [in] *The Girl's Own, Cultural Histories of the Anglo-American Girl, 1830-1915* edited by Claudia Nelson and Lynne Vallone. Footnote 12, p 97.

an, edited by Robert Edmund Graves and Sir Walter Armstrong, Vol II: L-Z 1899)

Emily Stackhouse (1811-1870)

Her watercolours were employed by the engravers to work the fine woodcuts and steel engravings that SPCK used for Charles Johns's publications. (See the appended memoir for a reprint of Clifford Evans's article written for and published by *Country Life*, July 6, 1995.) A few of her coloured plates are reproduced in *Gertrude Jekyll, the Making of a Garden, An Anthology* compiled by Cherry Lewis (New Edition, 2000), for which gratitude is also expressed to Clifford Evans. (See bibliographic sources for details of the publications.) An entry for Emily Stackhouse in the *Dictionary of National Biography* has been contributed by M Hardie and will appear in 2008.

Josiah Wood Whimper (1813-1903)
aka Whymper from 1840

Born in Ipswich, Suffolk, Whimper began work as a stonemason. However, his abiding interest and skill was in wood engraving, and he, with his apprentices, family members and employees, worked for the SPCK from at least 1846, if not earlier, a major work being the *Phenomena of Nature*. At least two of his wood engravings, including the frontispiece, feature in Johns's first popular work, *Botanical Rambles*, and increased in quantity throughout the publishing career of the author. Whimper established a firm of engravers in the 1830s in Lambeth and within 20 years was employing 20 people, amongst whom were others of his immediate family and relations. A namesake (b1834) was a watercolourist of note with a wife who also took up wood engraving. Both Whimper and Whymper are used in credit lines and also in the census records, and serve on illustrations to differentiate his early work (up to 1840) from his later, due to his adoption of what he considered to be the original spelling of his name.[211] His talents were especially suited to the subjects that Charles Johns chose to write about, his vignettes almost always including men and women about their work, within the context of nature – both animal and plant life. His classic portrayal of Johns's rather calamitous climb at Kynance, in a *Week at the Lizard*, is included in the text.

Joseph Wolff (1820-1899)
(also found written as Wolf)

Considered today to be the finest wildlife illustrator and painter of the Victorian era, Joseph Wolff arrived in London from his native Germany in 1848 to work at London's Natural History Museum (then part of the British Museum). He was already an acknowledged illustrator, having worked for Germany's leading bird experts. His style, unlike that of his contemporaries, was to paint wild creatures in their natural setting, allowing them the expression of their behaviours and lives, making his own art in painting and illustration unique. He received many outstanding commissions, collaborated with Charles Darwin, and illustrated for returning

---

[211]Lois Oliver, 'Whymper, Josiah Wood (1813-1903),' *Oxford Dictionary of National Biography*, Oxford University Press, 2004.

explorers, including Dr David Livingstone. Sir Edwin Landseer, eminent Victorian animal painter described him, without exception, as the 'best all-round animal artist who ever lived.' The choice of Wolff's paintings as the subjects for Whymper's woodcuts was an inspired one for John's *British Birds in their Haunts*, as Charles Johns's descriptions and commentaries also tell the story of how these birds lived. [Notes taken from www.nhm.ac.uk/nature-online, the website of the Natural History Museum.] He contributed illustrations to many books and journals, notably the collected works of poets and naturalists. The signature of Joseph Wolff appears in the Johns's Autograph Collection.

Appendix iii: Publications by Charles Alexander Johns

The attempt here is to include all publications by the author, rather than just those that qualify as natural history books within the author's life-time. It is compiled from the *Dictionary of National Biography* Oxford: OUP, 1885-1900 Vol 30, p 223, the publication lists found in his already published works, and references within his publications. The original *DNB* entry for Johns was contributed by George S Boulger, FLS, FGS, a lecturer, later Professor of Botany in the City of London College. A major contribution to 'Johnsiana' was his repeated revision (4 editions) of *Flowers of the Field*, from 1900 through to 1911. He was also responsible for the revision of the 11th edition of *Forest Trees of Britain* issued by London: SPCK in 1919. Some dates were incorrect (and family information) in the *DNB* and in the biographical memoir included in his final revision in 1911 [*Flowers of the Field*], due to Boulger's reliance upon F L Davey's account of Johns in the *Flora of Cornwall* (1909). Davey's account in turn relied upon the information listed earlier by Boase & Courtney, that Boase himself commented later in the *Collectanea*, as being open to question. Since the *Collectanea*, printed in 1890 in 130 copies only, was unlikely to have been seen by Boulger, due to its precious scarcity, the mistakes have been carried on in the public record.

Hence publication dates have been revised according to R B Freeman, *British Natural History Books 1495-1900: a Handlist*, 1980 [Catalogue numbers 1967-1982 as identified below], and gleaned through further investigation within the British Library Catalogues and multiple other sources (listed in bibliography), and from the actual publications themselves. The latter form a part of the Johns Archive, within the Hypatia Collection, though not every one of the smaller items have yet been located. An asterisk* before a title indicates that the item has been viewed and is in our collection unless indicated as elsewhere. The intent of this section is to be as definitive as possible for those publications appearing in his lifetime, though it is difficult as Freeman admits to trace off-prints, editions and reprints that are undated. A collection of his writings is a work-in-progress, and additions and corrections to this list are welcome. [Address: Johns Archive, Trevelyan House, 16 Chapel Street, Penzance, Cornwall TR18 4AW, or e-mail: info@hypatia-trust.org.uk]

1833

Chronological Rhymes on English History 1833 (further editions 1855, 1861). Written while Assistant Master at Helston Grammar School.

1840-1

*Flora Sacra 1840 Sub-title: *or, The Knowledge of the Works of Nature conducive to the knowledge of the God of Nature*. Copies of rare item are also found with the date 1841, but the editions are the same in every respect, so this is simply an indication of the printing year. This little book was issued with plant specimens dried and tipped in to labelled pages, with letterpress titles. Adjacent are the passages in the Bible

referenced. Family information received indicates that the book was researched in Ireland alongside the completion of his studies at Dublin. Published by J Parker, Strand: London. The printer was his brother-in-law Henry E Carrington at Bath. *The Index to the British Catalogue of Books* (1853) by Sampson Low lists this book as being published in December, 1841, however the fly-leaf clearly states 1840. [Freeman: Cat 1967]

1842
*'Note 137: List of Mosses &c collected chiefly at Leith Hill, Surrey' *The Phytologist* 1842 v I, part l. Dated 19 March 1842
Short Sermons for Children, illustrative of the Catechism & Liturgy November, 1842 by Rev C A Johns, Chaplain to the Central School, Westminster. Published by J W Parker & Sons, West Strand.

1845
*'Wistman's Wood' *The Phytologist*, January 1845

1846
**Botanical Rambles* 1846 by the 'Rev C A Johns, BA, FLS, Headmaster of Helston Grammar School' London: SPCK (Engraved by J W Whimper, based on the botanical watercolour paintings of Emily Stackhouse as signed and by Johns's sisters, all anonymously rendered). This compilation includes 8 chapters being the following: The Meadow, The Corn-Field, The Hedge-Bank, The Wood, The Heath, The Mountain, The Bog, The Sea-Shore. 187 pp + Index. R Trenoweth provides information of an edition clearly dated 1844, oblong in shape whereas in a following book (*A Ramble in Winter*, published in 1847, Johns refers to a square edition.) This was later issued in four parts following the seasons of the year. [Freeman: Cat 1968]

1847-52
*From the *Flora of Cornwall* (1909) Davey states: 'In 1847 he added *Trifolium strictum* to the British flora, and *T procumbens, T. filiforme, Thalictrum minus* to our local list. These contributions were made in *The Phytologist*.'

*'A Few Notes on Cornish Plants' *The Phytologist*, 1847 Vol ii, pp 725-6 (with special reference to 'Asparagus officinalis')

*'Observations on the Plants of the Land's End' *The Phytologist*, 1847 Vol ii, pp 906-9
*'Notes on British Plants' in *London Journal of Botany* (Hooker, editor) 1847 (includes a section on 'Finds in Cornwall' by CAJ, pp 474-7)

**Rambles in the Country* 1847-52 [Freeman: Cat 1969]
   A Winter Ramble in the Country London: SPCK 1847, 93pp
   A Ramble in Spring London: SPCK Sept 1849, 110pp
   A Ramble in Summer London: SPCK c1850, 98pp
   A Ramble in Autumn London: SPCK 1852, 89pp
All of the frontispieces for these small books were executed by Whymper (one from

a painting by B Foster), that for the *Winter Ramble* being the 'Holy Well' at Trelill, near Helston, Cornwall. Within the set of four, there are many plants drawn by Emily Stackhouse with monogram, many anonymously reprinted, but most notably in the *Spring Ramble*, are 13 drawings by Charles Johns himself.

Examination Questions on the historical parts of the Pentateuch 1847 For the use of families, national schools and the lower forms in Grammar Schools. London: J(oseph) Masters 70 pp

*Forest Trees of Britain in Two volumes: Vol 1: 1847; Vol II: 1849 London: SPCK. In the first instance the reader could purchase the chapters one by one, about two-three individual trees, for 8d each, or the first five bound in a volume for 3s 8s. In 1869, the two volumes were re-issued as one, and thenceforward through at least 12 editions continuing in print till 1929. In 1874 the New Edition was being advertised as containing 150 woodcuts. The Editor and reviser in 1909 through the tenth edition (1912) was G S Boulger. The illustrators were J W Whimper, Emily Stackhouse, JJ (Julia Johns), B Foster, and Charles Johns, again with some remaining unattributed. A selected edition of *Some British Forest Trees* was issued in 1907. Then in 1911, another edition of the two volume book was published entitled *British Trees, including the finer shrubs for garden and woodland*. [Freeman: Cat 1970]

1848
*'On the Landslip at the Lizard' in quarterly transactions, *Journal of the Geological Society London* 1848 vol iv: pp 193-4

*A Week at the Lizard May, 1848 London: SPCK. Second edition, 1863; Third edition, 1874; 4th ed, 1882; in print till 1948, with facsimile reprint in 1992. A delightful exploration of the Lizard Peninsula in Cornwall, and an interesting piece of early tourist literature. Virtually all of the botanical illustrations are woodcuts taken from Emily Stackhouse's watercolours (some acknowledged with Emily's cipher ES), with the 'action engravings and scenes' signed by Whimper. Drawings (one each) by CAJ and Philip Henry Gosse, FRS are also used. The map is drawn and engraved by W Hughes, 1848. This is still a good travelling companion for any visit to this part of Cornwall. Entertaining and well-written and illustrated, it is good literature in its own right. Though published by SPCK, it is not a religious book, but an excellent example of the rambling literature of the time. The Third edition, with updating and a new introduction, was the final book on which Johns worked in his life-time. [Freeman: Cat 1972]

*Gardening for Children 1848 London: SPCK. Published from Beenham, Berkshire (5,000 sold). Second edition: 1849 (issued at Sixth Thousand) chapters on Tools, Flower-garden (annuals, biennials, perennials, shrubs, hardy bulbs), Fruit-garden, Kitchen-garden, Parts of a Plant and concluding with maxims for the budding gardener. The second edition was issued by George Cox , 18 King Street, Covent Garden, in June 1849, and a third edition at 2s 6d, beautifully illustrated, handsome cloth gilt, in 1851. Whymper and B Foster collaborated on the Frontispiece, but no other illustrations are identified. [Not listed in Freeman]

1849
Gardening for Children, 2nd edition

Amnenon the Forgetful and Eustathes the Constant 1849. Advertised in 1851 in the publisher's list of George Cox, 18 King Street, Covent Garden under the banner of 'Books for the Young.' This was issued in 'limp cloth' with gilt edges for 1 shilling, complete with 14 engravings.

1851
Gardening for Children, 3rd edition

*Flowers of the Field 1851 in two volumes, in one volume from 1889. [Incorrect dates in Boase & Courtney, Simpson and in Freeman, all of whom wrongly indicate 1853 for the first edition.] Later editions with revisions were issued without dates, though dated advertisements help to establish when new editions appeared. Within Johns's lifetime there were 11-12 editions issued with revisions, a more-or-less constant flow of work. London: SPCK. Charles's *magnum opus* was *Flowers of the Field*. Over 50 editions were published stretching into 1949 from at least five different publishers both in Great Britain and the United States. The book was still on stockists' shelves in London in the 1970s which most certainly must make it one of the longest-lived scientific books of all time. Well over 200 of the book's original illustrations of plant life have come from the hands of Emily Stackhouse (165 signed), and his sisters, Emily and Julia (unsigned), with early Whimper/Whymper providing the woodcuts and engraving plates of 'scenes.' All of these were line drawings, woodcuts and engravings. Charles Henry (referred to as C H), Johns's eldest son, added posthumously a section on 'Grasses' into the 28th ed, 1892, that continued with the book thereafter.[Freeman: Cat 1982] The 29th edition was entirely revised by G S Boulger in 1899-1900 up to and including the 33rd edition (1911), then removed from SPCK's catalogue in 1925 (35th ed). Routledge & Kegan Paul Ltd paid for the rights to the work and published a parallel set of editions, (1-17), from 1907- 1949. The 1907 edition (3rd), issued by Routledge was revised throughout and edited by Clarence Elliott with 92 coloured illustrations by E N Gwatkin. The 1949 edition (17th), also by Routledge was revised throughout and edited by R A Blakelock FLS, with 266 coloured illustrations by Gwatkin.

The Governess; A First Lesson Book for Children Who Have Learned to Read...by a Schoolmaster of Twenty Years Standing 1851. This little book was first advertised in 1851 by George Cox of Covent Garden as 'Just Published, price 1 s. Post Free, 18 Stamps.' The British Library copy is dated 1855. Available on request from the British Library, Shelfmark 12203.b.4. Humanities collection.

*Simple Tales From Other Lands by Rev C A Johns and others, nd (c1851-59) The tales, issued in a series of small books over a number of years (1-8 known, but not listed in British Library) include the following: 1) *Good Little Christel*, etc. 2) *Little Blue Violet*, etc. 3) *The Cup of Cold Water*, etc. 4) *The Grandmother's Arm Chair* and *The Little Shepherd* (both tales from France) 5) *The Foster Sisters*, etc. 6) *Little Adolphus*, etc. 7) *Leonora*, etc. and 8) *The Covetous Boy*, etc. The Tales, origi-

nally published by the Society for the Diffusion of Useful Knowledge (SDUK) were re-published by Allman & Son, 42, Holborn Hill, London. Illustrations for 'Little Adolphus' and 'The Covetous Boy' are collated in the Princeton University Alexander Anderson Collection of wood engravings. With a different order and additional titles, these simple tales are advertised by the publishers George Cox of Covent Garden as early as 1851 with 12 tales in total 'by the same author.' Additional titles are Nos 2: *The Eve of Kipur; or, The Stolen Child* 4) *The Inundation, & c* 5) *The Witches' Hut* 7) *A Story for Boys* 10) *The Mason's Grandchild* 11) *The Foster Sisters* 12) *The Lily Boot*.

1852

*The Loss of the [RMS] *Amazon* 1852 London: SPCK. Illustrated with woodcuts, 124 pp An account of the wreck in the Bay of Biscay of the wooden passenger and mail steamer on its maiden voyage en route West Indies, Mexico and South America, departing from Plymouth. This book was compiled by CAJ for the SPCK, and dedicated to his former pupil at Helston Grammar School, Charles Henry Treweeke. A copy is available at the Cornish Studies Library, Redruth.

1853

First Steps to Botany 1853 Teaching material for schools undertaking botany within curricula. Published by the National Society for Promoting the Education of the Poor: London. Available on request from British Library, Shelfmarks 7030.a.19 and 7030.a.33 (1). This book was incorrectly stated by Boulger as being introductory to *Flowers of the Field*, giving rise to the common mistake of mis-dating the first edition of the earlier work, that appears in numerous later reports. [Freeman: Cat 1973]

1854

The Origin of the War 1854: a sermon on 2 Chronicles XX.15: 'And he said, Hearken ye, all Judah, and ye inhabitants of Jerusalem, and thou king Je-hosh-a-phat, Thus saith the Lord unto you, Be not afraid nor dismayed by reason of this great multitude; for the battle is not yours, but God's.' A sermon offered at the start of the Crimean war.

*Birds Nests and Eggs 1854 (2nd ed, 1865) London: SPCK. An on-line copy of this book is available on the Internet Archive, as contributed by the University of California Libraries. It was written for young people to encourage their respect for the needs of birds to build their homes and launch their young safely into the world. Keywords for finding this little volume are: Birds – Eggs. Johns refers readers to p 12 of this book (about the Nuthatch) in a footnote on p 313, of *British Birds in their Haunts*. [Freeman: Cat 1975]

1856

The Spirit of Peace 1856: a sermon based on Luke ii.14: 'Glory to God in the highest, and on earth peace, good will toward men.' (King James Version). A sermon preached at the close of the Crimean war.

1858

Monthly Flower Garden 1858 No detail currently, but this format appears to be the one adopted for the several 'monthly' titles that follow in the early 1860s.

1859

*Birds of the Wood and Field 1859 (second and third series 1862) Three sets of cards, and possibly bound. (12 cards in packet). SPCK: London. [Freeman: Cat 1977]

*Picture Books for Children – Animals 1859 Nos 1, 3 and 5, as part of the second series of The Picture Library, published by the SPCK and printed by the Clarendon Press, Oxford. No. 3 (includes 'The Hedgehog,' 'The Squirrel,' 'The Goldfinch,' 'The Reindeer,' 'The Monkey,' 'The Giraffe,' 'The Bat,' 'The Cuckoo,' 'The Beaver,' 'The Rhinoceros,' 'The Toad,' 'The Woodcock,' 'The Guinea-Pig,' 'The Mackerel,' and 'The Mouse.' No 5 includes a different list of animals such as 'The Esquimaux Dog' (Eskimo), 'The Hippopotamus,' 'The Gull,' 'The Seal,' 'The Sheep,' 'The Goat,' 'The Nightingale,' 'The Crab,' 'The Cock,' 'The Hen,' 'The Lion,' 'The Dove,' 'The Ant-Eater,' 'The Otter,' and the 'Long-tailed Tit.'(Further editions 1873, 1883, 1923) Many of the illustrations are identified as being supplied by Whimper, though some are anonymous. [Not listed in Freeman]

*Rambles about Paris 1859 London: SPCK; combining history with observation Johns leads the reader through 14 illustrated chapters from First Impressions, Place de la Concorde, The Louvre, The Tuileries, Notre Dame, The Madeleine, Pere La Chaise, etc. to the Bois De Boulogne. The same easy style of *A Week at the Lizard* makes this an educating read and a sufficient modern-day tour guide with a difference.

Child's First Book of Geography

This book was advertised under the banner of 'Books for Young Readers' in 8 volumes, by C A Johns, as published by George Bell & Son, 1859. As yet the other 7 volumes are unidentified, and the 1872 edition, of this volume only is available on request from the British Library, Shelfmark 10004.aa.17. It is not known if the others were published. In 2007, the 1872 edition was digitized for Google Books on-line, as made available by Oxford University.

*Monthly Gleanings from the Field and Garden (Editor) nd [1859-60] London: SPCK. This book is similar in construction to *Monthly Wild Flowers*, in that there is a series of 12 sections of 6 pages each, consisting of excerpts from poets and writers about specific garden and wild flowers within a floral frame (each signed by W Dickes and A (Anne) Johns. Headed by the title of the month, each section contains two original poems by EHC (Emily Heywood Carrington), a fine example of chromolithography illustrating a bouquet of flowers appropriate to the month (executed by J (?Julia or Jane) Johns and W Dickes, followed by a page of descriptions of the flowers included. [Freeman: Cat 1978]

1860

*Monthly Wild Flowers 1860 London: SPCK. A series of 12 illustrated meditations,

consisting of a full colour card with poetic excerpts from famous poets about specific flowers within a floral frame (each of the 12 by W Dickes, as signed), followed
by a six stanza poem for each month by Emily Heywood Carrington (EHC), on
the reverse of which is a spiritual meditation on nature by Charles Johns. The same
excerpts from famous poets about the flowers are used, along with their floral frame,
in both this and the *Monthly Gleanings*. [Freeman: Cat 1979]

Monthly Window Flowers 1860 (2nd ed. 1869) Edited by CAJ with illustrations by
J Johns (Julia or Jane, probably Julia). Advertised as No. 11 of 'Picture Tickets and
Cards' in packets and printed in colours. [Not listed in Freeman]

New edition, just published: *Flowers of the Field*, advertised by SPCK in the *Ecclesiastical Gazette* of June 1860.

1861
*Manual of Prayers for Schools,Public Institutions and Private Families, Compiled with-
out mutilation from the Holy Bible and Book of Common Prayer* 1861. Published by
Longman, Green, Longman & Roberts. Accessible on-line at Google Books in full
version, and available on request from British Library: Shelfmark 3456.c.37

1862
Birds of the Wood and Fields 2nd and 3rd series (3 volumes in total)

British Birds in their Haunts, xxxii+626 pp. June 1862 London: SPCK; second edition 1867 illustrated by Wolff; in print till 25th ed, (London: Routledge & Kegan
Paul, 1948). Early editions were illustrated by woodcuts drawn by the artist, Wolff,
and engraved by Whymper. Included as an Appendix is the 'Index of Systematic,
Common, and Provincial Names, and Glossary of Technical Terms' employed in
the volume, at the end of which is the comment 'The Author will be grateful for any
additions to his list of Provincial Names' (of birds). In 1874, this book advertised
as 'by the late C A Johns's, contained 190 engravings by Whymper of drawings by
Wolff. In 1904, the Eleventh edition was issued, and in 1911, the Twelfth, with 16
coloured plates. As further editions were produced, coloured plates replaced the
originals. Edited, revised and annotated by J A Owen in 1909, in 1948, the book
was advertised as being uniform with *Flowers of the Field*, by Routledge, and edited
and revised by W B Alexander, MBOU, with 64 coloured and 5 black and white
plates (by William Foster), making a total with vignettes of 251 figures.

1863
A Week at the Lizard, 2nd edition

Ductor in Elegias in usum puerorum Etonae limen insistentium 1863 Edited by CAJ,
published Londini: Longman, Green, Longman, Roberts et Green. Available on
request at British Library, in Humanities Collection. Shelfmark 12932.aa.6, and
available on-line in full version on Google Books. This is a textbook for pupils of
Latin on prosody.

Home Walks and Holiday Rambles 1863 London: Longman & Co, illustrated by daughter Katie Johns (ACJ monogram) and his friend Cornwall Simeon (CS monogram). Written in diary form, this volume covers the period of tours and walks and holidays that Johns took in the years beginning January 1st, 1861 to the time of publication, including nature experiences in Devon, Norfolk, Scotland, and at home in Winchester. References are also made to previous visits, in former years, to the locations described. [Freeman: Cat 1981]

1864
Sea Weeds nd [c1860s] (12 cards) Coloured cards with descriptions. Letterpress. Edited by CAJ. Published by SPCK, printed in London by William Clowes and Sons, Stamford Street, this small brown volume (also issued as cards) has no specified authorship on the title page. Every one of the twelve sections, however, is signed CAJ, and the text is explanatory to the very fine prints produced by the Baxter process (in colour). Google Book Search identifies this publication as one in 1864, but it may have been much earlier.

1866
The Cottage Flower Garden 1866 Plates, with instructions for cultivation, instructions signed CAJ. Available on request at British Library, Shelfmark 7055.aa.23. [Not listed in Freeman]

'Acherontia Atropos' in *Entomologist* 1866-7

1867
Monthly Window Flowers, 2nd edition

British Birds in Their Haunts, 2nd edition

1869
Forest Trees of Britain, Revised and re-issued in one volume

1874
A Week at the Lizard, 3rd edition significantly revised

Forest Trees of Britain, New edition also in one volume with 150 woodcuts

'The Fall of the Leaf' in *Journal of the Winchester Scientific Society* 1874

'Notes on a Collection of Land and Freshwater Shells' in *Journal of the WSS* 1874

'Vesuvias' in *Journal of the WSS* 1874

Birds of the Wood & Field 1874 SPCK Twelve cards with embossed design and trim, text to verso. [Not listed in Freeman]

Posthumous publications (selected by publishers from earlier works)

*In 1905 (1907 re-issue) a selected compilation from *British Birds in their Haunts* was published in Edinburgh, under the title of *I go a-walking through the lanes and meadows*, illustrated with photographs by Charles Reid. [Freeman: Cat 1980]

*The *'Look about you' Nature Study Books*, authored jointly by Thomas W Hoare, C A Johns and J G Wood. Edition(s) by T C & E C Jack nd [1904, 1907] Book V in this series is *Some British Forest Trees*, and the preface to it begins 'The lessons in this book were written by the late Rev. C. A. Johns, B.A., F.L.S....

Picture Book of Animals London: E & J B Young & Co 1883; SPCK 1886; Macmillan Co 1927. The title pages of these books generally state author as by 'The Late Rev C A Johns's.

*The *Look About You Nature Book, No. 5* Some British Forest Trees, Oak, Ash, Horse-chestnut, Elm, Birch, Willow, Beech, The Fir Tribe. London: T C & E C Jack, Ltd. Colour plates and steel engravings. It is not known whether or not the other 6 books in this series are also taken from Charles Johns's lessons for pupils of nature.

British Trees and Shrubs – Flowering and Evergreen London: George Routledge & Sons nd [1910]

British Trees including the Finer Shrubs for Garden and Woodland by The Late C A Johns, edited by E T Cook and W Dallimore (of Kew Gardens) London: George Routledge & Sons nd [1911]

British Birds in their Haunts 1911, by the late Rev C A Johns, B A, F L S, with illustrations on wood, drawn by Wolf [Wolff] engraved by Whymper, SPCK. Twelfth edition, with 16 coloured plates.

This is a citation list of authorities and friends referenced by Charles Johns in his major botanical works. It has been collated by Melissa Hardie, based on the referenced quotations* and poems employed by Johns in his major works, to discuss and juxtapose his observations and some arguments put by other explorer-naturalists. His method is always kindly and open, inviting correction, but it is clear when he does not agree with one of the authorities he quotes for the reasons he then puts forward. What impresses the student of Johns is the enormous scope of his reading and the 'conferencing' approach that he takes, quite aside from the comparative literature at his command. His quotations and translations from original sources in several languages, lead the historian to realise that somewhere, unless unfortunately destroyed, there must be botanical notebooks and diaries of extraordinary variety and richness kept by Johns over many years. Works of this magnitude, full of artistic and literary detail as well as historical intricacy could not have been produced with a few open volumes spread around even a large Victorian desk. No one authority is relied upon unduly, and the writers of this monograph are brought back immediately to the style in which his earliest known diary was written: approximately half being devoted to cuttings, poems, excerpts etc. in the form of a commonplace book, and the other half a personal record of his own daily walks and activities. To date, no further handwritten or hand-collated notebooks or diaries have been located other than that included in the main text of this volume [Cornwall Records Office].

NOTE: Some references are sketchy, i.e. only including a surname of a common nature, such as Mr Bourne, making further identification of the authority difficult to establish. Corrections or additions to this check-list are welcome.

Abbreviations: [Listed chronologically in terms of publication]
[FAC] Person represented in Family Autograph Collection (Appendix v)
FS (*Flora Sacra*) 1840
BR (*Botanical Rambles*) 1846
WR (*Winter Ramble*) 1847
FT (*Forest Trees of Britain*) Vol 1 and 2, 1847-49
FF (*Flowers of the Field*) Vol 1 and 2, 1851
MWF (*Monthly Wild Flowers*) 1860 [Applies also to *Monthly Gleanings*.]
BB (*British Birds in Their Haunts*) 1862, 1867 2nd edition
WL (*A Week at the Lizard*) [1848 original] The 3rd edition, revised in the year before his death and published 1874 is used for this index, and for the book as a whole. Page numbers differ from those of the first and second editions. This became the final work within his life-time, and contained references to his latest 'gleanings' as well as his earliest youthful adventures in Cornwall.

Addison, Joseph 1672-1719
FS, p 34: The Lord my pasture shall prepare

Aiken, Dr J (published Gilbert White's *Naturalist Calendar* in 1795)
FT, Vol 2 p 300: Suggests Yews were planted to supply boughs for Christmas with which Miss Kent disagrees by quoting Brand's *Popular Antiquities*, that they were only used by default of other evergreens

Akenside, Mark 1721-1770
FS, p 8: Whom Nature's works can charm, with God himself

Agricultural Journal of Bavaria
FT, Vol 1 p 271-2: Notes on the use of the Bird-cherry

Allan, J H (published before 1849)
FT, Vol 2 p 349: About the departed forests of Scotland from *Last Deer of Beann Doran*

Anon
FS, p 14: Mountains and oceans, plants, suns and systems,
BR, p 43: Oh! where can Nature, through her wide domains,
BR, p 69: The damsel donned her kirtle sheen
BR, p 105: ----The hardy Furze, In yellow lustre glows
BR, p 114: The shadow sleeps upon the hill! (from 'The Cathedral')
FT, Vol 2 p 214: Each leaf and bud/Doth know I AM. (? corruption of H Vaughan)
 p 278: The Guelder Rose-tree of gardens/

Audouin, M (contemporaneous publication with Mr Spence)
FT, Vol 2 pp 114-6: about insects that prey on the Elm

Audubon, John James 1785-1851
BB, p 509: About the nesting habits of the Eider Duck in Labrador
 p 564: Describes the cry of the Sandwich Tern
 p 574: Audubon should be read for a description of the habits of the Noddy Tern

Babington, Charles Cardale 1808-1895
FT, Vol 2 p 241: reduced Hooker's enumeration of Willows from 70 to 57

Banks, Sir Joseph 1743-1820
FT, Vol 2 p 429: Received Araucaria (Chili Pine) from Menzies who accompanied Vancouver in his expedition to Chili (sic) in 1795, one of which is still growing at Kew (in 1849).

Barrington, Judge (before 1770)
FT, Vol 2 p 313: measured the Fortingal Yew in the Grampians & found to be 52 feet in circumference.

Barton, Bernard 1784-1849
BR, p 73: Hast thou seen, in winter's stormiest day

Beckmann, Johann 1739-1811
FT, Vol 2 pp 62-3: about his history of the discovery of alum, and finding Holly

Bechstein, Johann M 1757-1822
BB, p 78: the sound of the Fieldfare is 'a mere harsh disagreeable warble'
    p 87: the song of the Blackbird is not without melody, but is agreeable only in open country

Bell, John G 1812-1899
BB, pp 273-5: Bell refers to Gilbert White's published account in *Selborne* of the Swallow, as an admirable form of bird-biography, in his own analysis of whether or not all Swallows migrate.

Berkeley, The Rev Miles Joseph 1803-1889
FT, Vol 1 pp 344-6: about truffles in abundance in Kent, used for catsup, and the high price and demand for them in France and other countries. Quotes from Berkeley's *English Flora*, vol v, part ii.

Berwickshire Naturalists Club
BB: p 38: the food of the Honey buzzard kept in captivity

Bewick, Thomas 1753-1828
BB, p 380: Refers to his drawing of the Collared Pratincole

Bible (Holy writ)
WR, p 1: Song of the Three Children (Apocrypha/Daniel)
FT, Vol 1 p 235-6: The use of creatures (insects, etc.) and other unknowns working in the environment, employed by the Almighty as national scourges, spreading famine and desolation (Irish potato famine, 1846). 'Go to the ant, thou sluggard, consider her ways and be wise.' Prov vi.6.
FT, Vol 2 p 10: references to the Chestnut-tree in the OT at Gen xxx 37 and Ezek xxi 8
    pp 133-4: Genesis xliii. 11: Pistachio-nuts and the Hazel
    p 240 Isaiah xliv. 4: They shall spring up as among the grass, as Willows by the watercourses.
    p 258: Mentioning Willows: Job xl. 22, Ezekiel xvii. 5
    pp 327-9: Frequent mention in Sacred Writings (Bible, Talmud, and the Romans) of the Cedar, Fir & of Cypress
    pp 411-3: The fragrance of the Cedar of Lebanon referred to as "smell of Lebanon" in Hosea xiv. 6, and quoting from Gilpin's remarks, Johns notes that the prophet Ezekiel gives the fullest description of the Cedar in Ezek. xxxi. 3-8.
    p 433: Elijah sat under the Juniper when flying from the persecution of Jezebel 1 Kings xix. 4
    BB, pp 4-6: The Golden Eagle
    p 239: The Raven

Bloomfield, Robert 1766-1823
MWF, April: Wild Hyacinth

Bochart, Samuel 1599-1667
FT, Vol 2 p 260: The Euphrates was lined with Willows

Boethius, Hector c 1465-1536
BB, p 373: The Scottish call the Bustard, the *Gustardoe*

Borlase, William 1696-1772
WL, p 46-8: Where the Cornish language survives, and the longevity of the Cornish people
    pp 61-3: His tour of the Lizard with the Dean of Exeter, Charles Littleton
    p 118: About the little horses, called Goonhillees, for which the wild downs were known [hence, Goonhilly Downs, where the earth station is now located]

Borrer, William (Senior) 1781-1862
FT, Vol 2 p 241: WB 'the first of living British botanists' and his arrangement of species of Willow, was that followed by Hooker, while Lindley follows first Sir J E Smith, then changes to Koch, for the identification of species of Willow.

Bosc, Louis Augustin Guillaume 1759-1828
FT, Vol 2 p 13: Quotes Bosc's analysis that Chestnuts grow where corn does not, only on rocky and flinty soils

Bourne, no further identification
FT, Vol 2 p 50: Quotes the Edict of Bracara about decorating houses with green boughs by Christians at the same time as pagans

Bowman, Mr No further identification
FT, Vol 2 p 301: His article in *Magazine of Natural History* theorises that Ancient Britons planted Yews for superstitious purposes and idolatrous rites.

Bowring, Sir John 1792-1872
BR, p 164: Beneath Thy all-directing nod/Both worlds and worms are equal, God!

Brand, Rev John (Published 1701 *Description of Orkney*)
FT, Vol 2 p 142: Quoting from *Grim, the Collier of Croydon* about 14th September being a nutting day

Bree, Rev T W (c1847)
FT, Vol 1 pp 215-6: From a letter in the *Gardeners Magazine*, vii 234
    Vol 2 pp 301-2: Believes that churches were frequently built in Yew-groves, rather than the reverse.

Bremontier, N T (c 1833)

FT, Vol 2 p 368: Methods of sowing Pinaster to thatch and protect from soil and sand erosion

Brook No further identification
FT, Vol 2 pp 361-2: In Sweden, at times of scarcity, the bark of the Pine is made into bread.

Browne, Sir Thomas 1605-1682
BB, p 404: Reference to his account of birds found in Norfolk with special information about Cranes
 p 417: The Ciconia Alba or Stork seen between Norwich and Yarmouth
 p 418: Enumerates the Spoonbill among the birds of Norfolk and Suffolk
 p 529: Describes the Great Crested Grebe, under the name of 'Loon'

Browne, William c1590-c1645
FT, Vol 2 p 92: The Alder, whose fat shadow nourisheth – Each plant set neere to him long flourisheth.

Brunner, M (c1840s)
FT, Vol 2 p 31: The 5 stems of which the Il Castagno del Nave in Sicily is composed of distinct trunks, proceeding from one root.

Bryant, William Cullen 1794-1878
MWF, October

Buckingham, James Silk 1786-1855
FT, Vol 2 p 207: Also describes the Plane-tree at Vostitza on the Gulf of Lepanto, Corinthia

Buffon, Georges-Louis Leclerc, Comte de Buffon 1707-1788
FT, Vol 2 p 22-3: B was the first to point out the strong resemblance of the Chestnut to Durmast Oak, or as **Lindley** would call it, English Oak
BB, pp 31-2: Admiration for the flight of the Kite
 p 226: The beak of the Common Crossbill said to be 'an error and defect of nature, and a useless deformity.'

Burckhardt, John Lewis 1784-1817
FT, Vol 2 pp 183-4: Notes the Tamarisk tree in his journey through the wilderness of Sinai
 p 260: Mentions a fountain in Syria, called the Willow Fountain
 p 433: Mentions the Juniper growing in the deserts south of Palestine
BB, p 368: Offers opinion about the identification of the Quail

Burns, Robert 1721-1784
FT, Vol 1 p 203: The milk-white Thorn that scents the evening gale
FT, Vol 2 p 146: About the custom of prognosticating about people from igniting nuts of the Hazel

MWF, May: Hawthorn

Carrington, Emily Heywood
MW, Twelve 6-stanza poems based on the months of the year, repeated in *Monthly Gleanings*, with an additional 12 named also for the months.

Carrington, Nicholas Toms 1777-1830
FS, p 20: How Nature through her ample reign displays
FT, Vol 1 p 15: How heavily/ That old wood sleeps in the sunshine – not a leaf

Caesar, Julius Gaius c100-44 BCE
FT, Vol 1 p 313-14: In reference to his invasion of Britain and report of the trees extant.
    Vol 2 p 248: in his *History of the Civil War*, tells of his use of coracles

Chandler, Dr No further identification
FT, Vol 2 p 50-1: Decking churches with greenery may have emanated from the Druids

Chaucer, Geoffrey c1343-1400
FT, Vol 1 p 202: Amongst the many buds proclaiming May
    p 296: reference to his mention of pears
MWF: May: Hawthorn
BB, p 323: Quoting 'It was a commone tale/ That it were gode to here the Nightingale,/ Moche rather than the lewde Cuckowe sings.'

Clare, John 1793-1864
MWF, July: The Ragged Robin
    August: Blue-Bottle
    October: Crab-Apple

Clark, Rev S (of St Mark's College 1840s)
FT, Vol 2 pp 206-7: Account of a noble Plane-tree at Vostitza, 8 centuries old

Clarke, Dr Edward Daniel 1769-1822
FT, Vol 2 p 158: the use made of Walnut-trees by the Tartars, for the making of sugar
    pp 205-6: On seeing the Plane Tree of Stanchio many years after the Earl of Sandwich
    pp 329-30: Fir-trees north of the Gulf of Bothnia in Sweden
    p 334: about conveying Fir-timber from Swedish forests to the sea
    pp 359-61: methods of procuring tar from the wood of the Pine in ancient Greece and in Scotland

Cobbett, William 1763-1835
FT, Vol 2 p 236: indebted to Cobbett for many Acacias, but perhaps not as profitable as promoted

Coleridge, Derwent 1800-1883 [FAC]
WL, p 3: Suggests that Meneage [district south of Helston] is a term identical with the Welsh maenawg, meaning stony.

Coleridge, Samuel Taylor 1772-1834 [FAC]
FS, p 46: Fair the vernal mead,
     Glory to Thee, Father of earth and heaven!
MWF, June: Forget-Me-Not

Collingwood, Cuthbert 1748-1810
BB, p 91: the note of the Golden Oriole is a very loud whistle

Cornwall, Cornish reference
BR, pp 104-7: Of Heath and Furze
FT, Vol 1 pp 98-9: Trees at Mount Edgecumbe in Devonshire, Clowance, Trelowarren and St Michael's Mount in Cornwall.
FT, Vol 2 p 28: Fine trees at Cotehele on the banks of the Tamar
     p 67: Fine specimen of Holly on the glebe of St Gluvias Vicarage, Cornwall
     p 103: Description of the Cornish Elm (*Ulmus stricta*)
     p 120: Engraving of a Wych Elm at Enys, Cornwall (signed WCS), and further comment pp 123-4 about the trees there
     pp 181-2: Tamarisk tree first observed in wild state on St Michael's Mount, and now common hedge-plant in many parts of the Cornish Coast.
     p 268-9: The great esteem in which the ancient Cornish held the Elder, is exhibited in the vocabulary explicated by Borlase, and in names, i.e. Boscawen (of which Lord Falmouth is one) and Scawens (of St Germans), in that the Cornu-British words for the Elder are *scau* and *scauan*.
     p 284: Engraving by Whimper of the Holy-Well at Trelill, near Helston
     pp 371-2: Sir Charles Lemon noticed a singular variety of Pinaster at Carclew [illustrations on page 370 and 371 of Pinus Lemoniana by Emily Stackhouse]
BB, pp 120-1: The Nightingale, questioning why it does not come to Cornwall?
     p 177: The Rock Pipit and the Meadow Pipit appear sociable in Devon and Cornwall. (CAJohns)
     pp 237-239: The Chough (or Red-legged Crow)
     p 242: A huge Ravens' nest at Bishop Rock, in Cornwall.
     p 261: Magpies numerous in Cornwall, and sometimes called 'Cornish pheasants'
     p 416: A dead specimen of the Night Heron was brought to CAJ in 1836, as shot on Goonhilly Downs
     p 439: The condition of the Woodcock when it visits the British Isles annually about 20 October
WL, Full text about Cornwall, its customs and inhabitants, and walks that may be taken in six sections.
     pp 151-158: Accounts of the losses by wreckage off the coast of the Lizard of the following: *Johnkheer* of Dordrecht 1867; *Jose Oscar of Bayonne* 1862 and *Maria Louisa of Padstow* 1868.
     p 162 n: Reference to buried treasure of Captain Avery at Gunwalloe or Kennack

Cove, as it was searched for by John Knill (collector of the customs at St Ives) c 1770.
pp 177-9: A description of Helston Flora Day annually on May 8th

Cornwall, Barry (*nom de plume* for Bryan Waller Procter) 1788-1874
FT, Vol 1 p 356: The green woods moved, and the light poplar shook

Cotton, Charles 1630-1687
BR, p 82: To be resigned when ills betide

Cowley, Abraham 1618-1667
FT, Vol 1 p 196: Where does the wisdom and the power Divine
p 213: Man does the savage Hawthorn teach
p 258: Although no part of mighty Nature be
p 342: If thou, without a sigh, or golden wish

Cowper, William 1731-1800
FS, p 6: What, though I trace each herb and flower
p 8: Strange there should be found
p 22: All we behold is miracle; but seen
      From dearth to plenty, and from death to life
WR, p 41: And the green/ And tender blade
WR, p 85: He marks the bounds which winter may not pass,
FT, Vol 1 p 111: Nor unnoticed pass/ The Sycamore
p 356: Poplar, that with silver lines his leaf
FT, Vol 2 p 272: About honeysuckle (Woodbine), 'As Woodbine weds the plant
within her reach/...'
MWF, January: Furze

Crabbe, George 1754-1832
MWF, January: Cup-Moss
      May: Thorn
      July: Water-Lily
      August: Poppy
      November: Hart's Tongue

Crawford, no further identification
BR, p 173: the perilous toil of collecting birds' nests

Cunnack, James (of Helston c 1873)
WL, pp 203-254: Thanked for additions to Appendix I of the new edition, by this
zealous botanist.
[A photo of James Cunnack is to be found, following that of Johns in the *Flora of
Cornwall* (1909) by Davey.]

Darwin, Charles 1809-1882 [FAC]
FT, Vol 1 p 183-4: from *The Voyage of H. M. S. Beagle*
      pp 305-6: lengthy reference to Darwin's observations on the apples of South

America, and the size and measurements of the trees on which they grow.

pp 318-19: his account of a beech-tree forest

pp 345-6: on edible fungi, and that fungus named by Mr Berkeley as 'Cittaria Darwinii' with illustration (engraving).

Drummond, Dr James Lawson 1783-1853
BR, p 169: quote from his *First Steps to Botany* (1823)

Dawson, R (of Tottenham, 1849)
FT, Vol 2 p 429: Dawson owned one of the finest and handsomest Chili Pines in England, 20 feet high with branches descending to the ground on all sides, planted out at the height of 4 inches (1832).

De Candolle, Augustin-Pyramus 1778-1841
FT, Vol 2 p 210: Computes that the largest tree in the world, the Plane-tree on the Bosphorus is 2,000 years old.

pp 255-6: about the Herbaceous Willow in Switzerland

pp 293-4: speaks of the ivy at Gigean near Montpelier

De la Roque (published 1772)
FT, Vol 2 p 414: Reports that the Maronites say that when the snows begin to fall, the Cedars change their figure, rising up and turning toward heaven.

De Saint Hilaire, Geoffrey (Etienne Geoffrey 1772-1844, Son Isidore Geoffrey 1805-1861)
BB, p 389: Confirmed the ancient report of Herodotus about Plovers cleaning the mouths of crocodiles

Dodd, Charles Edward (published 1818)
FT, Vol 2 pp 340-1: excerpt about rafts and living aboard them from *An Autumn near the Rhine*

Dovaston, John F M 1782-1854
FT, Vol 2 pp 44-7: A 'fanciful but graphic description' of the Horse Chestnut, quoting Linnaeus.

Drayton, Michael 1563-1631
MWF, June: Columbine

Drummond, William of Hawthornden 1685-1649
MWF: September: Eryngo

Dryden, John 1631-1700
FT, Vol 1 p 198: When first the tender blades of grass appear

Ducarel, Andrew Coltee 1713-1785
FT, Vol 2 p 4: quotes from his *Anglo-Norman Antiquities* about English chestnut

imported to France.

Dunn, Robert
BB, p 521: Refers the reader to his *Ornithologist's Guide to Orkney and Shetland*, p 95 about the Long-Tailed Duck

    p 591: Three places in Shetland where the Common Skua breeds: Foula, Rona's Hill and the Isle of Mist (from his *Ornithologist's Guide to Orkney and Shetland*, p 12)

Edmonston, Dr Laurence 1795-1879
BB, p 592: About the habits of the Common Skua (having been able to study them closely on Unst)

Edwards, George 1694-1773
BB, pp 374-5: *Edwards's Gleanings of Natural History* was used by Yarrell as a benchmark on the water-bearing capacity of the Great Bustard, which he checked out by dissection to find false, facts also found by Professor Owen.

Elliott, Ebenezer 1781-1849
MWF, April: Orchis
    May: Speedwell

Evelyn, John 1620-1706
FT, Vol 1 pp 139-54ff: from *Sylva or Discourse on Forest Trees* (1664)- many individual references to this author's comments

    p 339: comment that beeches grow where once oaks previously stood

    p 358: the white poplar as building material

FT, Vol 2 p 3: comments on the most sought-after wood for joiners – the Chestnut

    pp 17-18: chestnuts not used as article of food so much as they deserve, rather fed to swine

    p 22: Evelyn's mistake in quoting Fitz-Stephen about Chestnut forests near London

    p 28-31: Chestnuts at Fraiting, Essex, Gloucestershire and planted in Greenwich Park

    p 49: Holly the most important of all evergreens, an 'incomparable tree'

    p 61-2: E lavish in his praises of the Holly, and entertained Czar, Peter the Great with tours of it in a barrow

    p 63: E observes that Holly often indicates where coals are to be found

    p 82-3: his recipe for Birch wine, made from the sap and honey

    pp 108-9: about the Elm and its native plantations

    p 130: he is loud in his praises of the Hornbeam as making noble & stately hedges

    pp 134-6: Evelyn derives his name from the Hazel (Avelan, Avelin, alias Evelyn)

    pp 158-60: The plantations of Walnuts in Europe

    pp 167-8: about the Lime Tree (Linden-tree)

    pp 172-3: about Gibbon the sculptor and his use of Linden-wood

    p 204: re-telling the story of the love of Xerxes for the Plane-tree

    pp 210-11: from his diary of September 16th 1683, about the Oriental Plane-tree at Lee

    p 230: The Acacia deserves a place among our avenue trees and walks

p 265: the medicinal properties of the Elder

p 309-11: spectacular specimens of Yew at Crowhurst, Surrey and Scot's Hall in Kent [now (1849) dead as a result of the storm of 1845, according to the **Rev. James Brothers** of Brabourne]

p 400: about the values of British-grown Larch

pp 408-9: E claimed to have received cones and seeds from the few remaining Cedar trees on the mountains of Lebanon. There follows a discussion by Johns of when the Cedar of Lebanon may have been introduced (but not by Evelyn as Loudon contends). In 1683 four Cedars were planted in the Chelsea Garden, two of which are yet standing.* [*written in pencil at the bottom of the page in the handwriting of the former owner of the book 'Babb' is 'one of which has since fallen.']

Fitz-Stephen, William d c 1190
FT, Vol 2 pp 3-4, pp7-9: comments on a noble and large forest growing near London in 12th century, introducing a contested question of the indigenous (or non-) nature of the Chestnut, as extrapolated by following botanists (see Evelyn).

Fletcher, Phineas 1582-1650
FT, Vol 1 pp 330-331: No empty hopes, no courtly fears him fright (from *The Purple Island*)

Forsyth, Mr No further identification
FT, Vol 2 pp 357-8: Description of the Scotch Fir, and how pruning wounds the tree.

Frezier, Amedee-Francois (published 1717)
FT, Vol 2 p 74: account of St Bartholomew's herb (Mate) found in Chili [sic] and Peru 1712, and how wholesome it may become

Fuller No further identification
FT, Vol 2 p 250: the rapidity of growth of Willows

Fuller, Rev Fitzherbert
FT, Vol 2 p 310: provides a contemporaneous account of Yew-tree described by Evelyn

Gardener's Magazine / Gardener's Chronicle
FT, Vol 1 p 299-300: reference to vol ix 333 and the fungus sometimes attacking pears

p 310: reference to vol ix 334 and the destructive insect called 'American blight' ("for no other reason, one would suppose, than that it has been long the custom to ascribe the origin of most strange-looking things to the New World")

pp 342-3: vol vii p 375, the size of beeches in Tyrone Ireland
FT, Vol 2 pp 42-3: A writer in the *Gardener's Chronicle* reported that in Switzerland the horse chestnut is crushed and used for fattening sheep.

p 178: Note in *Gardeners' Chronicle* about a singular mildew occurring on the Barberry

p 311-12: oral history of the Old Yew Tree at Crom Castle, Fermanagh, Ireland p 347: Forsyth tells of clouds of rooks in search of food to the Highland forests of Pine

p 430: How to plant the Chili Pine

Gerard, John 1545-1612

FT, Vol 2 p 8: quotes from his *Generall Historie of Plants* 1597 about the Sycamore, a 'rare exotic'

p 35: G speaks of the Horse Chestnut in 1579 as a rare foreign tree

p 78: The Birch's branches serve well as decorations for banquets and houses

p 121: Long-bows made of the wood of the Wych Elm

p 160: The edible Walnut, in several forms

Gilpin, The Rev William 1757-1848

WL: pp 1-3: Travelled no further than Bodmin in his search for the picturesque, which he did not find in Cornwall

FT, Vol 1: from *Observations on the Western Parts of England* (frequent quotes, and pp 279-80 at length concerning the Mountain Ash)

p 323: describes WG as unable to divest himself of the feelings of the painter, and therefore is looking at nature for that which is 'picturesque.'

pp 334-337: In describing Boldrewood in the New Forest, WG is forced to qualify his own strictures on the beauty of the beech (from *Forest Scenery*).

pp 370-371: the peculiarities of the Lombardy Poplar

FT, Vol 2 p 5: Chestnut suspected to be the wood of the belfry beams at Sutton, Surrey

pp 11-12: The Chestnut trees of Calabria an inspiration to Salvator Rosa, the painter

p 27: A Chestnut at Wimley, nr Hitchin Priory, Hertfordshire had a girth of 42 feet in 1789, at 5 feet tall

p 41-2: Pronounces that the Horse Chestnut has no picturesque beauty.

p 60: States that Holly as an ornament of the landscape is a tree of singular beauty

p 92 Follow the banks of the Mole, in Surrey through vales of Dorking and Mitcham into groves of Esher to see the picturesque Alder in perfection

pp 109-11: Comparing the Oak and the Ash

pp 122-3: Wych Elm more picturesque than the common sort

p 213: The Occidental Plane-tree and its place in the Canon of the picturesque, from *Forest Scenery*

p 230: The frail beauty of the Acacia-tree

pp 248-9: Does not recommend the use of Willows in artificial landscapes

pp 260-1: The Weeping Willow a very picturesque tree, and the perfect contrast to the Lombardy poplar

pp 281-2: His opinions on ivy as a rich decoration to old trunks, and beautiful

pp 306-9: He professes himself a great admirer of the Yew, and underlines that in the New Forest, a post of Yew is said to outlast a post of iron.

pp 356-7: When in perfection, the Scotch Fir a very picturesque tree

pp 373-5: Description of the Stone Pine, promising little in youth but growing in beauty with age

pp 378-80: A description of the Spruce Fir (with illustration) from a pictur-esque point of view, but best seen as a single tree rather than in a group
p 390: In old age the Silver Fir stands its greatest chance of achieving beauty.
WL, pp 1-3: A distinguished writer of the picturesque could find little of interest in Cornwall, turning back at Bodmin

Goldsmith, Oliver c1728-1774
FT, Vol 1 p 203: The Hawthorn-bush, with seats beneath the shade

Good, Dr John Mason 1764-1827
BR, p 12: Not worlds on worlds in phalanx deep

Gorrie, Mr [could be David (1822-1856 Horticultural journalist) or William (1811-1881 President of the Edinburgh Botanical Society)]
FT, Vol 2 pp 401-2: Larch now raised by Scotch nurserymen more than any other timber-tree.

Gould, John 1804-1881
BB, pp 269-70: The constitution of the real nest of the Kingfisher, as found in the Thames, and preserved at the British Museum

Grahame, James 1765-1811 'The Poet of the Covenant'
BB, p 330: 'Deep toned/ The Cushat plains; nor is her changeless plaint/ Unmusi-cal, about the Wood Pigeon (Ring Dove) which has been named the Queest or Cushat

Gray, Thomas 1716-1771
FT, Vol 1 pp 347-8: relates Gray's description of beeches to Horace Walpole, 'And as they bow, their hoary tops, relate/ In murmuring sounds, the dark decrees of Fate/'
FT, Vol 2 p 112: Beneath those rugged Elms, that Yew-tree's shade/

Greville, Dr Robert Kaye 1794-1866
BR, p 175: How the Chinese employ algae for gloss and varnish on paper and silk
pp 184-5: Sea-weeds produced in the tropics

Grigor, James (published 1841)
FT, Vol 1 p 218-224: Account of the Hawthorn from *Eastern Arboretum, or Register of Remarkable Trees, Seats, Gardens &c in the County of Norfolk*
FT, Vol 2 p 96: See Grigor's *Eastern Arboretum* for excellent illustration of the Alder.

Hall, Mrs S C 1800-1881
FT, Vol 2 pp 192-4: a lengthy account of the Strawberry-tree in Ireland, especially at Killarney, from *Sketches of Irish Life and Character* (1829)
BB, p 306: Reprint of part of song that is sung in Cork about "The Wran, the Wran, the kind of all birds" [The Wren] and its legendary importance in the history of Ireland •

Hartlib, Samuel c1600-c1662
FT, Vol 2 pp 21-2: The use of Chestnut timbers in and about Gravesend, Kent for houses and barns

Hasselquist, Fredric 1722-1755
FT, Vol 2 p 206: Gave a specimen of the Oriental Plane-Tree to Linnaeus, which is now in his Herbarium
    pp 259-60: The water of the little Willow (Calaf) used medicinally for all manner of ailments in Egypt. Information from his *Letters from the Levant* (p 453)
BB, p 368: One of two naturalists worth listening to, in relation to the identification of the Quail

Hasted, Edward 1732-1812
FT, Vol 2 p 4: A quoted letter from Hasted to Philosophical Transactions confirming Ducarel's comments on the mutual traffick of building materials – stone and wood – between France and Britain

Heber, Bishop Reginald 1783-1826
FS, p 14: O hand of bounty, largely spread
    p 40: Lo, the lilies of the field
FT, Vol 1 p 281-2: notes from his *Indian Journal* about the Mountain Ash and superstitions connected to it.
    Vol 2 p 422: the splendour of the Deodar, striking the unscientific eye as resembling the Cedar of Lebanon

Hemans, Felicia 1793-1835
BR, p 165: What hid'st thou in thy treasure-caves and cells

Herodotus of Halicarnassus c 484-c 425 BCE
FT, Vol 2 p 204: about Xerxes and the Plane-tree at Lydia in Asia Minor
    pp 247-8: says that the Armenians, trafficking with Babylon, built their boats of Willow
    pp 328-9: the uses and challenges of the Fir-tribe of trees for both Greek and Romans
BB, p 389: The finding of H who stated the Trochilus (Plover) to give a friendly and courageous office to the Crocodile, by cleaning its teeth. Thought to be a fable, the French naturalist Geoffrey de Saint Hilaire has confirmed it in modern times.

Herrick, Robert 1591-1674
FT, Vol 2 p 53: quotes 'Ceremonies for Candlemas-Day' from H's *Hesperides*
    p 240: As beasts unto the altars go,/ With garlands dressed, so I/ Will, with my Willow wreath, also/ Come forth and sweetly die.
    p 300: The Holly hitherto did sway/ Let Box now domineer
MWF, April: Fled are the frosts, and now the fields appear

Hewitson, William C 1896-1878
BB, p 85: The Redwing

p 90: The Ring Ouzel
p 173: The eggs of the Tree Pipit present such a quantity of distinctive varieties
pp 397-8: an account of the habits of the Turnstone during the breeding season

Hill, Mr F V (of Helston, c 1873)
WL, pp 254-262: Catalogue of Birds observed in the Lizard District

Homer (of Ithaca) c 8th century BCE
FT, Vol 2 p 90: From out the cover'd rock…The bush Alders form'd a shady scene.

Hooker, Sir William Jackson 1785-1865 [FAC]
FS, p 35: *Dicranum Bryoides*
BR, p 180: Sea-weed as a source of winter food for cattle on Jura and Skye
FT, Vol 2 p 81: The branches of the Weeping Birch are more warty than the common Birch
   p 241: 70 species of Willow enumerated by WJH as native of Britain
   p 422: No distinctive botanical characters have been given for the Cedar and the Deodar

Horace, Quintus Horatius Flaccus 65-8 BCE
FT, Vol 2 p 189: Now stretch'd beneath the Arbutus' green shade [about the Strawberry Tree]

Hore, Rev William Strong 1807-1882
BB, pp 390-1: Observed the Grey Plover in full black plumage in Norfolk in May
   p 454: Acknowledges indebtedness to Hore for many valuable notes, incorporated in the text. Observations on this p about the Little Stint, specimens found in 1840 on the Laira mud banks
   p 503: The Garganey breeding in the Norfolk Broads

Horticultural Society's Transactions
FT, Vol 1 p 247-8: identifies 274 variety of plum from the sloe to the green-gage

Houel, Jean-Pierre Louis Laurent 1735-1813
FT, Vol 2 p31: A visit to the Chestnut trees of Sicily of mammoth proportions

Howison, Dr John 1797-1859
FT, Vol 2 pp 337-9: about bringing timber to market in the heart of Russia

Howitt, Mary 1799-1888
FS, p 32: 'The Use of Flowers'

Howitt, William 1792-1879
FT, Vol 2 p 275: notes that the poet has written an 'Ode to the Wayfaring-tree'

Hunter, Dr Alexander 1730-1809
FT, Vol 2 pp 130-1: The importance of Hornbeam in hedging

pp 231-5: Quotes in full a letter of Joseph Harrison, Esq of Bawtry to AH, as reprinted from Hunter's edition of Evelyn's *Sylva*, about the use of the Acacia (aka Locust-tree) in ship-building in Virginia, then in Rhode Island and New York through his promotion of it as superior to Oak in strength and duration.

p 415: Describes the 'feast of Cedars' in the Levant

Hurdis, James 1763-1801
MWF, March: Anemone

Ingram, Rev E W c1849
FT, Vol 2 p 315: Informant to Charles A Johns about the Ribbesford Yew & a violet hurricane

Irby, Charles Leonard and Mangles, James (c 1817 travels in the Middle East and Egypt)
FT, Vol 2 pp 415-6: reporting their observations in travelling to the Cedars of Lebanon, that names and dates as far back as 1640 are carved into the trunks

Jardine, Sir William 1800-1874
BB: p 54: the hoot of the older barn owls as a description of their cry

Jesse, Edward 1780-1868
FT, Vol 1 pp 206-8, p 218: quotations from *Gleanings from Natural History* 1832-1835

pp 346-347: the admiration and wonder one feels about beeches (*Gleanings*)
FT, Vol 2 p 119: Charles I on his execution day pointing out an Elm that his brother planted

Joan of Arc 1412-1431
FT, Vol 1 p 337: note on the legendary Beech-tree at Domremy, Lorraine, where Joan spoke with Saint Margaret and Saint Catharine.

Johns, Alexander Esq (Charles Johns's uncle/cousin)
FT, Vol 1 pp 226-8: account of the 'Witch Thorn' in County Antrim, Ireland (+engraving)

Johns, Charles Alexander 1821-1874
FS, pp 24-6: 'Sabbath Morning in the Country'
FT, Vol 2 p 255: Refers the reader back to his *Botanical Rambles*, p 123 [Scottish Highlands], where the Herbaceous Willow interested him particularly as being the least of known British trees. (Illus)
MWF, November: Mosses
    December: Holly
BB, pp 274-5: His observations relating to Swallows on the bank of the Plym in Devonshire, in deepest December.

pp 300-1: His personal observation about the Wryneck (*yunx torquilla*) and the appropriateness of its name (from the Latin *torqueo*, to twist), and setting it free after study

p 313: Refers the reader back to his *Birds' Nests*, p 12 (1854, SPCK) about the Nuthatch

p 314: Refers the reader to *Spring Ramble*, p 47 (1849, SPCK) about the food storage habits of the Nuthatch.

pp 598-560: From his own Journal: August 27th [Ed. note: This is *not* the only known diary/journal kept by the Cornwall Records Office as employed in this biography.] This excerpt is about the Gannet, watched through a telescope near the entrance of Belfast Lough, Ireland, possibly in the late 1830s when Johns was at University.

Johns, Henry Incledon 1776-1851
BR, p 57: Beneath the verdurous canopy, how sweet

Johnson, Dr Samuel 1709-1784
FT, Vol 2 pp 250-1: The White Willow was his favourite tree, under which he often rested

Jonson, Ben 1572-1637
FT, Vol 2 p 17: chestnut whilk hath larded (fattened) many a swine
MWF, September: Horned Poppy

Keble, John 1792-1866 [FAC]
FS, p 18: It was not then a poet's dream
p 28: The glorious sky embracing all
p 36: Thou wilt – for Thou art Israel's God

Kent, Elizabeth 1790-1861
FT, Vol 1 p 280: quotes from her *Sylvan Sketches, or a Companion to the Park and Shrubbery* (1825), 'by the author of the *Flora Domestica*,' a stanza of an ancient song: 'Their spells were vain; the boys returned,' about the 'roan tree.'
FT, Vol 2 p 267: Elder sometimes coupled with the Cypress and others emblematical of death or sorrow.
pp 298-9: quoting from Dr Hunter: planting Yew in churchyards, is for reasons of procession on Palm Sunday

Keppel, Rev Thomas 1811-1863
BB, p 477: Reports the letter sent to Yarrell, about the Pink-footed Goose killed by Lord Coke at Holkam in 1841

Kerby (also Kirby), William 1759-1850
FT, Vol 2 pp 116-7: Referring to his second vol written with Spence, *Entomology*, about the Elm

Kitto, Dr John 1804-1854
FT, Vol 2 p 433: K a fellow West Country poet and scholar from Plymouth, rising from the poor house to author of theological texts. Here he fixes on the Juniper as Elijah's tree of rest, possibly erroneously.

Knapp, John Leonard 1767-1845
FT, Vol 2 pp 51-2: quoting from his 'instructive and entertaining' *Journal of a Naturalist* comments on Christmas decorations and the use of Holly
   pp 282-5: a lengthy quotation from this 'amiable author' about the possessive qualities of ivy, covering much ruin, and covering it with fancy and imagination

Knight's London (1840-1)
FT, Vol 1: references to this written guide vol 1, p 174 regarding the largest telescope in the world

Kollar, Vincenz 1797-1860
FT, Vol 2 p 341: about insects destructive to the Fir-tribe of trees

Lamartine, Alphonse de 1790-1869
FT, Vol 2 p 417: The Cedars, and what more beautiful canopy for worship can exist?

Lauder, Sir Thomas Dick 1784-1848
FT, Vol 1 p 218: About the Hawthorne tree
   pp 323-6: Commenting on Gilpin's approach to the beauty of nature, and defending the nobility and beauty of the beech – and a grove of beeches.
FT, Vol 2 p 5: the use of chestnut for buildings in the Scottish capital, Edinburgh
   p 12-13: It is in Italy that the Chestnut is to be found in all its glory and usefulness
   p 27: A Chestnut at Finhaven, Forfarshire, long reported the largest tree in Scotland
   p 44: The large size of Horse Chestnuts at Peeble in Tweeddale
   p 81: The bumpiness of the Weeping Birch is due to fragrant gum/resin that hardens
   pp 92-4: The Alder always associated with river scenery
   p 123: Agrees with Gilpin about the picturesque interest of the Wych Elm and comments
   p 334-5: on meeting up with a Silver Fir-log being transported down the Jura mountains
   pp 343-6: about the Scotch Fir or Pine in the forests of Invercauld and Braemar
   p 348: the Pine forest and how it renews itself
   p 351: His observations about the Forest of Glenmore and its skeletons of trees
   pp 380-1: The Spruce Fir is the great tree of the Alps and the essence of Swiss sceneric grandeur

Layard, Sir Austen Henry 1817-1894 [FAC]
FT, Vol 2 p 329: At Nimroud, the ancient Nineveh, many representations of figures on sculptures are bearing Fir-cones.

Leland, John c 1503-1552

Tour of Cornwall c 1538
WL, p 118: The biographer of St Rumon, and a description of 'Gunhilly,' i.e. Hilly
Hethe

Lightfoot, Bishop Joseph Barber 1828-1889
FT, Vol 1 pp 367-8: references the Highlanders belief in the cross of Jesus being
made of aspen

Lindley, Dr John 1799-1865
FT, Vol 1 pp 244-5: Uses of the bark of the Blackthorn
    p 304: considered the Cornish Gilliflower to be the best eating apple
FT, Vol 2 p 104: describing a variety of Elm
    pp 218-219: about the Oriental Plane and its leaves and foliage
    pp 241-2: Further reduced Hooker's enumeration of 70 native Willows (Britain) from Babington's 57, following Karl Koch's (1809-1879) arrangement, to 30, relegating some specimens to 'mere varieties.' This little difference of opinion leads CAJ to ask his readers, if they are deeply interested in Willows, to select their own guide between Hooker, Babington and Lindley, as Willows are obviously very difficult to distinguish, even for botanists.
    p 289: L pronounces on varying opinions about ivy and its protective/destructive qualities
    p 432: L posits that a plant nearly the same as the Chili Pine once (long past) grew in Britain (remains in Dorsetshire), though it is said to have been introduced in 1793.

Linnaeus, Carolus [Carl von Linné] 1707-1778
FS, p 16: A condensation from *Flora Lapponica*
BR, Chp 5: pp 97-100 About Linnaeus's observations of the Reindeer Moss
FT, Vol 2: pp 10-11 The Chestnut placed in the same genus as the Beech
    p 132: Hornbeam used for dyeing yellow
    p 166: his name derived from the Swedish Lin (Linden-tree)
    pp 330-1: about the burning forests of firs in Lapland
    p 377: L is said by Johns to have mis-identified Picea (the Spruce Fir) as a Silver
Fir
    p 435: Juniper placed by L in a different class from other Firs, though allied
FF, Vol 1 p xv-lix: Introducing L, as the learned fixer of the first arrangement of plants, amounting to 7,300 species in 1753. Johns then both defends and explains the Linnaean system. He concludes: 'It is not, therefore, too much to say that the Artificial System of L has served a double purpose. Before a Natural Method was arranged, it was the only one that was available; and now that it is superseded, it is still eminently useful as an index, or catalogue of the contents of its successor;' Johns then outlines the system adopted in Britain, a modification of those of Jussieu and De Candolle.
BB, p 380: The Collared Pratincole, was named by L as *Hirundo pratincola*, and by that name is figured in Bewick.

Littleton (Lyttleton), Charles 1714-1768

Dean of Exeter, later Bishop of Carlisle
WL, pp 61-3: A description of his tour of the Lizard with Rev William Borlase

Longfellow, Henry Wadsworth 1807-1882
MWF, August: Autumn Flowers

Loudon, John Claudius 1783-1843 and his wife, **Jane Webb Loudon** 1807-1858
FT, Vol 1 p 240, p 246: account of the Blackthorn

p 317: account of the spread of the Beech in temperate zones internationally

p 341: the use of beech wood in Scotland for making the scabbards of swords, and much used for the smoking of herrings

p 345: references *Arboretum Britannicum* on the work of finding truffles

p 361: the nature of the name of the black poplar

FT, Vol 2 p 9: raps Loudon & others for misconception about the Chestnut in Italy as being introduced by Tiberius Caesar, probably from quoting it secondhand rather than reading in the original.

p 84: The multiple uses of the Birch tree made by the Scottish Highlanders

pp 103-4: about the Cornish Elm

pp 160-1: the preparing of Walnuts

pp 173-4: the various uses of the Lime wood in Russia, Sweden and Germany and in Switzerland in Evelyn's time

p 175: A Lime tree at Knowle

p 226: a pink and a green dye may be prepared from Privet berries

pp 230-1: quotes from JCL's elaborate account of the Acacia

pp 235-6: L reports on the American shipwrights and their heavy use of Locust-wood (See Hunter above) Acacias useful for tree-nails.

p 247: about the Willow down used for stuffing mattresses, and made into paper

p 254: tells of old Willow rooting itself into an oak prop, eventually making the support no longer necessary (at Karlsruhe)

p 256: with Selby, Loudon has a long list of insects that feed on Willows

p 260: Weeping Willows used throughout the East, Turkey and Algiers as plants for cemeteries to present the idea of grief for the departed.

pp 262-3: The Willow introduced into St Helena from Britain, becoming a favourite of Napoleon, and subsequently some planted around his grave. The oldest now (1849) in existence in Europe from that re-introduced stock from St H, stands in the garden of the Roebuck Tavern on Richmond Hill, Surrey

p 277: uses in basket-making and ties for the Wayfaring-tree in Germany, berries used in Switzerland for ink

p 293: L points to the largest plants of Ivy at Brockley Hall in Somerset and one at Morpeth

p 308: about the wood of the Yew, and the Englishman's use of it

p 313: description of the Mamhilad Yew near Pontypool

pp 383-4: describing the extreme beauty of winter scenery in a Spruce Fir forest in Sweden

pp 400-1: about the extensive planting of the Larch following the lead of the

Duke of Athol (c 1750) who found the timber so superior. His successor, John, Duke of Athol then planted between 1764 and 1826, Larches to occupy some 10,324 imperial acres (more than 14 million) [Johns here extracts from the *Transactions of the Highland Society*]

p 436: L mentions some Junipers that have grown to between 16-30 feet high

Low, George 1747-1795
BB, p 593: His observations about sheep being attacked by Skua on Orkney and Shetland

Lubbock, Rev Richard 1798-1876
BB, p 501: CAJ refers the reader to L's *Fauna of Norfolk* for the systematic method of capturing Ducks by a decoy.

p 580: Black-headed Gulls hawking for flies with a motion like Swallows

Macgillivray, William 1796-1852
BB, pp 185-7: About the Snow Bunting (*British Birds*, vol i, p 404)

p 222: About the Bullfinch

p 228: About observing hundreds of Crossbills in Scotland (*British Birds*, vol i, p 425)

p 241: The acute sight and smell of the Raven (British Birds, vol i, p 510)

p 280: Observations of his witnesses about the House Martin

p 283: Reference to his *British Birds*, vol iii, p 600, related to Sand Martins

p 336: Information he shares about the Rock Dove, based on year-round observations

p 382: The behaviour of the young Golden Plover

p 414: The mistaking of the Bittern's cry with that of the Snipe, by a brother naturalist

p 425: Quotes a writer in the *Naturalist* about the Common Redshank

p 431: About the incidence of the Greenshank in Scotland

p 458: The nesting habits of the Dunlin

pp 479-80: About this very beautiful bird, the Bernicle Goose

p 545: The mode of life of the Black Guillemot differs in no material respect from other G

Maddon (probably Madden, Edmund) (published 1847)
FT, Vol 2 p 420: says that the Kelon of Simla, is the true Deodar

Magazine of Natural History
BB: p 159: About the Bearded Tit

p 180: The style of the Skylark song is determined by whether it is ascending, stationary or descending.

p 229: About the numerous Crossbills in Suffolk in 1822 (No. for January, 1834)

p 309: Concerning the nest-building habits of the Wren

Mallet, David c1705-1765

BR, p 88: Fair Morn ascends; fresh Zephryr's breath

Marlowe, Christopher 1564-1593
BB, p 240: The sad presaging Raven tolls [*Jew of Malta*]

Martial, Marcus Valerius c40-c103 AD
FT, Vol 2 pp 17: And chestnuts, such as learned Naples boasted

Martyn, William Frederick (published 1785)
FT, Vol 2 p 43: Mentions Horse Chestnuts raised from the nut to great size rapidly
  p 299: The Yew used by our forefathers for processing to graves

Maundrell, Henry 1665-1701
FT, Vol 2 pp 414-5: A description, one of many, of the famous grove of Cedars on Mount Lebanon

McDougall, Dr Peter 1798-1834
BB, p 565: The discoverer of the Roseate Tern describes the bird

Melville, Hon William Leslie (1831 travels)
FT, Vol 2 p 423: M brought home some cones of the Deodar in 1831 and supplied seeds to the Horticultural Society &c.

Meredith, Mr and Mrs Louisa Anne 1812-1895
FT, Vol 2 p 431: Excerpt from her entertaining *Notes and Sketches of New South Wales* (c 1841 State Library of Tasmania presentation copies) about Pines

Merritt, T L (c 1835)
MWF, February: Hazel
  July: Pimpernel
  September: Star-wort, or Aster, and Thrift

Meyer, Henry Leonard 1797-1865
BB, p 220: Refers to information given in *Illustrations of British Birds*, vol iii, p 120 about the Lesser Redpole
  p 391: Reference to the character of the Grey Plover in *Illustrations of British Birds and their Eggs*, vol v p 162
  p 564: Comments on the Sandwich Tern

Michaux, Andre 1746-1802 and son **Francois Andre** 1770-1855
FT, Vol 2 p 319: description of process when vegetation ceases in the Fir-tribe of trees

Miller, [Philip]
FT, Vol 2 pp 20-21: grafting of chestnut fruit upon stocks raised from the nut, becoming *marroniers*

Millington, Thomas 1628-1704
FF, Vol 1 p xv: Is alluded to by Linnaeus as preceding him in plant arrangement systems, with 'characters' written for plants

Milton, John 1608-1674
FS, p 12: These are thy glorious works, Parent of good
FT, Vol 1 p 342: Let herbs to them a bloodless banquet give/ In Beechen goblets
FT, Vol 2 p 17: In whom shall I confide? Whose counsel find/
    p 112: Not always city pent, or pent at home...Of branching Elm,
    p 408: Over head up grew,/ Insuperable height of loftiest shade,/ Cedar, and Pine, and Fir, and branching Palm.
MWF, March: Primrose
    April: Cowslips
BB, p 323: Addressing the Nightingale: 'Thy liquid notes that close the eye of day/ First heard before the shallow Cuccoo's bill,/ Portend success in love.'

Montagu, George 1751-1815
BB, p 141: Nest of the Dartford Warbler
    p 151: About the Crested Tit
    p 176: The Rock Pipit never observed as gregarious
    p 374: Estimating how much water a Great Bustard can carry in its pouch (*Ornithological Dictionary*)
    p 411: The presence of the Buff-Backed Heron in England

Moorcroft, William c 1770-1825
FT, Vol 2 pp 422-3: The durability of the timber of the Deodar

Munro, Captain No further identification
FT, Vol 2 p 422: Considers the Deodars to be varieties of the Cedar of Lebanon

Naturalist
BB, p 204: The account of an affray amongst House Sparrows, leaving some dead and dying.

Neill, Dr Patrick 1776-1851
BR, p 178-9: Reporting the sea-weeds at the mouth of the Firth of Forth 1813-14
FT, Vol 2 p 313-14: The Fortingal Yew described by Barrington & later Pennant, has since 1770 been much injured by country people taking large branches of wood for making cups & other items.

Newton, Bishop Thomas 1704-1782
FS, Title-page: True philosophy is the handmaid of true religion

Norden, John c 1547-1625
WL, p 40: Quoting from his survey of Cornwall (date misprinted as 1384/prob 1584) about the smoking and drying of fish

Ogelvie, W c 1848
FT, Vol 2 p 423: O was secretary of the Zoological Society, and owned the largest plantation of Deodars made in Europe, on his Altinachree estate in Tyrone (11 acres of Deodar).

Ousely, Sir William 1767-1842
FT, Vol 2 p 207: notes the hanging of old clothes as sacrifice in Persian gardens on the Plane-tree. Similar customs exist in Ireland, Arabia and South America.

Owen, Professor Richard 1804-1892 [FAC]
BB, p 375: Brought in on the question of the pouch of the Great Bustard

Palladius, 4th c AD specialist on agriculture (14-15 vols)
FT, Vol 2 p 17: Bids the rough Chestnut change its prickly kind

Parkinson, John 1567-1650
FT, Vol 2 p 35: quoting from his (1629) *Paradisi in Sole Paradisus Terrestris* placing the Horse chestnut as a fruit-tree between the Walnut and the Mulberry.

Parr, Rev Dr Samuel 1747-1825
FT, Vol 1 pp 193-6: Festivities to keep up May-day in the annual calendar.

Patterson, Robert 1802-1872 (written as Paterson)
FT, Vol 2 p 65: References to his *Insects Mentioned in Shakespeare's Plays*, with special note of Holly infested with honey-dew

Pennant, Thomas 1726-1798
BB, p 385: About the Dotterel, referring the reader to the poet Drayton who mentions 'Dottrels'
    p 404: About the incidence of the Common Crane
    p 408: Counted 80 Herons in one tree
    p 492: Refers the reader to vol ii, p 257 about the Common Sheldrake
    p 511: The Eider Duck and its down/the plucking of her breast

Pepys, Samuel 1603-1703
BB, pp 87-8: from the diary 22d May 1663, about the Blackbird.

Perrault, M (c1676)
BB, pp 373-4: An account of a tame Bustard.

Philips, John 1676-1709
BB, p 337: 'The cuckoo calls aloud his wand'ring love/ The Turtle's moan is heard in ev'ry grove;

Phillips, Henry 1779-1840 Author of *Sylva Florifera*
FT, Vol 2 pp 145-6: about gathering Hazel nuts
    p 175: describes an enormous Lime in Vaud, Switzerland

p 299: A consecrated Yew, its value is a pound;

p 435: Juniper wood and berries burned to fumigate rooms of the sick. In Sweden, the berries are made into conserve, and sometimes used as a substitute for coffee.

Pliny the Elder 23-79 AD

FT, Vol 1 p 261: account of the Cherry tree from book xv, chapter 30

p 296: enumerates 32 varieties of pear

p 315: ties his description of the Fagus with the Beech tree

p 362: the black poplar known to Pliny

p 365: Aspen described by P in the name of Libyan Poplar

FT, Vol 2 p 9: the varieties of Chestnut

p 35: Aesculus, from *esca*, food, was applied originally to a species of Oak

pp 77-80: The Birch, a slender tree inhabiting Gaul

pp 107-9: about the Elm and its habitats

p 133: about the Hazel

pp 165-6: about the Linden or Lime-Tree, called Philyra by the Greeks, and its thousand uses.

p 181: Pliny described the Tamarisk as an evergreen [unmerited], and it was known to the Greeks and Romans under the name of *Myrica*

p 189: Pliny terms the Strawberry-Tree (*Arbutus Unedo*) as *Unedo*, or *One-I-Eat*, the fruit being not pleasant enough to eat a second.

p 201: allusion to the Dogwood as a 'bloody-twig'

p 203: quoting P that Trees were the first inducement to the Gauls to cross the Alps

p 242: Pliny mentions only 8 species of Willow, and finds them useful and valuable

pp 265-6: the medicinal qualities and uses of the Elder

p 297: The Yew is a symbol of evil omen, neither verdant, nor graceful, but gloomy, terrible, and sapless.

p 377: P writes of the Spruce Fir (as *Picea*) as delighting in a lofty and cold situation

BB, p 31: The Kite by the movement of its tail has taught mankind the art of steering.

pp 268-9: Reference to his lib. x, cap 32. xxxii. cap 8: the original meaning of 'halcyon days' and the gestation period of the Kingfisher

pp317-8: Lib x, cap ix, contributes to a discussion of the Cuckoo and its biography

pp 368-9: P says, "Quails always arrive before Cranes..." (*Natural History*, lib x cap xxiii)

pp 376-7: The name given the Little Bustard, a bird classed by Pliny with geese

Plot, Dr Robert 1640-1696

FT, Vol 2 p 147: Referring to his *Natural History of Oxfordshire* and a finding of Hazel nuts

pp 253-4: Pollard Willows and seeds of Ash trees becoming cross-rooted

Pope, Alexander 1688-1744
FT, Vol 1 p 192: 'Amidst the area wide they took their stand'
FT, Vol 2 p 262: The Willow may have been introduced into Britain by Pope, or a Mr Vernon (merchant of Aleppo). Another account states that it was first planted at Kew in 1692.

Rauwoolf, Leonhard c 1535-1596
FT, Vol 2 pp 258-9: About Willow-trees near Aleppo and their peculiarities in medicinal distillation when can be used to comfort the heart

Ray, John 1627-1705
WR, p A: *Wisdom of God in Creation*
FT, Vol 2 p 269: The inner bark of the Elder to be used for the dropsie
BB, p 480: With Willughby in 1676 disposed of the fable of the tree-bird, the Bernicle Goose

Rennie, James 1787-1867
BB, p 141: Whereabouts of the Dartford Warbler in February
    p 177: The sociability of the Rock Pipit, observed in Normandy
    p 283: Reference to his description of the Sand Martin in his book, *Bird Architecture*

Richardson, Dr
BB, p 61: Tengmalm's Owl is called by Cree Indians, the 'Death-bird'
    p 453: Tells of Captain Lyon observing breeding of Knots on Melville Peninsula

Rigby, Elizabeth 1809-1893
FT, Vol 2 pp 381-3: Describing a country on the Baltic as a 'land of Pines' with powerful prose, an excerpt from *Letters from the Baltic*

Robinson, Rev Mr Vyvyan
WL, p 9: An oral account of the wrecks in 1872 of the *Marianna* and *Rafflino*, two barks from Genoa, on the Stag rocks at the Lizard

Rogers, Samuel 1763-1855
MWF, December: Now Christmas revels in a world of snow

Ross, Captain Sir John 1777-1856
BR: p 185-6: The reporting of 'red snow' from his Polar expedition of 1819, due to minute plant as later determined
BB, p 576: The Cuneate-tailed Gull received its name in honour of Captain Ross

Sandwich, Earl of
FT, Vol 2 p 205: called the Plane-tree a Sycamore (1739) on seeing it on the island Stanchio (Cos)

Scott, Sir Walter 1771-1832
FT, Vol 1 p 203: From the Whitethorn the May-flower shed

p 366: 'Aspen' With every change his features play'd/
FT, Vol 2 p 308: But here, 'twixt rock and river, grew/ A dismal grove of sable hue
MWF, December: Mistletoe
BB, p 382: His poems which so often include the singular cry of the Golden Plover

Selby, Prideaux John 1788-1867
FT, Vol 1 p 264-5, 268: quotation from *British Forest Trees* about the Cherry tree
FT, Vol 2 p 131-2: Hornbeam to be planted in cold, stiff, clayey soils & burns
freely, the best of fuels
    pp 251-2: about the Crack Willow (*Salix fragilis*) and its brittleness
    p 256: with Loudon, Selby has a long list of insects that feed on Willows
    p 350: about the remains of the Forest of Glenmore between river Spey and the
Cairngorm range
BB: p 476: Gives an interesting account of several young broods of the Bean Goose
    p 538: Observed the Black-Throated Diver in the Outer Hebrides

Shakespeare, William c 1564-1616
FT, Vol 1 p 202: Gives not the Hawthorn-bush a sweeter shade
    p 280: A puzzling expression in *Macbeth* about a 'roan tree'
    p 305: Reference to the Apple-John of Shakespeare
FT, Vol 2 p 17: The sailor's wife with chestnuts in her lap
    p 204: The Queen of Carthage standing – With a Willow in her hand/Upon
the wild sea banks;
    p 272: So doth the Woodbine – the sweet Honeysuckle, Gently entwist the
Maple.
    p 299: My shroud of white, stuck all with Yew,/O prepare it!
MWF, February: Look'd like a Daisie in a field of grass
    March: Violet
    June: Honeysuckle, Fumitory
    August: Corn Marigold
BB, p 240: The Raven being a bird of dire omen
    p 533: A di-dapper peering through a wave,/ Who, being looked on, ducks as
quickly in

Sharpe's *London Magazine*
FT, Vol 2 pp 405-8: Relates the history of the introduction of the Cedar into France;
the date of its introduction into Great Britain is not known

Smith, Colonel C H (c 1841)
BB, pp 369-70: Reports on the flights of the Quail abroad, Malta, Russia, etc.

Smith, Charlotte Turner 1749-1806
FT, Vol 1 p 203: The Gorse is yellow on the heath
MWF, April: Cowslip

Smith, Sir James Edward 1759-1828
FS, p 38: 'The character of natural science'

FT, Vol 2 p 11: The Chestnut as a stately and majestic tree rivalling the English Oak
  p 127: about the Hornbeam (*Carpinus Betulus*)
  p 190: Notes that in the Levant the produce of the Strawberry Tree is agreeable
& wholesome
  p 267: an infusion of Elder leaves proves fatal to various insects

Smollett, Tobias George 1721-1771
FS, p 8: Nature I'll court, in her sequester'd haunts

Snow, R
BR, pp 109-110: Admire, as close the insect lies

Southey, Robert 1774-1843 [FAC]
FT, Vol 1 p 132: Here amid the brook
FT, Vol 2 pp58-9: O Reader! has thou ever stood to see/The Holly-tree?
  p 247: notes on coracles made of Willow rods used on the Severn (*Madoc*)
  p 414: It was a Cedar-tree/ Which woke him from that deadly drowsiness (*Thalaba*)

Spence, William 1783-1860
FT, Vol 2 pp 114-6: the insects that prey on the Elm

Spenser, Edmund 1552-1599
FT, Vol 1 p 62: A huge Oak, dry and dead
  p 77: the gray moss mars his rime
  p 366: His hand did quake/ And tremble like a leaf of Aspen green
FT, Vol 2 p 240: makes the Willow the fitting garb of the forlorn
  p 267: The water-nymphs, that wont with her to sing and dance/
  p 408: High on a hill a goodly Cedar grew/
MWF, January: Yon naked trees
  February: The little Dazie [Daisy]
  March: Primrose
  June: Wild Rose, Eglantine, Columbine
  October: Bramble, Juniper, Nuts
BB, p 18: *Fairy Queen*, Book VI, Canto VII, the *faulcons*

Stanley, Bishop Edward 1779-1849 [Bishop of Norwich]
BB, p 236: Refers to his *Familiar History of Birds* for revealing accounts of the
Starling
  p 323: Reports two instances of a young Cuckoo in captivity fed by a young
Thrush

Staunton, Sir George Thomas 1781-1859
FT, Vol 2 p 375: Nuts of the Stone Pine much prized by the Chinese

St John, Charles 1809-1856
BB, p 591: Gave the name of Wagel to the Great Grey Gull

pp 594-6: A fully-observed account of Richardson's Skua, taken from SJ's *Wild Sports of the Highlands*

Strabo, Greek 7th c BCE
FT, Vol 2 p 270: The Palm-tree has 360 uses

Strickland, Agnes 1806-1874
FT, pp188-92: From *Lives of the Queens of England* about the Hawthorn and its worthiness to be presented to royalty
MWF, July: Borage

Strutt, Jacob George 1784-1867
FT, Vol 2 pp 24-8: Illustration of the Tortworth Chestnut, and Strutt's complete description, from *Sylva Britannica* (1826)
    p 312: About the Great Yew at Ankerwyke, near Staines, said to have flourished upwards of a thousand years – the place of conference for King John to sign Magna Charta, and a favoured meeting place of Henry 8th and Anne Boleyn. Also describes the Yew at Fountain's Abbey. (Woodcut from his *Sylva Britannica* on p 314)

Taylor, Jeremy 1613-1667
FS, p 42: So I have seen a rose newly springing from the clefts

Taylor, R C (published 1840)
FT, Vol 2 pp 332-4: About a dramatic 'ice-storm' in the Alleghany Mts of Pennsylvania where Fir-trees cracked and wasted under the weight of ice, crashing into one another.

Temminck, Coenraad Jacob 1778-1858
BB, p 427: About the Green Sandpiper and its nest-building
    p 454: About Temminck's Stint (*Tringa Temminckii*)
    p 573: A description of the White-Winged Black Tern
    p 576: The exceedingly rare species called the Masked Gull & where it is to be found

Tengmalm, Dr Peter Gustaf 1754-1803
BB, p 61: Tengmalm's Owl, named after the Swedish naturalist who pointed out the difference between this and the 'Little Owl'

Tennyson, Alfred Lord 1809-1892
BB, p 198: Then as a little helpless innocent bird/ That has but one plain passage of few notes/ in the section about the Chaffinch.

Theophrastus of Eresus c371-c286 BCE
FT, Vol 2 p 10: Quotes the name 'Jupiter's nut' for the Chestnut
    p 90: Alders used in the dyeing of leather

Thomson, James 1700-1748
FS, p 10: Should fate command me to the farthest verge

BR, p 14: Rent is the fleecy mantle of the sky
FT, Vol 1 p 367: Gradual sinks the breeze/ Into a perfect calm
FT, Vol 2 p 143: Ye swains, now hasten to the Hazel-bank/
MWF, February: As yet the trembling year is unconfirmed
    July: These, in successive turn, with lavish hand
    October: The last smiles/ Of autumn beaming o'er the yellow woods
    November: But see the fading, many-coloured woods

Tibullus, Albius 54-19 BCE
FT, Vol 1 p 341: No wars did men molest/ When only Beechen bowls were in request

Toussenel, Alphonse 1803-1885
BB, p 78: the song of the Fieldfare

Train, Joseph FSA (Scotland) 1779-1852
FT, Vol 1 p 280: account of the Mountain Ash on the Isle of Man

Turner, Dr William 1508-1568
FT, Vol 2 p 50: 'Our earliest writer on plants' entitles the Holly tree the Holy-tree
    p 211: quotes from WT's *Herbal* (1541-1568) about 2 young Playn-trees (Oriental Plane) seen in England

Vaughan, Henry 1622-1695
FS, p 22: Not a sprig or leaf

Vergnaud, M (c1840s)
FT, p 43: His pamphlet proposes converting extracted starch of the horse chestnut into sugar to be used in distillation

Vetch, Captain c1821
BB, p 593: Referring to his account of the Island of Foula (Shetland) in 1821 about the Skua and its defense against Ravens, Eagles and much larger quadrupeds.

Virgil 70-19 BCE
FT, Vol 1 p 314-17: the use of the Fagus (Beech) for making into bowls, and that it is often grafted onto the Chestnut (Castanea).
FT, Vol 2 pp 16: Ripe apples and soft chestnuts we have there/ And curd abundant to supply our fare
    p 18: chestnuts eaten with milk or cheese
    p 90: Then rivers first the hollowed Alder knew,
        And the light Alder skimm'd the torrent wave [translated, from original]
    p 107: About the Elm
    pp 157-8: about the Walnut and its indicators for corn-harvest
    p 189: With leafy Arbutus your goats supply [about the Strawberry Tree]
    pp 244-5: In the time of V. willows were planted in apiaries to afford nourishment to the bees: "The Willow-hedge, which parts your neighbour's land, To bees

of Hybla yields unfailing store…"
    p 297: V agrees with Pliny in condemning the Yew-tree, & calls it noxious

Vitruvius, Marcus V Pollio, 1ˢᵗ century BCE
FT, Vol 2 p 90: notes that the city of Ravenna is built upon piles of Alder

Walpole, Horace 1717-1797
FT, Vol 2 p 173: the genius of Gibbon's carvings of wood from the Lime-tree

Walsh, Dr No further identification
FT, Vol 2 p 210: Measured the largest existing Plane-tree (at the same time the largest tree in the world) in 1831, at Buyukdere, on the Bosphorous (140 feet circumference).

Walton, Isaac 1593-1683
FT, Vol 1 p 304: account from his *Complete Angler* of the delicious syllabub to be made from apples, lard, and rose-water
    p 330: I was for that time lifted above earth,
FT, Vol 2 p 293: W says a fragrant resin, exuding from ivy makes bait attractive to fish

Warburton, Eliot B G (c 1844 published)
FT, Vol 2 p 416: At publication date only 7 (seven) Cedars of Lebanon remained, these trees being the most renowned natural monuments in the universe, celebrated in religion, poetry and history.

Waterton, Charles 1782-1865 [FAC]
FT, Vol 1 pp 280-2: account of anti-witch quality of Mountain Ash in Yorkshire, as reported in his *Essays on Natural History* (1838-1857, 3 series)
BB, p 53: The service of the Barn Owl to the agriculturist by its consumption of rats and mice
    p 258: Strongly defends the Jackdaw from the charge of molesting the eggs or the young of the pigeon.
    p 259: Verbally protects the Magpie, because it has noone to stand up for it.

Webber, Rev F (c 1847) Friend of Charles Johns
FT, Vol 1 pp 193-6: Account of a meeting with celebrated scholar Dr Samuel Parr

Weir, Denham
BB, pp 69-70: About the Spotted Flycatcher
    p 181: About the Skylark

Whitaker, John 1735-1808
WL, pp 120-1: Quoting from his 1804 study of the church at St Germans

White, Gilbert 1720-1793
FT, Vol 1 pp 133-4 'from his classical history of Selborne'
    p 240: Reference in notes to country people's definition of 'Blackthorn winter'

p 320-23: Engraving of the village of Selborne with the surrounding trees and quotation from GW, about the beech tree and his descriptions of it as 'a genuine lover of Nature.'

p 339: Beeches like to grow in crowded situations.

BB, pp 125-6: Describing the cry of the Blackcap

pp 131-2: The Lesser Whitethroat frequenting his garden

pp 273-275: A 'round-robin' discussion of the Swallow and its habits, especially related to migration

p 277: Account of the House Martin

pp 291-2: About the Nightjar

pp 333-4: The Stock Dove abundant at Selborne

p 434: *Selborne* has interesting remarks on the Black-Winged Stilt

Willughby, Francis 1635-1672

BB, p 319: In relation to his work with John Ray published in 1676 (posthumously) *Ornothologia*, containing some errors in relation to the Cuckoo and its destruction of found eggs, errors that persist amongst some to Johns's day.

pp 372-3: Gives a lengthy account of the Great Bustard

p 404: About Cranes and their haunts

pp 414-5: The Bittern or Mire-drum is the bird popularly known as the Night Raven

p 417: The Stork rarely if ever seen in England – only when blown by the wind or by accident

p 452: About the Knot and its name, deriving from being a favourite dish of King Canutus (Knute)

p 502-3: With Ray in 1676, p 286, defines and explains decoys, a corruption of Duck-coy

p 506: With Ray, provides a description of the Wigeon, under the name of Whewer

p 517: The Ferruginous Duck appears to be the 'Morillon' as described by W

pp 578-9: Describes a colony of Black-headed Gulls (Black-caps) in Stafford

p 590: Naming the Wagell (probably the Great Black-backed Gull)

p 600: About the Manx Shearwater ('Puffin')

Wilson, Professor James 1795-1856

BB, p 543: Refers to his *Voyage round the Coasts of Scotland and the Islands*, with special reference to the feeding of Guillemots

p 562: Directs the reader to an interesting account about Gannets at St Kilda

p 597: About the habitat of the Fulmar Petrel (in the Outer Hebrides on Fulmar)

Dr Woodhouse, late Rector of Donington from 1690-1703

FT, Vol 1 pp 83-8: An account of the Royal Oak (King Charles II) in Latin & in translation

Wordsworth, William 1770-1850 [FAC]

FS, p 2: Happy is he who lives to understand

p 4: Among these rocks and stones, methinks, I see

How beautiful this dome of sky!

p 10: To me the meanest flower that blows can give

BR, p 31: To me the meanest flower that blows can give
BR, pp 112-13: Poor Robin
FT, Vol 1 p 189: That only night in all the year
    p 203: Yon reverend Hawthorns, harden'd to the rod
    p 209: There is a Thorn – it looks so old –
    p 278: The Mountain Ash/ No eye can overlook
    p 342: A Beechen bowl/ A Maple dish, my furniture should be
    p 367: Into a gradual calm the zephyrs sink
FT, Vol 2 pp 59-60: Where leafless Oaks towered high above
    p 91: But now to form a shade/For thee, green Alders have together wound/
    p 112: Our days glide on; …That he hath been an Elm without his Vine
    pp 143-4: quoting at length for its beauty: "It seems a day/ (I speak of one from
many singled out)/
    p 272/1: So, pleased with purple clusters to entwine/
    p 272/2: Brought from the woods the Honeysuckle twines/
    p 298: about the Yew: Of vast circumference, and gloom profound/ This solitary Tree!
MWF, January: Snowdrop
    July: Foxglove, Water-Lily
    November: Yew
BB, p 291: The busy Dor-Hawk chases the white moth/ With burring note----
[about the Nightjar]
    p 330: 'I heard a Stock Dove sing or say/ His homely tale, this very day;

Xenophon c431-355 BCE
BB, p 372: In the *Anabasis*, Johns finds the earliest mention which he can find of
the Great Bustard (*Otis tarda*)

Yarrell, William 1784-1856 [FAC]
BB, pp vi-viii: the present volume contains an account, more or less detailed, of all
the birds figured in the second edition of Yarrell, as well as of some few which have
been observed since the date of that publication.
    p 78: The song of the Fieldfare is soft and melodious
    p 411: Buff-backed Heron, 1805 near Kingsbridge, Devon
    p 160: The nests of the Bearded Tit
    pp 172-3: His description of the Tree Pipit (Vol i, p 432) is comprehensive and
accurate.
    p 175: The nest of the Meadow Pipit is often a depository for the eggs of a
Cuckoo. (vol i, p 429)
    p 226: Disagrees with Buffon about the useless nature of the Common Cross-
bill's beak (Vol ii, p 22)
    p 261: See *British Birds*, vol ii, p 113 about the then recent introduction of
Magpies to Ireland.
    p 275-6: The Swallow as a migratory bird
    p 295: Structure and mode of life of the Green Woodpecker in *British Birds*,
vol ii, p 138
    p 301: The number of eggs laid by the Wryneck in one nest being 22
    p 334: Y wrote of two old Stock Doves brought to sale with Ring Doves

p 375: Y delivered a paper, Linnean Transactions, vol xxi, p 155, with many interesting observations about the Great Bustard.

p 489: Provides a full account of the Polish Swan

p 490: The Ruddy Sheldrake placed first in the list of Ducks

p 526: CAJ refers the reader to an account found in Yarrell, from Audubon, about the Hooded Merganser, an American species, only very few having been seen in Britain

p 536: Y quotes Sir Thomas Browne as the authority on Great Northern Divers

pp 579-80: About the Black-headed Gull

The Zoologist

BB, p 25-6: Reference to a male Kestril, "Billy" as told in Pet Animals, published by SPCK

p 48: The Long-eared Owl and its plaintive cry

p 59: The cry of the Little Owl a pleasant sound of the country, not as a French proverb of reproach

pp 64-5: The Red-backed Shrike and its attachment to its mate and young. Vol XI, p 3981

p 78: The song of the Fieldfare combines the whistle of the Blackbird with the voice of the Missel Thrush. Vol IV, page 1297

p 203: The quantity of grain consumed by the House Sparrow is enough to consider it a pest to the agriculturist (Vol vi, p 2299)

p 228: A writer describes the manoeuvres of a flock of Crossbills in County Durham (Vol vii, p 2527.

p 241: A writer describes the acute senses of the Raven (Vol i, p 215)

p 262: The complete lack of fear of man amongst Norwegian Magpies (Vol viii, p 3085)

pp 285-6: Quoting from the September issue, 1856, p 5249 about the Common Swift

pp 296-7: Referring to Vol viii, p 3115, where a writer observes the attraction of fallen timber to the Great Spotted Woodpecker

p 315: An amusing account of the Nuthatch is referred in vol i, p 213 of the magazine

p 345: The story of a male Pheasant and his vicious killing spree. The female pheasant is a timid, unoffending bird.

pp 355-6: Rev. A C Smith writes in vol viii, p 2977, his observations of the Ptarmigan

p 397: An account of two Turnstones successfully turning over the dead body of a cod-fish 3 ½ feet long, imbedded two inches in the sand.

pp 443-4: A writer reports 4 young solitary Great Snipes in county Durham

p 469: Record of a female Gallinule (Moor-Hen) carrying a young one in each foot

p 539: Numerous Red-throated Divers in winter off the coast of the Isle of Wight

p 585: About the Common Gull by Mr W R Fisher in the Zoologist, vol i, p 248

p 594: About the Skua, vol iii, p 880

All of the whys and wherefores of the following alphabetic list of autographs and photographs are elusive. Educated guesses may be made in some cases, but not in all. The reader of the cache of letters, envelopes, notes, signatures is aided in this collection by the addition in many cases of small vignette photographs (indicated by (P) following name) of the sender and a handwritten inscription below. The formality of the period does not allow consistently for interpretation of who the receiver is, unless the correspondent has added the name of the person addressed, usually at the end of the document. The common address, even amongst closer friends was 'Dear Sir' and 'Madam.' Hence, unless the envelope is also saved by the collector, which is sometimes done in this collection, or within the letter other hints allow for who is being addressed, this may remain a mystery until a matching correspondent is found. Basically, an Autograph Collection and its study is one of finding connections and networks within class structures, and indicates who was considered noteworthy to the collector(s) over the lifetime of the collection. It is not, of course, a stash of personal correspondence, and usually only one example, sometimes two, of each individual is saved. Weighted as this one is toward science, education, and the arts, it serves as a reflection of the interests of Johns and his family within the various sectors of society in which they mixed.

The earliest item that is dated is the signature of George III (1790), and the latest dated note from Dr Henry Liddell, Christ Church, Oxford, to Mrs Johns (1880). Other undated entries may have been both earlier and later than the dates mentioned, but the collection spans virtually a century. From internal reading of the correspondence, the main correspondents, collectors and arrangers appear to have been Mrs Johns and her daughter, Katie. Some items will have come to the family after the death of Charles's parents (such as the signature above, a receipt to J St Aubyn, and a letter from Charles Incledon, their cousin). Some early letters to Johns himself, from Henry de la Beche, Bishop Philpotts (Cornwall), William Wordsworth, the Hookers, Robert Graham, Charles Darwin etc. would have been kept by him because of their sentimental and scientific interest to him and his work. There is little personal or family correspondence (that would have been of even greater interest to this memoir), though close friendships with the families of former pupils are discernable through a study of content. Examples are the Evans family (Sir Arthur Evans of Knossos, a pupil) and the Monckton-Milnes family (Baron Houghton, his son a pupil), both of these enjoying large circles of talented friends of wide influence.

It is suggested, after careful surveillance of the entire collection, that the Collection was probably begun in the late 1850s or early 1860s, when Katie and her mother, Ellen, took it up as a project together – which they could both enjoy and expand through their own correspondence, and to which they could invite their friends to contribute. The sections deliberately labelled are 1) Royal 2) Political 3) Literary 4) Scientific 5) Artistic. A large number are not categorised or labelled, and these form a Miscellaneous section. Throughout there is a plethora of clergymen but no section marked theological, and this for the simple reason that most of the distinguished names would overlap, as ordination was common amongst educated men. The external contributors of batches of autographs to the collection are obvious due to the repetition of names as recipients: Derwent Coleridge, Mrs Charles Kingsley (née Grenfell), Mrs Robert Holland, Lord and Lady Elcho and John Noble. The primary collector was Mrs Johns, and the letters continue to be inserted following CAJ's death due to her own wide correspondence and friendship network. But, as in all such collections some signatures are indecipherable, whether sender or receiver, and many are undated. Handwritten attributions under items are often faded, and in several cases are out of scanning order with their labels, mainly due to letters extending to several pages, having originally been written on both sides of the stationery employed. Hence, careful checking of photographs has been required, and this has been made much easier, due to the good offices of the Complete Catalogue of the National Portrait Gallery, where many portraits of these same distinguished people are held. However, of interest is the fact that only some of the photographs in the Johns Album match exactly those in the NPG. Hence, in some cases in the Johns Album we have another visual image for the historical record.

Any researcher desiring particular information about a specific item, should address: Curator, Johns Archive, Trevelyan House, 16 Chapel Street, Penzance, Cornwall, TR18 4AW. The identification code for the entire CY Reel 2846, is ML (Mitchell Library) A27, Frames 1-275, and is catalogued in the Mitchell Library of the State Library of New South Wales, Sydney, Australia. It is through their prescience and courtesy that this has been made available for personal study.

Item from	Item to	Date	Content in brief
Acland, Dr Henry	Peter	August 12, 18--	Personal friendly
Addington, Henry (Vt Sidmouth)	Unidentified Madam	1786 (?96)	Opportunities for Mr Gent
Adelaide, Queen/Lord Howe for	Rev Charles Johns (CAJ)	12 July 1841	Thanks for Flora Sacra
Ainsworth, William	Unknown	Undated	Birthday dinner invite
Airey, Sir G	J W G Gutch Esq	January 11, 1842	Meterological Journal
Arnold, Matthew	Warburton	Mar-15	Pension Minute in review
Auerbach, Berthold	Unknown	Undated	
Babbage, Charles	John Evans Esq	January 23, 1865	Envelope
Baker, Sir Samuel	Mrs Charles Kingsley	May/Mar? 1866	Autograph letter
Balfour, Professor J H	Introduction letter for CAJ	Undated	Opening doors for collecting
Barker, Lady M A	Mrs CAJ	November 29, 1877	Sending autograph
Beche, De La	CAJ	Undated	To visit Coverack with CAJ
Bell, Thomas FLS	My dear Sir (CAJ)	March 11, 1861	Permission for Land Birds reprint
Bench, R C	Unidentified Sir	October 25, 1861	Information not available
Berkeley, W J	Kings Cliff (?)	November 14, 1861	Sending Kew specimen
Bernand, F C	John Noble	1866	Delightfully funny personal
Bethell, Richard (Westbury)	Earl Russell KG	Undated	Envelope
Birkbeck, George	Mr White	June 21, 1841	Meterological Society
Blessington, Lady	Unknown	April 30, 1849	Returning proofs/contact in Paris
Boyd, Professor/ St Andrews	Charles Kingsley	Aug-03	Delighted to welcome him/St A
Brand, HBW, Speaker HoC	Mrs Maria Jacob	1877	Cannot assist nephew at BM
Bright, John	Wm Marshall MP	1867	Thanks for superb grapes

Name	Recipient/Type	Date	Description
Brougham, Henry Peter, Lord	J I Luscombe Esq	Undated	Envelope
Brunel, Isambard K	My dear ?Newham	February 8, 1858	Reply to friend not seen
Buckle, Henry Thomas (P)	Mrs Robert Holland	22-Dec	Has written to W Parker
Cambridge, HRH Duke of	Lord Elcho	December 15, 1875	Prince George considering
Cameron, Verney Lovet	Autograph	Undated	Central African traveller
Carlyle, Thomas	Unknown Sir	Undated	Frenchman's Reminiscences
Carpenter, William B	CAJ	March 18, 1871	Arrangements for speaking visit
Chatham, Lord	Mrs John Eliot	1774	Calling card
Clarendon, Lord (His agent)	CAJ	Undated (c 1863)	Permission for boys to fish canal
Cobbe, Frances Power (P)	My dear Mary (?Coleridge)	Undated	Friendly reply to letter
Cohen, C W	Duncan Dunbar	October 28, 1861	Engagements prevent attending
Coleridge, S T manuscript[1]	Given by Derwent Coleridge	Attached 1860	
Collins, F Payne	John Noble	August 29, 1865	Cannot come to Billiards
Collins, Wilkie	Autograph	July 17, 1866	Card
Craik, Mrs Dinah Maria Mulock	Charles Kingsley	Undated	Inviting the Kingsleys to visit
Creswick, Thomas	Duncan Dunbar	November 4, 1861	Unable to attend/friends visiting
Darwin, Charles[2]	CAJ	Aug 13, [1868]	Friendly reply to botanical query
De la Beche, see Beche			
Delane, John	Unknown	Undated	Note from the Editor of Times
Derby, Lord	CAJ	May 13, 1867	Cannot agree idea for solicitors
Dickens, Charles	Autograph	November, 1865	From Gad's Hill
Disraeli, Benjamin	Lord Elcho	May 25, 1875	Declines due to Cabinet Meeting
Duff, M E Grant	CAJ	1872	Lady Portsmouth refers Winton
Durham, Joseph	Autograph	Undated	Signature of sculptor
Edwards, Amelia B	Mrs Woodroffe	May-08	About printing plates
Elcho, Lord[3]	CAJ	1870	His son & school report
Elliott, Sir Henry	Lord Elcho	Undated	Dining with Lord Derby tomorrow
Etty, William	Mrs Robert Holland	July 10, 1849	Declines due to illness
Evans, Arthur John[4]	Mrs Ellen Johns	Undated [1875]	Memorial tribute to CAJ received
Evans, John Sir	Autograph	Undated	Bro of Sebastian, Father of AJE
Evans, John Sir	Anne C (Katie) Johns	February 10, 1866	Thanks for gold coin impression
Evans, Sebastian	Anne C (Katie) Johns	1866	Religious beliefs to a friend
Faed, Mr	W Duncan Dunbar	October 26, 1861	Pleased to accept invitation
Falconer, Dr	Mr & Mrs Evans	25-Jul	Invited to meet the M & M Sartet
Fitzgerald, Lord John	Indecipherable (?Peel)	Undated	At home
Flint, Professor R	Mrs Hamilton	December 21, 1876	Progress in mathematical truths
Fox-Maule, Lord Panmure	CAJ	1853	Will call on him about Crimea
Fraser, J Esq	Edwards	Mar-05	Invitation
Gardiner, William (1808-1852)	End scrap (CAJ)	Undated scrap	Thanks for specs from Lizard
Gaskell, Mrs E C	Mrs Robert Holland	June 4, 1853	Will be at F D Maurice's
Gatty, Mrs Margaret	Anne C (Katie) Johns	July 9, 1867	Rejects MSS but encourages K
George III	Duke of Clarence at Plymouth	1790	Calling card
Gladstone, William	Unknown Mr Purly	1863	Note
Goodall, Mr Frederick	W Duncan Dunbar	October 28, 1861	Pleased to accept invitation
Goschen, Lord	Autograph	Undated scrap	Yours truly, signature
Graham, Professor Robert	CAJ	December 7, 1836	Eagerly awaiting his specimens
Grey, Charles	J St Aubyn	October 24, 1831	Postmarked envelope
Grote, George	Mrs Robert Holland	Friday, May 11	Delighted to accept dinner invite
Grove, W R	Mrs John Bullar	1864	Not heard from Fairfax Hse
Gull, Dr William W	Mrs Johns	March 11, 1873	Enquiring about CAJ treatment
Hallam, Henry	Mrs Holland	Undated	Declines, due at Buck House
Hare, Julius Charles	Dear Sir (? CAJ)	December 24, 1851	C Kingsley's Hypatia chapters
Harvey, Sir George, RS Pres	Autograph scrap	1820	Signature
Hawker, R S	Sir T D Acland, Bart	Faint postmark	Envelope
Haydon, B R (Painter)	Autograph	March 1, 1839	Signature from Bath, Somerset
Helena, Princess (1846-1923)	Autograph	Undated	Ever your affect., Helena
Henslow, Professor J S	CAJ	January 25, 1860	Thanks for prize books, regards
Hibberd, Shirley	CAJ	November 23, 1860	Declines Pampas Grass article
Hill, Octavia	Lady Elcho	February 23, 1877	Accepting invite for March 3
Holmes, Oliver Wendell (P)	Mrs (Ellen) Johns & Katie	December 23, 1872	Thoughtful letter about his work
Hooker, Dr J D (from Kew)	Cousin Effie	March 15, 1873	Remembrance of Sir A Helps
Hooker, W J from Glasgow	CAJ	Nov 20, 1835	Give specimens to Miss Warren

Houghton, Lord	CAJ	1868	Son a pupil at Winton House
Houghton, Lord	Henry Johns	July 10, 1874	Envelope at CAJ's death
Hughes, Thomas	My dear Sir (CAJ)	March 5, 1861	About teaching at Rugby for H
Hughes, Thomas	Mrs Holland	September 6, 1865	About prizes to give to Corps
Hunt, W Holman	Lowes Dickinson	April 10, 1863	Writing a painter's paper
Incledon, Charles Benjamin	Henry Incledon Johns	December 1, 1815	Performing at Exeter Monday
Ingelow, Jean	Charles Kingsley	Undated	Responding to his letter
Irving, Washington	George Harvey at Plymouth	August 14, 1831	Envelope
Jeffery ? (cardiologist)	John Noble, Esq	Tuesday	Indecipherable
Jeffreys, John Gwyn (1809-1885)	Sir John Evans	2 pm, Monday	Returned from Italy to find yours
Jesse, Edward	John Noble, Esq	September 19, 1866	Remember friend in Brighton
Kean, Charles	Mrs Deane	November 15, 1858	Much Ado About Nothing ticket
Keble, John	Autograph	Undated	Signature
Keppel, Wm Coutts (Vt. Bury)(P)	Mrs Johns (Ellen)	Undated	Card
Kingsley, Charles	Mrs Johns (Ellen)	1869	Thanks for off-print
Kingsley, Charles	Anne C (Katie) Johns	Undated [1869]	Madam How & Lady Why
Layard, A Henry	John Evans, Esq	?1860	Faded postmarked envelope
Leighton, Lord Frederic	Mrs Holland	Undated	A photo from that night
Lhoyd, H	My dear Sir	May-04	Forward letter from Capt Ross
Liddell, Dr (Christ Church, Oxon)	Mrs Johns	March 4, 1880	Returning birth reg document
Lockhart, John Gibson	Unidentified	July 19, 1836	Asking for magazine ref
Longfellow, Henry Wadsworth	Charles Kingsley	1868	Envelope
Lorne, Marquess of	Unknown Dear Sir	1868	About Gaming laws & farmers
Lund?, John	Wm Longman Esq	January 14, 1860	Publication idea of young friend
Lyell, Sir Charles	Charles Kingsley	February 21, 1866	Hooker's Herbarium & USA
MacDonald, George	Photographs only	Undated	Youthful
Martineau, Dr James	Mrs Johns	December 8, 1873	Envelope
Maurice, F D	Miss Field (later Mrs Johns)	May 1 [1842]	Arranging to visit her in Chelsea
McAdam, William	J L McAdam, grandson	July 6, 1835	Scrap of a note
Mill, John Stuart[5]	Charles Kingsley	July 9, 1870	Women's suffrage reply
Mitford, Miss	Mrs Kingsley	Friday aft	Thanks for sending Hypatia
Monckton-Milnes, Richard, see Lord Houghton			
Moore, George (?)	Labelled G Moore	Undated	2 pages tightly written mss
Morley, Dr Henry	Mrs Johns	1869 postmark	In Winchester again Friday week
Morley, J L	Autograph	Undated	Signature
Morpeth, Lord	Lady Stovin	November 26, 1875	Envelope: Dublin to Sthampton
Moultrie, John	My dear Sir (CAJ)	April, 1867	Seek schoolmistress for Rugby
Muller, Max	Charles Kingsley	Nov-11	Antiquities in Cornwall
Munro, Alexander (1825-1871)	Anne C (Katie) Johns	1867	Exchange plaster casts lent
Nares, George Strong (later Sir)	Calling card	Undated	Stoneham House, Winchester
Northbrook, Lord (War Office)(P)	CAJ	February 22, 1871	Requesting school-leave for son
Norton, Hon Mrs	Lady Elcho	Undated	Now Lady Stirling-Maxwell
O'Connell, Daniel	Bearer	March 29, 1836	Admit to House of Commons
Oliphant, Mrs Margaret	Mrs Hamilton	Undated	Friendly 4 pp correspondence
O'Neil, Henry Nelson	Lowes Cato Dickinson Esq	Jan-28	Thanks for lending monk's dress
Ouseley, Frederick Gore	Mrs Johns (for son Henry)	March 17, 1863	Son's music studies at Oxford
Owen, Professor Richard	John Noble	July 7, 1860	Thanks for scientific exchange
Page-Roberts, Rev W (Canon)	Lady Elcho	March 3, 1877	Meaning to visit town, but not yet
Palmerston, Lord	John Russell KG	1861	Cover note for letter unknown
Panmure, Lord see Fox-Maule			
Pascoe, William	Mr St Aubyn	October 16, 1804	Receipt to Plymouth Dock Bank
Philpotts, Bishop H	CAJ	1846	Regrets CAJ to leave Helston
Philpotts, Bishop H	CAJ	1847	Refs for dearly beloved friend
Poole, Reginald Stuart	Mrs Johns	January 18?, 1875	Friendly catch-up on travels
Praed, Winthrop Mackworth	Derwent Coleridge	July 28, 1835	Envelope: Pridham's, Plymouth
Praed (clipped)	W M Praed	1842	Envelope: No 7 Manchester Sq
Proctor, R A	Mrs Johns	December 30, 186?	Astronomy at Manchester RI

Name	Addressee	Date	Note
Ramsay, Professor Andrew	John Evans	Sep-10	Interest in numismatics
Richmond, George RA	My dear William (?Longman)	September 20, 1866	Long letter to ailing friend
Ruskin, John (*see* Tywhitt) (P)[6]	Mrs Johns	December 26, 1871	Ill, sorry for late reply
Russell, Earl KG	Place card		I.D. as at Foreign Office
Schaeffer, Ary	Mrs Holland	Undated	Indecipherable note
Seeley, J R	Mrs Kingsley	Jul-14	Accepting invitation for Saturday
Shaftesbury, Lord	John Noble Esq	Feb-05	100 girls' outfits for Australia
Sidmouth, Viscount *see* H Addington			
Somerville, Mary	Charlotte [? Grenfell]	Sep-04	Seeking connections in Italy
Southey, Robert	Given by Derwent Coleridge	Attached 1860	Note 1
Stanley, Dean Arthur	Rev Dr Turner	Indecipherable PM	Envelope, scrap
Swanwick, Anna	Mrs Johns	August 10, 1876	Reply on spiritual matters
Talford F or T N	Bearer	Jun 3, 1841	Admit to House of Commons
Tennent FRS, J Emerson	Mrs Longman	Sept 22, 1862	Enquiring about prep school
Tyndall, John	CAJ	Sept 22, 1873	About rainbows/optical images
Tywhitt, St John	CAJ	Jan 9 & 12, 1872	Encl Ruskin letter re: rasores
Unknown	Rev Dr Yates	1823	Envelope to Tavern/ London
Unknown	Autograph with umlaut	Undated	Signature
Unknown	John Noble Esq	Tuesday	? Jeffery (cardiologist)
Unknown ?Longham	My kind Friend ?CAJ	Jul-14	Locating Alleyne fr W Indies to Falmouth/his mother has died
Unknown	Autograph (? G I Kiallmark)	Jun 25, 1862	Dated signature
Vaughan, Charles J.	CAJ (privately)	Nov 23 1857	About applicant to Harrow
Victoria, Queen	Photo-postcard frontispiece	Undated	Seated older monarch reading
Victoria, Queen	Duchess of Kent	Undated	Calling card
Victoria, Queen	Signature	Undated	At Windsor, paper strip
Victoria, Queen	Count Platen	May 17, 1860	Invitation for 1/2 3 today
Wales, Prince of	Charles Kingsley	October 25, 1867	Dated autograph
Walpole, Spencer Horatio	Autograph	Undated	Signature
Warburton, Rev Wm	Mrs Johns	January 26, 1877	Note
Ward, Nathaniel Bagshaw (P)	CAJ	January 25, 1865	Photographer to visit Winton H
Waterton, Charles	CAJ	1854 (?)	Praising work & thanks for book
Wedgwood, Hensleigh	Derwent Coleridge	Nov-20	Etymological Dictionary
Wellington, Duke of	Unknown	Jan-05	Why dogs not listed/ quantity
Wesley, Dr Samuel S	Charles Mays Esq	Sept 10, 1867	Envelope
Wigan, Alfred	Lady Elcho	July 27, 1877	Enclosing vouchers for theatre
Wilkinson, Sir John	Unknown	Undated	Party invite from Egyptologist
Williams, J E	Lowes Dickinson	Jan 20, 1866	Note
Winchester, Bishop of (P)	B Whiteford	1877	Note addressed Winton Hse
Wolff, Joseph	Autograph	Undated	Signature of CAJ illustrator
Wordsworth, William	CAJ	July 29, 1841	Response to gift of Flora Sacra
Yarrell, William	Sir (CAJ)	January 26, 1842	Appt at Entomological Society
Yonge, Charlotte M	Mrs Johns	December 5, 1870	Envelope
Yonge, Charlotte M	Mrs Johns	2 letters c 1865-70	Arr to meet; CAJ lectures

---

Note 1: A joint (S T Coleridge/R Southey) working document about the poem 'Before Gleim's Cottage' & Schiller's writings.

Note 2: Dated by Darwin Letters Project, Cambridge

Note 3: Douglas, Francis Wemyss-Charteris, 8th Earl of Wemyss (1818-1914).

Note 4: Sir Arthur Evans of Knossos, was a former pupil of CAJ at Callipers Hall, and the whole family became friends.

Note 5: This Mills letter was the subject of an article (Dec 1946) in the *Australian Quarterly* Vol XVIII, No 4: pp 30-34.

Note 6: Tywhitt offers Ruskin's letter, after receiving an answer from CAJ, to Mrs Johns and Katie for their collection.

BIBLIOGRAPHY

Books and monographs

Acton, Bob (1991) *A Second View from Carn Marth,* Truro: Landfall Publications

Acton, Bob (2000) *In and Around Perranwell* Truro: Landfall Publications

Adburgham, Alison (1992) *A Radical Aristocrat* Padstow: Tabb House

Allen, David Elliston (1976) *The Naturalist in Britain, A Social History* London: Allen Lane

Allen, David Elliston (1986) *The Botanists* Winchester: St Paul's Bibliographies

Armstrong, Patrick (2000) *The English Parson-Naturalist* Leominster: Gracewing

Ashton, Rosemary (2006) *142 Strand, A Radical Address in Victorian London* London: Chatto & Windus

Bates, Selina, and Keith Spurgin (1994) *Stars in the Grass, the Story of Cornish Naturalist Frederick Hamilton Davey, 1868-1915* Redruth: Dyllansow Truran

Batho, Edith C and Professor Dobrée, Bonamy (1962 rev of 1938 first) *The Victorians and After 1830-1914*, Vol IV Introductions to English Literature. London: The Cresset Press.

Bennett, Alan (1987) *Cornwall through the Mid Nineteenth Century* Plymouth: Kingfisher Railway Productions

Bere, Rennie (1982) *The Nature of Cornwall, The Wildlife and Ecology of the County*, illustrated with drawings by M Blamey & Franklin Coombs, and photographs, Buckingham: Barracuda Books Ltd in association with The Cornwall Naturalists' Trust. Introduction by HRH the Prince Charles

Board of Trinity College Dublin (1989) *Trinity, One of the Great European Centres of Learning*

Bracken, C W (1934) *A History of Plymouth and her Neighbours,* 2nd ed., Plymouth: Underhill

Brett, R L (1979) *Barclay Fox's Journal* London: Bell and Hyman

Briggs, Asa (1996 revised from earlier editions) The Victorian Trilogy: *Victorian People: A Reassessment of Persons and Themes 1851-67* (1st published 1954); *Victorian Cities* (1st, 1963); Victorian Things (1st, 1988). Published as *The Victorian Trilogy* (1996) London: Folio Society

Brown, Jane (1999) *The Pursuit of Paradise, A Social History of Gardens and Gardening* London: HarperCollins Publishers

Butler, Samuel (1903, 1953 reprint) *The Way of All Flesh* London & Glasgow: Collins

Charnwood, Lady (1930) *An Autograph Collection and the making of it* London: Ernest Benn Ltd.

Chitty, Susan (1974) *The Beast and the Monk, A Life of Charles Kingsley* London: Hodder and Stoughton

Collins, Wilkie (1851) *Rambles beyond Railways* London: Bentley

Colloms, Brenda (1975) *Charles Kingsley, The Lion of Eversley* London: Constable; (1977) *Victorian Country Parsons*, London: Book Club Associates

Cowls, Bert (1982) *Looking Back to Yesterday* Helston: Cowls

Dare, Deirdre (1996) *The Unknown Founder: The Story of Helston Grammar School from 1550-1972* Truro: Kelynen Publications

Darton, F J Harvey (1966, 2nd ed of 1932 lst) *Children's Books in England, Five Centuries of Social Life* Cambridge: The University Press. Especially chapter XIV: The 'Sixties: *Alice* and After.

Davey, F H, FLS (1909) *The Flora of Cornwall being an account of the Flowering Plants and Ferns found in the County of Cornwall including the Scilly Isles* Penryn: F Chegwidden. Contains a map and six portraits of foremost botanists, the first of which is Charles Johns.

Deacon, Bernard (2004) *The Cornish Family, The Roots of our Future* Fowey: Cornwall Editions

Dixon, Joy (2003) *Divine Feminine: Theosophy and Feminism in England* Maryland: Johns Hopkins University Press. In this book Dr Dixon refers to Katie as 'Lilian Lloyd,' a hitherto unknown reference to A C Lloyd as she was most often listed, if not Mrs Lloyd.

Fortey, Richard (2008) *Dry Store Room No. 1: The Secret Life of the Natural History Museum* London: HarperPress (an imprint of HarperCollins)

Fox, Barclay, see R L Brett (Editor, 1979)

Fox, Caroline (1882) *Memories of Old Friends* London: Smith, Elder & Co

Gates, Barbara T (1998) *Kindred Nature, Victorian and Edwardian Women Embrace the Living World* Chicago & London: University of Chicago Press

Gates, Barbara T and Ann B Shteir (Editors, 1997) *Natural Eloquence, Women Reinscribe Science* Madison: University of Wisconsin Press

Gathorne-Hardy, Jonathan (1972) *The Rise and Fall of the British Nanny* London: Hodder & Stoughton

Gerrard, John (1982) *The Book of Plymouth* Buckingham: Barracuda Books

Gill, Crispin (1979) *Plymouth, a New History, 1603-Present Day,* Vol 2 Newton Abbot: David & Charles

Gill, Crispin (1995) *The Great Cornish Families* Tiverton: Cornwall Books

Hainton, Raymonde and Godfrey (1996) *The Unknown Coleridge* London: Janus

Hughes, Kathryn (1993) *The Victorian Governess* London: Hambledon & London

Jacob, John (1836) *West Devon and Cornwall Flora.* Plymouth: E Nettleton, and London: Longman, Rees, etc.

Jacob, Maria (1853) *Days, Months, and Seasons of the Year, Explained to the Little People of England* No 2 in the series of 'Flowers From the Gardens of Knowledge' London: Nathaniel Cooke

Johns, Henry Incledon (1831) *Poems addressed by a father to his children: with extracts from the diary of a pedestrian and a memoir of the author, &c.* Available to view at Plymouth Public Library, Devon County Records.

Kendall, Guy (nd, c 1945) *Charles Kingsley and His Ideas* London: Hutchinson & Co

Kent, Alan M (2000) *The Literature of Cornwall: Continuity – Identity – Difference 1000-2000* Bristol: Redcliffe Press

Kingsley, Charles (1870) *Madam How and Lady Why, or First Lessons in Earth Lore for Children* London: Bell and Daldy

Kingsley, Charles, edited by his wife, F E K (1877) *Charles Kingsley, His Letters and Memories of his Life,* 2nd ed. London: Henry S King & Co

Kingsley, Charles, *Poems of Charles Kingsley, containing The Saint's Tragedy, Andromeda, and Other Poems 1848-1870,* Oxford Edition, OUP, 1913

Lamb, Keith & Bowe, Patrick (1995) *A history of gardening in Ireland,* Dublin: National Botanic Gardens, Glasnevin, published by the Stationery Office, Dublin

Leinster-Mackay, Donald (1984) *The Rise of the English Prep School* UK: Falmer Press, Taylor & Francis Group, with particular reference to the amalgamation of Winton House and Dunchurch School in Rugby during WWII.

Lewis, Cherry, compiler (1984, New Edition 2000) *The Making of a Garden: Gertrude Jekyll, An anthology.* Antique Collectors' Club. The edition in 2000 reverses the title, and became *Gertrude Jekyll: The Making of a Garden,* and is enhanced by the addition of coloured plates by Emily Stackhouse pp 16-17 (six original watercolours created for *Flowers of the Field*), p 61 (Common honeysuckle, September), p 76 (Common hemp nettle, September), p 77 (Field thistle, July), p 94 (Common daffodil, May), p 116 (Wild hyacinth – bluebell, May), p 171 (Common hazel, September), p 188 (Common holly, January). Coloured plates provided courtesy of Clifford B Evans.

Lewis, Roy and Maude, Angus (1949) *The English Middle Classes* London: Phoenix House

Luce, John Victor (1992) *Trinity College Dublin, The First 400 Years* Dublin: Trinity College Dublin Press

Lundberg, Patricia Lorimer (2003) *"An Inward Necessity" The Writer's Life of Lucas Malet* New York: Peter Lang

Maber, Richard and Angela Tregoning, eds, (1989) *Kilvert's Cornish Diary,* [Journal No 4, 1870] Penzance: Alison Hodge, 1989

Mare, Margaret and Percival, Alicia C (1949 reprint of 1948 lst) *Victorian Bestseller, The World of Charlotte M Yonge* London: George G Harrap & Co

Martin, E W (1951) *A Wanderer in the West Country* London: Phoenix House

Martin, R B (1959) *The Dust of Combat, A Life of Charles Kingsley* London: Faber & Faber

Matthews, C M (lst 1976, Repr 1977, Rev 1982) *Your Family History And How to Discover It* Guildford: Lutterworth Press. The sample trees in this volume relate to the Johns, Carrington, and Incledon families.

McDowell, R B & Webb, D A (2004 reprint of 1982 lst published by Cambridge University Press) *Trinity College Dublin 1592-1952 An academic history* Dublin: Trinity College Press in association with Environmental Publications

Pavord, Anna (2005) *The Naming of Names, The Search for Order in the World of Plants* London: Bloomsbury

Pudney, John (1974) *Brunel and his world* London: Thames and Hudson

Pym, Horace N (1882, 3rd edition) *Memories of Old Friends*, being extracts from the Journals and Letters of Caroline Fox of Penjerrick, Cornwall from 1835 to 1871. London: Smith, Elder & Co

Ralling, Christopher (1979 reprint with corrections of 1978 lst edition) *The Voyage of Charles Darwin, His autobiographical writings selected and arranged* London: British Broadcasting Corporation

Robinson, Chris (1991) *Victorian Plymouth Illustrated, As Time Draws On* Plymouth: Pen & Ink Publishing

Routh, H V (1935) *Money, Morals and Manners as Revealed in Modern Literature* London: Ivor Nicholson and Watson Ltd

Sadleir, Michael (1944) *Things Past* London: Constable, with particular reference to 'Henry Kingsley (1830-1876)' Chp 1.

Seed, John (2005) *Training Female Schoolteachers in Victorian London: A Study of*

Three Colleges, Chap 1: 'A superior class of parochial schoolmistress' Whitelands College 1841-70. www.billygriff.sathosting.net

Shteir, Ann B (1996) *Cultivating women, Cultivating Science, Flora's Daughters and Botany in England 1760 to 1860* Baltimore & London: Johns Hopkins University Press

Thorp, Margaret Farrand (1969) *Charles Kingsley 1819-1875* New York: Octagon Books

Toy, H Spencer (1936) *The History of Helston* Oxford: OUP

Trewin, J C and Willmott, H J (1950) *London-Bodmin, An Exchange of Letters* London: Westaway Books

Turner, Barbara Carpenter (1979) *Winchester-100 Years Ago* Southampton: Paul Cave

Vicinus, Martha (1985) *Independent Women, Work and Community for Single Women 1850-1920* London: Virago

Wulf, Andrea (2008) *The Brother Gardeners, Botany, Empire and the Birth of an Obsession* London: William Heinemann

---

Collections, archives and catalogues

National Register of Archives: Winton House School, Winchester c1867-1943; Record ref 12M61, NRA Catalogue ref 38096 (26 items including School Chronicles, registers from 1895, photo album of the school and private photograph album (no family portraits). Most of the records post-date CAJ's death and record the concurrent activities of the school and its fellows. Sited at Hampshire Records Office, Winchester.

Royal Botanic Gardens, Kew archives: Thirty-one letters between CAJ and WJ Hooker are held in the Directors' Correspondence files, between 1834 and 1847.

Saywell, David and Simon, Jacob (Editors, 2004) *Complete Illustrated Catalogue: National Portrait Gallery, London.* London: Unicorn Press

Simpson, N Douglas, M A, F L S (7 Dec 2004 version) *Bibliographical Index of the British Flora*, including Floras, Herbals, Periodicals, Societies and References relating to the identification, distribution and occurrence of Phanerogams, Vascular Cryptogams and Charophytes in the British Isles. Privately printed PDF on-line index of 1960 original edition.

Wolstenholme, Leander (2008) ' Catalogued list of botanical specimen records for Rev C A Johns's, Manchester Museum, University of Manchester. Some un-catalogued specimens of CAJ also preserved there.

Yonge, Charlotte Mary (1864-1878) Letters of CMY to Anne Catherine Johns (1) Princeton University Parrish Collection; to Ellen Julia Johns: University of Delaware (8), University of Iowa (1), Princeton University (3), Mitchell Library, Sydney (2), and Dr Charlotte Mitchell (2).

Dictionaries, directories and guides

Anderson, P J and Rose, J, Editors (1991) *British Literary Publishing Houses, 1820-1880* Detroit: Gale Research Inc. [in] series Vol 106: *Dictionary of Literary Biography*. See article: 'J H Parker' by R M Healey pp 230-2, official publishers for SPCK.

Bates, Robin & Scolding, Bill (1996 & 2001) *Five Walks from the Lizard*, Cornwall: Serpentine Design, published by Cornwall County Council (in reference to Johns).
(2002) *Wild Flowers of The Lizard*, Cornwall: Serpentine Design, published by Cornwall County Council (Johns reference).

Benezit, E (1976 edition) *Dictionary of Painters, Sculptors, Designers and Engravers*, Paris: Librairie Grund

Boase, George Clement (1890) *Collectanea, A collection of Biographical & Topographical Notes related to the County of Cornwall*

Boase, George Clement and Courtney, William Prideaux (1882) *Bibliotheca Cornubiensis*, Catalogue of the Writings, both Manuscript and Printed of Cornishmen, Vol I and II, plus Supplement. London: Longmans, Green, Reader and Dyer.

British Library, *Integrated Catalogue*, On-line: catalogue.bl.uk

Burtchaell, G D and Sadleir, T U (First edition 1924) *Alumni Dublinenses* Ireland: Archive CD Books

Crockford's Clerical Directory 1868, 1874 UK: Archive CD Books College and Ecclesiastical Series, www.archivecdbooks.org

Dean, Dennis R, 'Parker, John William (1792-1870),' *Oxford Dictionary of National Biography*, OUP, 2004. Also 'John W. Parker' in Anderson & Rose (1991), pp 233-6.

Desmond, Ray (1977) *Dictionary of British and Irish Botanists and Horticulturists* London: Taylor & Francis 1977

Dictionary of National Biography (DNB), From the Earliest times to 1900, edited by Sir Leslie Stephen & Sir Sidney Lee, Oxford University Press. Original entry for Johns: G S Boulger; *New Dictionary of National Biography* contains a considerably truncated version contributed by Giles Hudson, to which some revision has been offered, due to further findings.

Ellis, Roger (1977) *Who's Who in Victorian Britain* London: Shepheard-Walwyn Ltd. Series editor: Geoffrey Treasure

Henderson, Charles (1925, repr 1964) *Cornish Church Guide and Parochial History of Cornwall* Truro: D Bradford Barton

Houfe, Simon (1978, rev 1981, 1986) *The Dictionary of 19th Century British Book Illustrators and Caricaturists* Suffolk: Antique Collectors' Club

Low, Sampson (1853) *Index to the British Catalogue of Books* Book search on-line: Google.

Ogilvie, Marilyn and Harvey, Joy (Editors, 2000) *The Biographical Dictionary of Women in Science, Pioneering Lives from Ancient times to the Mid-20th Century*, New York & London: Routledge

Pigot's Directory of Somerset 1822, Archive CD Books Directories Series

Wright, W H Kearley, FRHS (1896) *West-Country Poets: Their Lives and Works*, London: Elliot Stock.

Journals, newspapers and articles

Boulger, Professor G S (1911) 'Memoir of the Rev Charles Alexander Johns' [in] *Flowers of the Field* (33rd edition), pp ix-xii. Written at the suggestion of Sir Joseph Dalton Hooker (1817-1911) who had known Johns, and seen the progress of expanding on the original work. Boulger also wrote the original entry for Johns in the Dictionary of National Biography, in use until 2004.

The British Magazine (Maitland and Rose, editors) 1843: 'Births and Marriages' July number.

Collier, W F (1899) 'Helleston Grammar School under Derwent Coleridge' *Cornish Magazine*, Vol II: pp 116-125

Cowls, P (1952) 'Johns of Helston' in two parts. Transcription (edited) of the Diary of C A Johns, Summer number, pp 88-95. Autumn number, pp 167-176. *West Country Magazine*. Facsimile articles by P Cowles are lodged in the Cornwall Records Office, Ref. 3512 Xll/1 (CAJ Notebook and Journal), 3513 X11/2 (Facsimiles).

Ecclesiastical Gazette (1859, 1860) London. Miscellany of information on civil and liturgical preferments and appointments. Also book-lists by scripture unions and religious publishers.

Evans, Clifford (1995) 'Forgotten Field' [in] *Country Life*, 6 July issue. Available on-line at www.foxhillantiques.com/countlife.htm.

Jenkyn, Ann Trevenen (1996) 'Appendix A: Emily Trevenen 1786-1856 and Her Influence on Education in Helston' [in] Dare, D *The Unknown Founder* Truro: Kelynen Publications

La Nauze, J A (1946) 'A Letter of J S Mill to Charles Kingsley' [in] *Australian Quarterly*, Vol XVIII, No 4 (December 1946): pp 30-34. The original of this letter, which is the reply of J S Mill to a letter from Charles Kingsley included in *CK: his letters and memories of his life*, is in the 'Johns Album of Letters and Photographs.' The topic of this important, lengthy letter is the women's suffrage movement, and the general conduct of its supporters.

Penzance Gazette (1852) Issues for January 14, 21 and 28, relating the news of the loss of the mail ship *RMS Amazon* with 115 (actually 104) lives lost. The subject of CAJ's book for SPCK in that year.

RICJ, Journal of the Royal Institution of Cornwall Vol XXI, Part 1 1922 includes the Supplement to F Hamilton Davey's *Flora of Cornwall* by Edgar Thurston, CLE and Chambré C Vigurs, BA, MD (Contains some corrections on p xvi to the brief biography of Johns published in the *Flora of Cornwall* 1909).

Stackhouse, Emily (1866) 'Rare Plants in the neighbourhood of Truro' *Journal of the Royal Institution of Cornwall*, Vol II 1866-67 pp 245-50

Trehane, David (1989) 'Emily Stackhouse 1811-1870' [in] *The Cornish Garden*: *The Journal of the Cornwall Garden Society* No 32, March issue, pp 38-44

Trenoweth, Roger (2007) 'A botanical adventure, C A Johns in Cornwall' *The Cornish Garden*, No 50, March issue.

Victor, Helen (on-line essay entered 05/03/08) 'Victorian Periodicals' with special reference to *Fraser's Magazine* (under J Parker) and *Good Words*.

General Index

Abbreviations: App (Appendix); g-pts (grandparents); gg-pts (great grandparents); n (numbered footnote); illus (illustrator); nn (multiple footnotes); TP (title page). Numbers in **bold** indicate visual images. The Appendix iv Reading List and its numerous references, is not included in this Index, as it is alphabetized for ease of checking. From Appendix v: Autograph album, only those names which appear in the main text are cross-referenced.

ABOUT THE AUTHORS

Deirdre Dare has lived in Cornwall for over 50 years. She is the author of *The Unknown Founder*, a history of Helston Grammar School, where she and her husband taught. Research for that book led her to the diary of the youthful C A Johns, later the past headmaster from whom this book evolved.

Melissa Hardie is a social historian and author living in West Cornwall. She is the founder-director of the Hypatia Trust (www.hypatia-trust.org.uk), an international documentary and educational organisation, and an Honorary Fellow of the English department of the University of Exeter in Cornwall.